Meiner lieben Frau

Air Chemistry and Radioactivity

Christian E. Junge

*Institute for Meteorology
and Geophysics
Johannes Gutenberg University
Mainz, Germany*

1963

Academic Press
New York and London

ACADEMIC PRESS, INC.
111 Fifth Avenue, New York, New York 10003

United Kingdom Edition published by
ACADEMIC PRESS, INC. (LONDON) LTD.
Berkeley Square House, London W1X 6BA

LIBRARY OF CONGRESS CATALOG CARD NUMBER: 62-13090

Third Printing, 1972

PRINTED IN THE UNITED STATES OF AMERICA

*Air Chemistry
and Radioactivity*

International Geophysics Series

Editor

J. VAN MIEGHEM

Royal Belgian Meteorological Institute
Uccle, Belgium

Volume 1 BENO GUTENBERG. Physics of the Earth's Interior. 1959

Volume 2 JOSEPH W. CHAMBERLAIN. Physics of the Aurora and Airglow. 1961

Volume 3 S. K. RUNCORN (ed.). Continental Drift. 1962

Volume 4 C. E. JUNGE. Air Chemistry and Radioactivity. 1963

Volume 5 ROBERT C. FLEAGLE AND JOOST A. BUSINGER. An Introduction to Atmospheric Physics. 1963

Volume 6 L. DUFOUR AND R. DEFAY. Thermodynamics of Clouds. 1963

Volume 7 H. U. ROLL. Physics of the Marine Atmosphere. 1965

Volume 8 RICHARD A. CRAIG. The Upper Atmosphere: Meteorology and Physics. 1965

Volume 9 WILLIS L. WEBB. Structure of the Stratosphere and Mesosphere. 1966

Volume 10 MICHELE CAPUTO. The Gravity Field of the Earth from Classical and Modern Methods. 1967

Volume 11 S. MATSUSHITA AND WALLACE H. CAMPBELL (eds.). Physics of Geomagnetic Phenomena. (In two volumes.) 1967

Volume 12 K. YA. KONDRATYEV. Radiation in the Atmosphere. 1969

Volume 13 E. PALMEN AND C. W. NEWTON. Atmospheric Circulation Systems: Their Structure and Physical Interpretation. 1969

Volume 14 HENRY RISHBETH AND OWEN K. GARRIOTT. Introduction to Ionospheric Physics. 1969

Volume 15 C. S. RAMAGE. Monsoon Meteorology. 1971

Volume 16 JAMES R. HOLTON. An Introduction to Dynamic Meteorology. 1972

In preparation

K. C. YEH AND C. H. LIU. Theory of Ionospheric Waves

Preface

Air chemistry is defined in this volume as the branch of atmospheric science concerned with the constituents and chemical processes of the atmosphere below the mesopeak, i.e., below about 50 km. It includes all gaseous, particulate, and radioactive substances and covers the altitude range of the stratosphere and mesosphere which can be probed with balloons and high altitude aircraft. The dynamics and composition of this region are still, though sometimes only loosely, associated with the troposphere. Above the mesopeak the composition of the atmosphere is dominated by phototochemical and corpuscular processes which are so specific that a special name for this field, aeronomy, seems to be justified. It represents the altitude range probed by rockets. The region around the mesopeak itself is difficult to explore and very little is known about it with respect to both meteorology and composition.

Atmospheric chemistry began in the second half of the 19th century with investigations of trace substances in precipitation and of particulate material, concentrated for quite some time on the study of emanations and ozone, and gained real momentum recently with the discovery and observation of radioactive and inactive isotopes and their large scale injection into the atmosphere. This opened new aspects of study of the cycle of atmospheric constituents and of world-wide circulation. C. G. Rossby was one of the first to recognize these potentialities and his initiative and enthusiasm provided unique leadership and stimulation in this field.

Primarily for methodical reasons most of the investigations were made by chemists, physicists, and nuclear chemists and the papers are scattered in the journals of such diverse fields as physics, nuclear chemistry, chemistry, geology, geochemistry, oceanography, biology, ecology, agriculture, geophysics, and meteorology. Therefore, a survey of the present state of the art seems justified and may serve a useful purpose. In our attempt to give a comprehensive and critical account of atmospheric chemistry and radioactivity we soon became aware of the difficulties involved in summarizing a field which is in a state of flux and rapid expansion and we are certain that shortcomings in the treatment will become apparent. However, if this book helps to close the gap between meteorology, chemistry, and nuclear chemistry and helps to stimulate research in this field, the effort will have been worthwhile.

The emphasis throughout the book is on the basic and large scale phenomena and the discussion is critical rather than exhaustive. Subdivision of the field can be made on the basis either of the chemical compounds or of their phases, and overlapping of chapters and sections is inevitable in both cases. We decided to subdivide by phase, i.e., by gases, aerosols, and precipitation. This means that the discussion of most compounds will be continued in subsequent chapters. An exception was made in Chapter 3, where all radioactive substances were treated together, irrespective of phase, since radioactive decay cuts across the phases and allows no other treatment. A final brief chapter provides information on air pollution insofar as it is of general, not local importance for air chemistry.

The book covers the literature through 1960 and a good portion of 1961, as illustrated in the diagram of references, which shows that the information can be considered representative of the state of knowledge as of summer 1961.

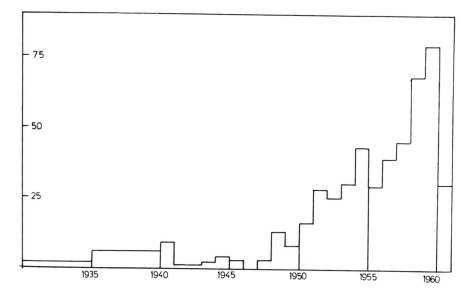

We have attempted to use the same symbols for quantities as those that appeared in the original papers, but because of the complexity of the field this led to the multiple use of some symbols. To minimize this difficulty, we have listed them separately for each chapter.

It is a pleasure to express my sincere gratitude to those who helped me to prepare this book. The management of the Air Force Cambridge Research Laboratories made it possible for me to devote considerable time and effort to this work.

I am much indebted to some colleagues who were kind enough to review some of the chapters and made useful suggestions and comments: Dr. E. A. Martell, Dr. M. I. Kalkstein, and Mr. I. H. Blifford, Jr. (Chapter 3); Dr. H.-W. Georgii (Chapters 2 and 4); Dr. K. Bullrich (Chapter 2).

A number of persons made unpublished reports available to be included in the text. I am particularly indebted to Mr. David Kraus and Mrs. Lee Ariemma, without whose invaluable assistance in preparing the text and the typescript this work would not have been possible.

CHRISTIAN E. JUNGE

Air Force Cambridge Research Laboratories
Bedford, Massachusetts

Universitätsinstitut für Meteorologie und Geophysik
Mainz, Germany

Contents

PREFACE vii

1. Gases

1.1 Introduction 1
1.2 Water Vapor 4
1.3 Carbon Dioxide 21
1.4 Ozone 37
1.5 Sulfur Dioxide and Hydrogen Sulfide 59
1.6 Hydrogen and Helium 74
1.7 Nitrogen Compounds 81
1.8 Halogens 91
1.9 Methane, Carbon Monoxide, and Formaldehyde . . 94
List of Symbols 99
References 100

2. Aerosols

2.1 Introduction 111
2.2 Physical Properties of Tropospheric Aerosol Particles 113
2.3 Chemical Composition of Tropospheric Aerosols . . 153
2.4 Distribution of Aerosols in the Troposphere and Stratospheric Aerosols 183
List of Symbols 200
References 202

3. Atmospheric Radioactivity

3.1 Introduction 209
3.2 Radon and Thoron and Their Decay Products . . . 211
3.3 Radioisotopes Produced by Cosmic Radiation . . . 230
3.4 Artificial Radioactivity 238
List of Symbols 282
References 283

4. Chemistry of Precipitation

4.1 Introduction 289
4.2 Physico-Chemistry of Wet and Dry Removal from the
Atmosphere 291

4.3 Chemical Composition of Precipitation   311
    List of Symbols   347
    References   348

5.   *The Role of Air Pollution In Air Chemistry*

5.1 Introduction   353
5.2 Composition of Polluted Atmospheres   354
5.3 Variation of Pollution in and around Polluted Areas   362
    References   365

AUTHOR INDEX   367
SUBJECT INDEX   375

1. *Gases*

1.1 Introduction

Atmospheric gases are usually classified as permanent or variable, but this is only a differentiation of degree. If time scales are extended, all gases can be considered variable, but the variations of oxygen, nitrogen, and most of the noble gases are so slow that these gases will not be considered in this monograph.

Except for water vapor, the first variable gases which attracted general attention were carbon dioxide and ozone. Originally, their study was stimulated primarily because of their importance for life and solar radiation, but gradually it was realized that they also constitute useful tracers for atmospheric circulation and exchange processes. In the course of time quite a number of other gases, mostly of very small concentrations, have been identified, some only very recently. Each of these gases has very special characteristics and has to be treated differently. As far as it is possible, our discussion will be concerned with the following questions:

(1) the observed distribution in time and space;

(2) the sources and sinks in the atmosphere and at its boundaries;

(3) the budget and cycle of these gases.

In most cases our information is so incomplete that we can barely cover the first point. Thanks to recent studies of the isotopic composition, especially of the radioactive isotopes tritium and carbon-14, considerable progress has been made for water vapor and particularly for carbon dioxide. We hope that the study of other gases will follow.

The atmospheric behavior of the various gases differs widely, primarily due to the differences in the distribution of the source and sink areas. This variety in behavior makes the study of atmospheric gases very attractive. As a consequence of this variety, there are almost no common features. One general feature is the relationship of the variability of a gas

1

to its life or residence time τ in the atmosphere. This lifetime or its reciprocal value, the rate of turnover, τ^{-1}, together with the spatial distribution of sources and sinks within the atmosphere and at its boundaries, is responsible for the amplitude of time and space variations of the atmospheric gases due to the local and general weather. If the space and time distribution of sources and sinks were the same for *all* gases, the time and space variations of all constituents would be similar and the amplitudes would be proportional to τ^{-1}. Since this is not the case, the relationship between τ^{-1} and these variations is only loose. Nevertheless, the magnitude of the fluctuations does allow at least some estimation of τ^{-1}. Gases with a variability as great as that of water vapor will have correspondingly short residence times, viz., a few days to a few weeks. Most of the chemically active trace gases fall into this category. This is not surprising since removal by precipitation plays an important part in their cycles.

There is another category of gases, such as CO_2, O_3, N_2O, and perhaps CH_4 and H_2, for which the water cycle is not important. As far as we know, their residence times range from a few years to a few hundred years. But reliable values of τ, are known for only a few gases and are listed in Table 1 together with other important information. Nitrogen, oxygen, and most of the noble gases can be considered permanent. Data on their concentrations were carefully reviewed by Glueckauf (1951) and will not be included in our discussion. Helium is an exception; it is not a permanent gas and its cycle can be estimated.

Table 1 seems to indicate that on the basis of residence times one can distinguish three major categories of gases:

(1) highly variable gases with τ of the order of days to weeks,

(2) variable gases with τ of the order of a few to many years, and

(3) quasi-permanent gases with much longer residence times.

The residence time of a reservoir like the atmosphere can be related to other important quantities. If M is the total amount of a gas in the reservoir, F the rate of its formation or release, R the rate of its removal or decomposition, equilibrium is defined by $F = R$. R is generally a function of M, $R = R(M)$, and the total amount of the gas is thus determined by $F = R(M)$. The residence time is $\tau = M/F = M/R$. In general, τ depends on M and only if the removal rate R is of the first order, i.e., if $R = \text{constant} \cdot M$, is τ independent of M. It is clear that for steady state conditions the concept of τ does not depend on the function $R = R(M)$. However, for non-steady state conditions, as in stratospheric radioactive fallout, the concept of a fixed value for τ is valid only for first-order removal processes.

TABLE 1 ATMOSPHERIC GASES OTHER THAN OXYGEN AND NITROGEN

Gas		Conversion of units			Atmospheric values		
					Ground level		
Name	Formula	1 ppm = $x \times \mu g/m^3$ STP	1 $\mu g/m^3$ STP = $x \times 10^{-4}$ ppm	1 $\mu g/m^3$ STP = $x \times 10^{-7}$ mm Hg partial pressure	ppm	$\mu g/m^3$ STP	Residence time
Argon	Ar	1784	5.61	4.23	9300	1.6×10^7	—
Neon	Ne	900	11.11	8.37	18	1.6×10^4	—
Helium	He	178	56.20	42.40	5.2	920	~ 2×10^6 years
Krypton	Kr	3708	2.70	2.04	1.1	4100	—
Xenon	Xe	5851	1.71	1.29	0.086	500	—
Water vapor	H_2O	800	12.50	9.40	$(0.4-400) \times 10^2$	$(3-3000) \times 10^4$	10 days
Ozone	O_3	2140	4.67	3.55	$(0-5) \times 10^{-2}$	0-100	? 2 years
Hydrogen	H_2	89	112.00	84.50	0.4-1.0	36-90	—
Carbon dioxide	CO_2	1960	5.10	3.87	$(2-4) \times 10^2$	$(4-8) + 10^5$	4 years
Carbon monoxide	CO	1259	8.10	6.10	$(1-20) \times 10^{-2}$	$(1-20) \times 10^1$	? 0.3 years
Methane	CH_4	712	14.05	10.70	1.2-1.5	$(8.5-11) \times 10^2$	100 years
Formaldehyde	CH_2O	1340	7.46	5.67	$(0-1) \times 10^{-2}$	0-16	—
Nitrous oxide	N_2O	1960	5.10	3.87	$(2.5-6.0) \times 10^{-1}$	$(5-12) \times 10^2$	? 4 years
Nitrogen dioxide	NO_2	2050	4.88	3.71	$(0-3) \times 10^{-3}$	0-6	—
Ammonia	NH_3	760	13.15	10.00	$(0-2) \times 10^{-2}$	0-15	—
Sulfur dioxide	SO_2	2850	3.51	2.61	$(0-20) \times 10^{-3}$	0-50	? 5 days
Hydrogen sulfide	H_2S	1520	6.58	5.00	$(2-20) \times 10^{-3}$	3-30	? 40 days
Chlorine[a]	Cl_2	3165	3.16	2.41	$(3-15) \times 10^{-4}$	1-5	—
Iodine[b]	I_2	11300	0.88	0.67	$(0.4-4) \times 10^{-5}$	0.05-0.5	—

[a] Gaseous Cl compound; not proven to be Cl_2.
[b] Fraction of I_2 likely to be adsorbed on aerosols.

In discussing the cycles of gases it is often necessary to subdivide the atmosphere into two reservoirs, the troposphere and the stratosphere, for which the residence times can be very different. The relations among F, R, M, and τ then apply to each of the reservoirs separately. For some gases, e.g., CO_2, the hydrosphere and the biosphere constitute important reservoirs and have to be taken into consideration.

Tables 1 and 2 define and explain the units used for atmospheric gases and give some important conversion factors. For easy comparison with aerosol data, the gas concentrations in this book will be expressed preferentially in $\mu g/m^3$, unless custom has established some special units as, for example, in the case of ozone.

1.2 Water Vapor

1.2.1 The Distribution and Cycle of Water Vapor in the Atmosphere

Water vapor is a highly variable gas and one of the oldest and best-known atmospheric tracers. Meteorology has gained invaluable information on tropospheric motions by the observation of clouds and cloud systems. The reason, however, for a treatment of it in air chemistry is based on other characteristics. First of all, condensation of water is of paramount importance for the cleansing of the atmosphere and thus for the cycle of numerous trace substances. Further, the study of the isotopic composition of water provided new and interesting insight into global aspects of the water cycle, which are of general importance for geochemistry, and, finally, evidence is accumulating that water vapor may be one of the most useful tracers for the study of stratospheric circulation.

We will start with a discussion of the vertical distribution of water vapor in the atmosphere. Figure 1 is based on the latest available data and contains all the reliable information. This figure shows the mass mixing ratio, which is a conservative property *above* the tropopause and thus is important for considerations of mass exchange. In the troposphere the mixing ratio decreases rapidly with altitude under the influence of the temperature distribution, but this decrease continues above the tropopause until a frostpoint of about — 83°C is reached. This fact was first observed by Brewer (1949) and later was well established by an extensive program of about 400 flights made by the Meteorological Research Flight Establishment (MRF) in Farnsborough, England, over a period of several years. Tucker (1957) has made the most comprehensive compilation of these data. The stratospheric values show a surprisingly small scatter and the average profile, given in Fig. 1, is fairly representative of all the individual flights.

TABLE 2

UNITS FOR GASES

Designation	Definition	Units
Volume or mole mixing ratio	Ratio of volumes at equal temperature and pressure conditions of moles, or of number of molecules of gas to air; independent of ambient conditions	10^{-2} = per cent by volume = per cent by mole 10^{-6} = part per million, ppm 10^{-8} = parts per hundred million, pphm 10^{-12} = parts per billion, ppb
Mass or weight mixing ratio	Volume ratio times ratio of molecular weight of gas to air; independent of ambient conditions	g/g g/kg ($\mu g = 10^{-6}$ g, sometimes called γ) μg/kg
Volume concentration at ambient conditions	Amount of gas in mass or moles per unit volume of air under conditions of ambient pressure and temperature; varies with ambient conditions	g/cm^3 or mole/cm^3, etc. g/m^3 $\mu g/m^3$ $\mu\mu g/m^3$ For atmospheric gases (e.g., O_3) cm of gas at STP per km altitude is sometimes used; 1 cm STP/km = ($10^4 \times$ density in g/liter STP) $\mu g/m^3$
Volume concentration at standard pressure and temperature (STP)	Amount of gas in mass or moles per unit volume of air under conditions of standard pressure and temperature; independent of ambient conditions	g/cm^3 STP etc., or mole/cm^3 STP, etc.

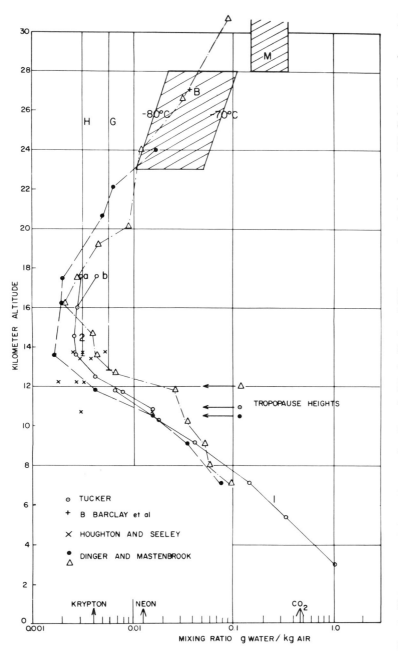

FIG. 1. Water vapor mixing ratio as a function of altitude. Tucker (1957), curves 1 and 2 based on 399 flights with a dew point meter over England. Data for the stratosphere are averaged separately with the troposphere as a datum level (curve 2). Top values a and b are explained in the text. Barclay *et al.* (1960), point B obtained by water vapor absorption. Houghton and Seeley (1960), spectroscopic measurements. Mastenbrook and Dinger (1960), dew point radiosondes. Hatched area between 23 and 28 km indicates range of frost points between $-70°$ and $-80°$ C for mother-of-pearl clouds. Gates *et al.* (1958), line G, average value above 12.8 km by spectroscopy. Houghton *et al.* (1957), line H, average value above 13.5 km by spectroscopy. Murcray *et al.* (1960), column M, range of average values above 28 km by spectroscopy.

Measurements in North Africa at 33°N (Helliwell and Mackenzie, 1957) also give very similar profiles and constant-level flights made at about 14 km between 30° and 70°N indicate that the frostpoint varies but little (around — 80°C) with latitude and weather. The spectroscopic data by Houghton and Seeley (1960) confirm these results at the tropopause level.

It was generally expected that the mixing ratio above 14 km would be constant throughout the stratosphere. In recent years, however, evidence has been accumulated which indicates that the mixing ratio increases in the middle and upper stratosphere. *

The MRF data seem to show this trend just at the maximum altitude, depending on the way the peak value of curve 2 is computed. Curve 2 was obtained by weighing the individual values with respect to the frequency of the tropopause level at which they occurred, and thus the peak value b, which is given by only one tropopause group in three seasons, may not be representative. Consequently, Tucker computed an alternative value a by applying the lapse rate of this group to the mean value at 16 km.

A few data from quite different sources are available for higher layers. Some of these data are fairly reliable, some are merely estimates. The mother-of-pearl clouds, which appear from December to February, primarily over southern Scandinavia, offer an opportunity to estimate the frostpoint for the altitude range of their appearance, viz., 23-28 km (Störmer, 1940). These clouds consist of water droplets or, more likely, of ice spheres about 3 μ in diameter. Unfortunately, no temperature soundings are available for these altitudes when mother-of-pearl clouds were present. According to Hesstvedt (1959), in 21 cases the temperature was — 67°C at 16 km and —70°C at 19 km, with an indication of a further decrease with altitude. From average data for latitudes 60-70°N, one can expect temperatures between —65°C and —75°C for the level at which these clouds appear. Assuming some additional cooling during the formation of these clouds, we arrive at an estimated temperature range of — 70° to —80°C. The corresponding area of mixing ratios is indicated by the hatched area in Fig. 1.

Barclay et al. (1960) measured the moisture content of the stratosphere by condensing water and carbon dioxide in a liquid nitrogen cold trap during a 3.5-hour balloon flight at 27 km. The volume of air was determined by the amount of carbon dioxide. The value of the water vapor mixing ratio is marked by B in Fig. 1 and falls in line with the other data. During 1959 and 1960 Brown et al. (1961) obtained six more measurements in about the same altitude ranging between 0.034 and 0.077 gr/kg except for one low value of 0.009 gr/kg at the lowest altitude of 24 km. These data are not included in Fig. 1, but agree reasonably well with the others.

---

* The following standard designation is used: lower stratosphere = tropopause to 20 km; middle stratosphere = 20-30 km; upper stratosphere = above 30 km.

There are a few independent spectroscopic measurements. Murcray *et al.* (1960) determined the average water vapor mixing ratio above 28 km, and the range of values is indicated in column M. Their values for the altitude range between 28 and 12 km are not too reliable and therefore are omitted. The values are at least one order of magnitude lower. Gates *et al.* (1958) and Houghton *et al.* (1957) obtained average values above 12.8 and 13.5 km, respectively, as indicated by lines G and H. The possible error of G is about 100%, but no limits were given for H.

Recently, Mastenbrook and Dinger (1960) discussed the results of dew point radiosonde measurements. Earlier data obtained by this method (Barrett *et al.*, 1950; Brasefield, 1954) showed much higher mixing ratios in the lower stratosphere than those indicated in Fig. 1. Water vapor released from the balloon or the equipment during ascent may introduce considerable errors. Unless it is assumed that the water vapor distribution differs considerably with longitude, these measurements cannot be reconciled with the MRF findings and must be regarded as unreliable. Mastenbrook and Dinger eliminated water vapor contamination and accepted only flights for which the ascent and descent values agreed. The values obtained during two of their three good flights are included in Fig. 1. The third flight showed higher mixing ratios in the lower stratosphere, but agreement for ascent and descent was not complete.

The various independent measurements shown in Fig. 1 indicate the same trend, i.e., an increase of the water vapor mixing ratio with altitude, although there are still too few data to determine how general this phenomenon may be. There can be little doubt that the air between 13 and 17 km in middle latitudes, with a frostpoint around $-80°C$, passed somehow through the region of the tropical tropopause. This is the only area in the atmosphere which has temperatures low enough to act as a cold trap for tropospheric water vapor. For the same reason, the higher water vapor mixing ratios found in the upper stratosphere could hardly have arrived with tropospheric air from latitudes lower than about 50°. We may get an idea of where the exchange occurs by calculating the mixing ratio at the tropopause level as a function of latitude. The possible mixing ratios at the tropical tropopause are around 0.002 g/kg and are certainly much too low. Table 3 shows data for higher latitudes. Mixing ratios between 0.04 and 0.1 g/kg would be expected if air were to penetrate through the tropopause in the middle latitudes, but the MRF data seem to exclude this possibility. Therefore, we must conclude that the exchange of moisture occurs through the polar tropopause. The highest mixing ratios, 0.1 g/kg, are found in summer and should represent the upper limit of mixing ratios in the stratosphere. If the exchange occurred during winter, the maximum possible mixing ratio in the stratosphere would be 0.02 g/kg.

A comparison of Table 3 with Fig. 1 suggests an exchange over the summer pole, but the data are not good enough for a decision.

TABLE 3

AVERAGE TEMPERATURE, PRESSURE, AND WATER VAPOR MIXING RATIO AT THE
TROPOPAUSE AS A FUNCTION OF LATITUDE [a]

	Latitude (degrees)					
	40	50	60	70	80	90
January						
Tropopause temperature (°C):	—55	—54	—56	—57	—59	—60
Pressure (mb):	235	285	330	355	355	330
Mixing ratio at 100% relative humidity (g/kg):	0.056	0.052	0.037	0.029	0.022	0.021
July						
Tropopause temperature (°C):	—55	—49	—50	—46	—48	—46
Pressure (mb):	170	230	265	295	305	305
Mixing ratio at 100% relative humidity (g/kg):	0.077	0.125	0.098	0.138	0.11	0.13

[a] Based on data from Hare and Orvig (1958).

Other information points to the winter pole. Ozone and rhodium-102 data demonstrate large-scale and high-reaching downward transport within the polar stratosphere only during winter. The stratospheric temperature structure over the winter pole is more favorable for vertical motions than is the structure over the summer pole. Most striking are the pronounced vertical movements, in both directions, in the middle stratosphere of the winter hemisphere as indicated by dynamic temperature fluctuations (Hare, 1960). These fluctuations are completely absent during the summer and culminate in the famous "explosive" warnings which are associated with the breakdown of the polar vortex in January and February.

As a tentative explanation for the high water vapor mixing ratios in the upper stratosphere, we suggest large-scale exchange processes in both directions over the winter pole. If further data confirm the increase in mixing ratio with altitude, water vapor may become a very important tracer for studying stratospheric circulation.

It is not unlikely that there is a longitudinal difference indicated between higher water vapor mixing ratios in the lower stratosphere over the United States and Western Europe. The possibility cannot be ex-

cluded that occasionally high-reaching convective clouds over a large continent can penetrate far into the lower stratosphere and carry moisture
with them. We feel, however, that this transport cannot be of global importance.

In a recent discussion (de Turville, 1961; Frith, 1961) it
was proposed that the oceans have resulted from the accreation of solar
protons, which by oxidation form water in the atmosphere. However, measurements of the flux of positive particles by Explorer X for instance
(Bridge et al., 1961) give values which are by one order of magnitude too
small to account for the ocean water if the age of the earth is taken as 4×10^9
years. This explanation would also be in contradiction to the concept that
the oxygen in the atmosphere originated from photodissociation of water
vapor and subsequent escape of hydrogen into space. Further data on stratospheric water vapor will decide between these possibilities. If the dry
layer at 15 km is a persistent feature over the polar regions, particularily
over the winter poles, it will be very difficult to invoke terrestrial sources
for the high humidity in the upper stratosphere and mesosphere.

The average residence time $\tau = M/R$ of water vapor in the
troposphere is about 10 days. M is the average amount of precipitable water
in a vertical column of air and R is the average rate of precipitation (Lettau, 1954). It can be expected that the residence time of those trace substances which are washed out by rain will be of similar magnitude. The residence time of water is, therefore, of importance for air chemistry and will
be discussed here in more detail.

The actual value of τ for water vapor varies considerably
with climatological conditions. To gain an idea of this variation with latitude, Table 4 was prepared on the basis of Bannon and Steele's (1957)

TABLE 4

AVERAGE RESIDENCE TIME OF WATER VAPOR IN THE ATMOSPHERE
AS A FUNCTION OF LATITUDE

	Latitude range (degrees)								
	0-10	10-20	20-30	30-40	40-50	50-60	60-70	70-80	80-90
Average precipitable water (g/cm²):	4.1	3.5	2.7	2.1	1.6	1.3	1.0	0.7[a]	0.45[a]
Average precipitation (g/cm² year):	186	114	82	89	91	77	42	19	11
Residence time (days):	8.1	11.2	12.0	8.7	6.4	6.2	8.7	(13.4)	(15.0)

[a] Values extrapolated.

maps of precipitable water. These data for the residence time would be correct if water vapor stayed within the same latitude belt for a time that was long as compared to the residence time. This is certainly an approximation and thus the values can give only the general trend and the magnitude of the possible variation. From the data in Table 4 we may infer that the average residence time of water vapor in the subtropics is about twice that in the middle latitudes.

The distribution of liquid cloud water within the atmosphere is of interest for considerations of the washout of trace materials in the troposphere, which will be discussed in detail in the chapter on rain chemistry. From studies in cloud physics (e.g., Cunningham, 1952), we know that most rain is formed in the lowest layers of the troposphere. This is also obvious from the gradient of the water vapor mixing ratio m in Fig. 1. If we assume steady state conditions, the removal rate of water vapor, i. e., the rate of precipitation p, is given by

$$ p = \frac{\partial}{\partial z} \left(D \frac{\partial m}{\partial z} \right). $$

With the assumptions that D is independent of altitude and that m is represented by an exponential function, p also decreases exponentially with altitude.

De Bary and Moeller (1960) recently gave data on the vertical distribution of cloud frequencies, based on 4 years of aircraft observations in Central Europe. Table 5 shows the annual average frequency of

TABLE 5

FREQUENCY OF CLOUDS AS A FUNCTION OF ALTITUDE FOR CENTRAL EUROPE [a]

Altitude (km):	0	1	2	3	4	5	Av: 0-5
Frequency (%):	0	44	49	36	33	28	Av: 32%

[a] De Bary and Moeller (1960).

all types of clouds as a function of altitude. We see that in these latitudes more than 30% of the lower troposphere is filled with clouds. This value decreases much more slowly with altitude than is indicated by the decrease of the water vapor mixing ratio. If we assume an average liquid water content in clouds of 0.5 g/m^3 and peak altitudes around 5.5 km for all clouds, the average liquid water present over 1 cm^2 of the earth's surface will be 9×10^{-2} g/cm^2. If the average annual precipitation rate is 70 cm, this liquid water must have an average residence time of 11 hours.

This is longer than the average lifetime of clouds and indicates the fact that most clouds evaporate. This estimate will be of interest for the modification of atmospheric aerosols, discussed in Chapter 2.

1.2.2 The Deuterium and Oxygen-18 Content of Water

Within the past 10 years, the stable isotopic species of water have become important tracers for studies of the atmospheric water cycle, as indicated by the work of Epstein (e. g., 1959), Dansgaard (1953), Friedman (1953), and others. The hydrogen and oxygen isotopes H, D, O^{16}, O^{17}, and O^{18} can form a total of nine different water molecules. Their over-all abundance in natural waters with respect to H and to O^{16} is respectively, $D = 1.38 \times 10^{-4}$, $O^{17} = 4.2 \times 10^{-4}$, and $O^{18} = 19.8 \times 10^{-4}$. Due to these abundances, the most prominent members of the isotopic family of water molecules are HDO^{16}, H_2O^{17}, and H_2O^{18}. The other members are much less abundant and can be neglected. Since it is difficult to measure H_2O^{17} and since it can be inferred that the variations of the ratios O^{18}/O^{17} and O^{17}/O^{16} are about half the variations of the ratio O^{18}/O^{16}, only the ratio O^{18}/O^{16} is considered when dealing with natural abundances (e.g., Epstein, 1959). Table 6 gives some data for HDO^{16} and H_2O^{18}. Fractionation of isotopic

TABLE 6

SOME DATA FOR HDO^{16} AND H_2O^{18}

Species	Mass	Relative abundance in ocean water	Observed variation range of abundance	
			Ocean	Fresh water and precipitation
HDO^{16}	19	3.10×10^{-4}	$\pm 2\%$	0 to -27%
H_2O^{18}	20	20×10^{-4}	$\pm 3\%_{00}$	$+6$ to $-50\%_{00}$

species in physical and chemical processes depends on the relative difference in molecular weight and therefore is fairly efficient for substances of low molecular weight, such as water. In the case of atmospheric water, fractionation occurs primarily by evaporation and condensation, due to differences in the vapor pressures of the isotopic species. The fractionation factor α is defined as the ratio of the abundances of the liquid to the vapor phase in the case of H_2O^{18}

$$a_{O^{18}} = (H_2O^{18}/H_2O^{16})_{liquid}/(H_2O^{18}/H_2O^{16})_{vapor} \equiv R_{l_{O^{18}}}/R_{v_{O^{18}}}.$$

It can be shown that α is a function of temperature alone and is independent of the relative composition. Since $R_{v_{O}18}$ is equal to the pressure ratio $p(H_2O^{18})/p(H_2O^{16})$, α_{O18} is equal to the ratios of the saturation pressures. The same is true of α_D. Table 7 gives these data as a function of temperature.

TABLE 7

RATIOS OF VAPOR SATURATION PRESSURES p_s AND
PHASE ENRICHMENTS FOR H_2O^{18} AND HDO^{16} [a]

Temperature (°C):	0	+10	+20	+30
$p_s(H_2O^{16})/p_s(H_2O^{18}) = a_{O18}$:	1.0114	1.0104	1.0095	1.0087
$p_s(H_2O^{16})/p_s(HDO) = a_D$:	1.120	1.087	1.074	1.066
$(a_D - 1)/(a_{O18} - 1)$:	10.5	8.4	7.8	7.5

[a] Kirschenbaum (1951), pp. 25, 29.

If the phase transitions are slow enough for equilibrium conditions to prevail, and if the newly formed phase is always removed, the composition of the remaining and decreasing phase will change progressively. If the vapor condenses, the condensate will contain a higher concentration of O^{18} and D than does the vapor, and if the condensed phase is currently removed, as in atmospheric precipitation, the vapor phase will continually be depleted of O^{18} and D. This process is described by the Rayleigh equation and was first used by Dansgaard (1953) to explain the isotopic variations of precipitation. The Rayleigh distillation formula for the liquid phase is

$$R_l/R_{l0} = f^{1-\alpha}$$

where R_l denotes the isotopic ratio of the remaining liquid, R_{l0} the ratio at the start of the distillation, and f the fraction of liquid left with $1 \geq f > 0$. The corresponding formula for vapor is

$$R_v/R_{v0} = f^{1-1/\alpha} \cong f^{\alpha-1}, \qquad \text{if } \alpha - 1 \ll 1.$$

It can be demonstrated that the Rayleigh formula describes the isotopic changes in atmospheric water fairly well. If the Rayleigh equation is valid, the changes for O^{18} and D should show a definite relationship. This relationship is confirmed by observations.

Before we discuss this, we will define the units in which the H_2O^{18} and the HDO^{16} content of water are usually expressed. If R_0 denotes the isotopic ratio of a standard, the variation of composition is given by $E = R/R_0 - 1$. For convenience, the numerical values for H_2O^{18} are given in per mill and for HDO^{16} in per cent:

$$\delta_{O^{18}} = 1000 \cdot E_{O^{18}}; \qquad \delta_D = 100 \cdot E_D.$$

Average ocean water is usually used as the standard.

If E is used to express changes in composition during phase transitions, it is called the phase enrichment with respect to the original composition R_0. Since $\mid \alpha - 1 \mid \ll 1$, the Rayleigh equation can be simplified and we obtain

$$E_l \cong (1 - \alpha) \ln f \qquad \text{and} \qquad E_v \cong (\alpha - 1) \ln f.$$

The ratio of the phase enrichment for H_2O^{18} and HDO^{16} is then

$$E_{D_l}/E_{O^{18}_l} \cong E_{D_v}/E_{O^{18}_v} \cong (1 - \alpha_D)/(1 - \alpha_{O^{18}}).$$

This approximation is accurate enough for a wide range of f between $1 \geq f > 0.05$. The values of $E_{D_v}/E_{O^{18}_v}$ depend only on the temperature and are given in Table 7. Since the calculation of differences is involved, the accuracy of these figures is not considered to be better than 10%. We see that the ratio of the phase enrichment is about 8 to 9 and changes very little within the normal temperature range. The investigations of Epstein and Mayeda (1953), Friedman (1953), and Craig and Boato (1955) confirmed this value for a large variety of ocean and fresh water samples and thus proved that the phase transitions in the hydrological cycle are indeed in equilibrium. A few deviations occur in stagnant lakes (e.g., Great Salt Lake) and in thermal waters, which show a larger variation of O^{18} for the same difference in D. Kinetic processes or an exchange of oxygen isotopes with minerals may be responsible for these deviations.

With fast phase transitions (i.e., under nonequilibrium conditions), the controlling factor in fractionation may not be the vapor pressure ratio, but gas kinetic properties such as the average molecular velocity, the collision frequency, or the molecular diffusion constant. These, in turn, are controlled by the mass ratio of the isotope species and should result in phase enrichment ratios $E_{O^{18}}/E_D$ of 0.5 to $\sqrt{0,5}$, compared with 9 under equilibrium conditions. Therefore, the ratio of phase enrichment is quite sensitive to deviations from equilibrium conditions.

The Rayleigh equation is based on the assumption that the forming phase is constantly removed and that the distillation proceeds under equilibrium. We saw that the phase enrichment ratio of about 9 for D/O^{18} is proof that the latter assumption is fairly correct for the atmospheric water cycle and that the Rayleigh equation can be applied. Figure 2 gives the $\delta_{O^{18}}$ values for liquid water and water vapor as a function of f. Starting with average ocean water where $\delta_{o18} = 0$, the water vapor in the atmosphere in close contact with the ocean surface has $\delta_{o18} = -8$. Very few data are available for atmospheric water vapor, but they are in general agreement with this value (Dansgaard, 1953). Since evaporation from the ocean is the major source of atmospheric water vapor, the value $\delta_{o18} = -8$ should prevail over wide areas of the low and middle latitudes.

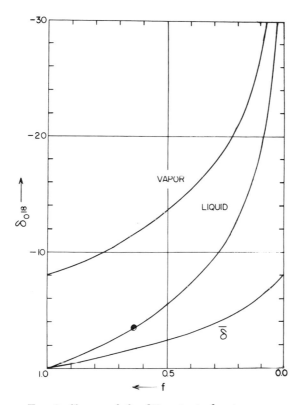

FIG. 2. Change of the O^{18} content of water vapor submitted to condensation according to the Rayleigh equation. The vapor starts with $\delta = -8$, which is the equilibrium value for average ocean water of $\delta = 0$. The condensed liquid starts with $\delta = 0$. $\bar{\delta}$ is the average δ value for all condensed water. f is the fraction of vapor remaining in the vapor phase (Epstein, 1959).

Figure 2 shows the change in composition when this water vapor is subjected to condensation. The δ_{o18} values of the remaining vapor and the condensed phase at the moment of its formation are plotted as a function of f. The first liquid water, perhaps in the form of some light rainfall, should have values close to zero. However, the data on precipitation and on fresh water generally indicate lower levels. Epstein and Mayeda (1953) give the following values for δ_{O18}: rain, Bermuda, $-$ 6.6; rain, Chicago, $-$ 7.1; Lake Michigan, $-$ 6.1; Mississippi River (St. Louis), $-$ 8.9; Mississippi River (mouth), $-$ 4.9. The first two rain values may not be representative, but they are in agreement with the lake and river water, which certainly reflect the average composition of precipitation over the central United States fairly well, except for some re-evaporation, resulting in a slight increase of O^{18} (mouth of the Mississippi). A value of $\delta_{O18} = -$ 8 would imply that all important rains in this area are formed by processes in which a large percentage of the original oceanic water vapor is removed in a single step. The *average* value for the water removed as a function of f is obtained easily by integration of the liquid phase curve in Fig. 2 and is included in the same figure. If all the vapor in an air mass is condensed, $\overline{\delta}_{O18}$ must equal the δ_{O18} of the vapor when condensation began. Precipitation with $\overline{\delta}_{O18} = -$ 6 to $-$ 7 would correspond to f-values of 0.1 to 0.05. But the f-values may also be lowered by recycling of fresh water over land or by precipitation in air masses which have already lost part of the water vapor, as in the case of snow from polar air masses. The actual average f-values for precipitation may therefore be higher than 0.1. Clearly, more data are needed to separate the various effects.

The water vapor of air masses which have lost a substantial fraction of their original ocean water vapor content can easily assume δ_{O18} values of $-$ 15 and less, and subsequent precipitation in such air masses should have similar values. Snow deposits on mountains and in polar regions represent such conditions and observed O^{18} data [e.g., Epstein and Mayeda] are in agreement with the expected values: snow, Chicago, $-$ 15; glaciers, Canada, $-$ 20; Columbia River, British Columbia (melt water), $-$ 15; polar ice caps, $-$ 30 to $-$ 50. Low δ_{O18} values in precipitation should also be expected in the lee of high mountain barriers and at the onset of a warm-front rain. Dansgaard (1953) observed that the O^{18} content drops very sharply at the beginning of a warm front rain and increases again as the surface warm front approaches. Precipitation in showers preceding the warm front showed much less O^{18} depletion. This is in agreement with the conventional concepts of the formation of such rains.

We see that the O^{18} content decreases systematically with latitude, altitude, and, to a lesser degree, with distance from the coast. Since temperature is the overruling factor in the degree of O^{18} depletion in atmospheric water vapor, the O^{18} content should show considerable seasonal variations in higher latitudes. Epstein and Sharp (1959) were able to identify the annual precipitation cycle in polar ice. In Greenland ice, summer and winter values of δ_{O18} range between $-$ 25 and $-$ 45 and provide an excellent tool for studying the stratigraphy of the ice even in deeper layers where other characteristics of the ice, such as density, begin to lose their validity (Fig. 3). The lowest values, — 50, were found at the South Pole.

The deposits of water with a low O^{18} content, which are found at high altitudes and primarily in the polar ice shields at high latitudes, must return to the ocean in a closed hydrological cycle. Epstein and Mayeda (1953) studied the relationship between salinity and O^{18} content in ocean waters. Both the salinity and the O^{18} content change with the addition of fresh water or by evaporation, but in different ways. If we start

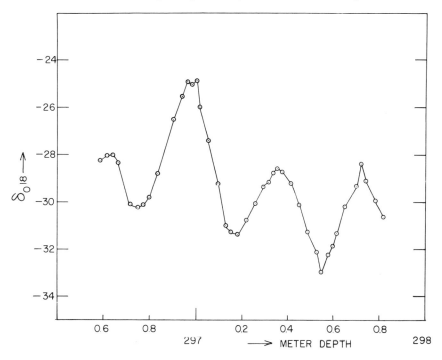

FIG. 3. Seasonal variation of the O^{18} content in Greenland ice, 300 meters below the surface, corresponding to an age of approximately 700 years. High values indicate summer (Epstein and Sharp, 1959).

with average ocean water with salinity $S = 35^0/_{00}$ and $\delta_{o18} = 0$, we should expect a 2.9 decrease of δ_{o18} for a $5^0/_{00}$ decrease of S by the addition of melt water with $\delta_{o18} = — 20$, a 0.9 decrease of δ_{o18} for a $5^0/_{00}$ decrease of S by the addition of river water with $\delta_{o18} = — 6$, and a 1.1 increase of δ_{o18} for a $5^0/_{00}$ increase of S through evaporation ($\delta_{o18} = + 8$).

Water samples from ocean currents into which melt water can flow, e.g., the California current off the west coast of the United States, show a relation between S and δ_{o18} that can be explained by an admixture of fresh water of $\delta_{o18} = — 20$, which is close to the composition of snow and ice deposits. There is also some indication of a similar relationship for deep sea samples, which may represent sinking polar waters.

On the other hand, samples from areas which cannot be influenced by fresh water, e.g., most regions with warm and temperate water, show an increase of δ_{O18} and S, but the relationship between the two values is poor. More surprising is the fact that the O^{18} increase per unit of salinity is greater than one would expect from evaporation and is closer to what one would get for the addition of fresh water with $\delta_{O18} = + 20$. Epstein and Mayeda point out that, budgetwise, the vast deposits of O^{18}-depleted water in the arctic regions must result in correspondingly enriched surface areas of the oceans, since vertical mixing in the oceans is slow. The process of this enrichment is obviously not simple Rayleigh distillation, where the new phase is always completely removed, but corresponds to a multiple-stage distillation with reflux. Precipitation is not negligible even in areas with considerable net evaporation. A net removal of water vapor with $\delta_{O18} = - 20$ can result from the repetition of evaporation and partial precipitation. The scatter of the δ_{O18}/S values for most. ocean areas indicates that the number of cycles in this multiple-stage distillation varies considerably with time and location.

We may include here a few remarks about the isotopic composition of atmospheric oxygen. Lane and Dole (1956) give the following values: oxygen in air, 0.2039% O^{18}; oxygen in ocean water, 0.1995% O^{18}; oxygen in fresh water, 0.1981% O^{18}. The O^{18} content of atmospheric oxygen is thus higher than in terrestrial waters by $\delta_{O18} = + 29^0/_{00}$ (Dole effect), and measurements have confirmed this result up to altitudes of 25 km (Dole *et al.*, 1954).

This finding is somewhat surprising in view of the concept that atmospheric oxygen is supposed to have originated by photodissociation of water vapor and subsequent escape of hydrogen into space. Experiments indicate that oxygen generated in this way has practically the same composition as in water. This is in apparent contradiction to the alledged origin of oxygen, unless there is a mechanism by which the composition can be modified subsequent to formation. Mechanisms of this kind are the thermodynamic equilibration with water in the atmosphere and/or oxygen production by living systems, but they must be excluded because they again yield an oxygen composition very close to that of water.

Lane and Dole (1956) suggested as a possible explanation the preferential *consumption* of O^{16} by the biosphere, i.e., by the respiration. Their experimental investigations show that the uptake of O^{16} for a variety of living systems, plants and animals, is indeed higher by the same ratio as the production of O^{16} in photosynthesis is lower than the O^{16} content in atmospheric oxygen. The O^{18}/O^{16} ratio of atmospheric oxygen, which originally must have been equal to that of water, thus appears to be adjusted to a steady state by recycling through the biosphere.

This explanation implies that the adjustment rate for the thermal equilibrium is small compared to the oxygen cycle. It further implies that the total amount of O^{16} "missing" in the atmosphere must be accumulated in the biosphere. The average amount of atmospheric O_2 is 230 g per cm^2 of the earth surface and the average amount of carbon in the terrestrial biosphere is about 0.3 g/cm^2 (see, e.g., Fig. 9). Even if the considerable amount of organic material in the oceans is included the O^{16} enrichment in organic material has to be one to two orders of magnitude higher than the depletion in the atmosphere, which is unlikely. It is also possible that O^{16} was preferentially used in the oxidation of the earth crust.

1.2.3 The Tritium Content of Water

The abudance and distribution of *natural* tritium in the atmosphere and hydrosphere was severely disturbed since the testing of thermonuclear weapons began with the Castle Series in spring 1954 (see Table 46). For this reason the present distribution of tritium will be discussed in connection with artificial radioactivity in Section 3.4.5. The *natural* tritium on the other hand will be discussed here, because of its intimate connection with the water cycle.

Tritium has a radioactive half-life of 12.5 years. The tritium content of a compound is usually expressed by the atomic ratio T/H, which is of the order of 10^{-18} in the hydrosphere. A T/H ratio of 10^{-18} is thus used as a convenient unit for tritium (tritium unit, T.U.). Tritium was discovered in atmospheric hydrogen as HT by Faltings and Harteck (1950) and in water as HTO by Grosse *et al.* (1951). Recently, Bishop *et al.* (1961) measured tritium in methane, probably as CH_3T.

For the determination of natural tritium, only data prior to 1953 can be used. The number of such measurements is very small and this is the reason why certain questions concerning natural tritium still remain open. The over-all distribution of natural tritium is given by the data in the accompanying tabulation (Begemann, 1961; see also Table 49).

Reservoir	T/H ratio (T. U.)	Per cent of total amount of tritium on earth
Hydrosphere		
Ocean	~1	~99
Fresh water	~5	—
Atmosphere		
H_2, 0.5 ppm	4×10^4	~0.1
H_2O, ~1000 ppm	5–20	~0.1
CH_4, 1.5 ppm	1×10^4	~0.1

We see that the specific activity of H_2 and CH_4 is about 1000 times higher than in water and that almost all natural tritium is contained in the ocean.

Natural tritium is produced by cosmic radiation with an altitude distribution very similar to that of Be^7 in Fig. 55 (see Section 3.3). Older calculations gave a total production rate of 2 atoms/cm² sec as an average value for the whole earth. More recently, Craig and Lal (1961) reconsidered the question of the production rate and obtained the revised figure of 0.25 $\pm$ 0.08 atoms/cm² sec which was also accepted by Begemann (1961). Because of fluctuations of the cosmic radiation by the activity of the sun, it is possible that this figure can vary by about 10%.

Under equilibrium conditions the total production rate must equal the total decay rate which is given by the total amount of tritium times the radioactive decay rate. The total amount of tritium in the various reservoirs can be determined, but the few data available for natural tritium are not sufficiently representative, so that the total amount can only be estimated on the basis of certain assumptions of the latitude dependence of the deposition rate of tritium with rain and other meteorological factors. The estimations of the total decay rate yielded: Craig and Lal (1961), 0.5 $\pm$ 0.3 atoms/cm² sec; Begemann (1961), 0.6 $\pm$ 0.2 atoms/cm² sec. Craig and Lal concluded that the limits of accuracy overlap with the calculated production rate of 0.25 and suggested that the data obtained between 1952 and 1954 were already contaminated to some degree by some smaller tests prior to Castle, so that agreement can be assumed. Begemann (1961) thinks that there is still a discrepancy between the production and decay rate, which may be due to the accretion of tritium from the sun or due to a solar component of the cosmic radiation, which cannot be determined in the low atmosphere. We have already discussed the possibility of the accretion of hydrogen from the solar wind in connection with the observed increase of the water vapor mixing ratio with altitude. Because of the complexity of this question and the unknown T/H ratio in the solar particle flux, nothing can be said at the present time. But both effects, accretion and production by a solar component of the cosmic radiation, should vary *in phase* with the sunspot cycle, and this gives a possibility to check this question. Begemann analyzed ice samples from the center of Greenland back to 1944 and found an indication of a slight variation of the specific activity in *antiphase* with the sunspot number. This seems to esclude a direct influence of the sun if the assumption is correct that the specific activity of the ice samples is proportional to the production rate of tritium in the atmosphere and not affected by the variation in the precipitation rate over Greenland or by other meteorological factors.

1.3 Carbon Dioxide

1.3.1 The Exchange of Carbon Dioxide at the Land and Ocean Surface

Carbon dioxide is not involved in any important reaction within the troposphere and stratosphere and has only little influence on rain water chemistry. Rather, since the turn of the century, interest of air chemistry in CO_2 is based on its cycle and on its slow, steady increase.

All important processes in which atmospheric CO_2 is involved occur at the earth's surface, and the atmosphere acts only as a *passsive buffer reservoir* with a large, but still limited, capacity. The rate of exchange with the ocean and the biosphere is relatively slow, but the ocean represents a huge reservoir compared to the atmosphere. The balance between these two reservoirs is, e.g., very sensitive to small variations of the temperature and the pH value of ocean water and also to fluctuations in the marine biosphere. The equilibrium may perhaps not even be stable and may be subject to secular variations of unknown magnitude. In addition, man currently generates large quantities of CO_2 and is about to upset the natural conditions. Since CO_2 plays an important role in the radiation budget of the atmosphere, effects on the world climate are not excluded (Kaplan, 1960).

Carbon dioxide is the major source for organic carbon and realization of this stimulated an early interest in its role for plant life. The amount used annually by the biosphere amounts to 3% of the total atmospheric CO_2. Therefore, it is to be expected that plant life has a considerable effect on the concentration of CO_2 near the earth's surface.

The intake of CO_2 by the plants, i.e., the CO_2 assimilation, is largely controlled by radiation, and, for the same amount of light, is approximately proportional to the CO_2 partial pressure P_{CO_2} in air (Lundegardh, 1954); no assimilation can occur during the night. This intake of CO_2 by the living plant material must be counterbalanced by a corresponding production of CO_2 from decaying organic material, which occurs mostly in the soil through the activity of bacteria. This release of CO_2 from the soil depends on the type, structure, moisture, and temperature of the soil. The temperature dependence results in a small daily variation over uncovered ground with a minimum release of CO_2 occurring during the night. The carbon concentration in soil air can be 100 times higher than in air. The use of CO_2 for assimilation, and the production of CO_2 in the soil, results in a biological cycle which is confined to a fairly shallow layer of the atmosphere and is responsible for the fluctuations observed at the land surface. The amounts involved can be best demonstrated by an example: The intake of CO_2 from the air over an oat field during the 8-hour period of assimilation in summer was $8 \times 15 = 120$ kg CO_2 per hectare. At the same time, the release of CO_2 from the soil during the day was $24 \times 5 \times 120$ kg per hectare. For the most part there is no complete balance between assimilation and release in one location. Over farmlands and forests more CO_2 is picked up during the growing season from the air, whereas, in other areas or during the rest of the year, more CO_2 is released from the soil. The release of CO_2 from soil can be as low as 1 kg CO_2 per hectare and per hour over clay soils, and as high as 15 kg over forest soils.

The 120 kg CO_2 in our example of the oat field corresponds to the total CO_2 in an air column of 20 meters. If the fluctuation of the CO_2 concentration at the bottom of this column were only 40% instead of 100% and if the decrease with altitude were exponential, one would expect a 1 to 2% variation of CO_2 even at 1 to 2 km. These estimates demonstrate the thickness of the layers which may be involved in the daily CO_2 cycle.

In his extensive studies of atmospheric CO_2, Lundegardh (1924) gave the first comprehensive data on fluctuations of CO_2 concentration near the ground under various conditions. The average variation for several years was $\pm 15\%$, with a maximum difference of more than 100% between the maximum and minimum at his station in Sweden. From his data we drew a schematic picture of the vertical profiles of CO_2 for two typical forms of vegetation (Fig. 4) to demonstrate the approximate magnitude of the fluctuations involved and the direction of the vertical fluxes. The vertical fluxes are given as the product of the vertical gradient times

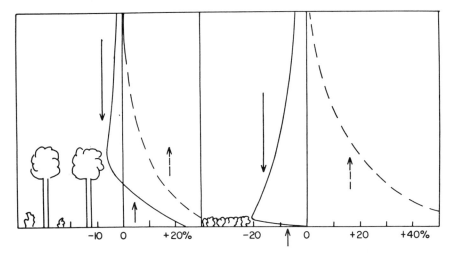

FIG. 4. Schematic diagram of the vertical distribution of CO_2 over a forest and a vegetable field. The abscissa indicates per cent deviation from the average concentration. The solid lines represent daytime conditions with assimilation, the dashed lines represent nighttime conditions. The arrows indicate the direction and the relative magnitude of the CO_2 flux.

the eddy diffusion coefficient. Because of the strong daily variation of the latter, the steeper CO_2 gradients during night, in fact, represent smaller fluxes.

Because soil and vegetation are so close together, part of the CO_2 cycle is "short-circuited" and involves only the lowest layer of the atmosphere. The thickness of the layer above the vegetation, which is involved in the cycle, depends on the intensity of the fluxes, on the turbulent state of the atmosphere, and to a considerable degree, on the horizontal extent of the active area. It is readily understandable that the interaction of these factors will produce a large variety of profiles and amplitudes. During summer, for instance, forests generally have a net consumption but the production of CO_2 from the soil is considerable and results in positive deviations up to 200% near the ground. In potato fields, e.g., CO_2 concentration was found to be 30% higher below the leaves than above them.

The daily variation of concentration controlled by the rhythm of assimilation and eddy diffusion is well illustrated in Fig. 5 by Huber (1952). The CO_2 concentration was recorded at heights of 1, 4.5, and 22.5 meters above a field of sugar beets during a day with fine weather. The lowest value was reached before sunset and the highest at sunrise. The small decrease of CO_2 with height during the day and the large increase during the night do not reflect the flux, but rather reflect the daily trend of the eddy diffusion coefficient. The record was quite different during cloudy and windy weather because of reduced assimilation and smaller variation of the eddy diffusion as demonstrated in the lower part of Fig. 5.

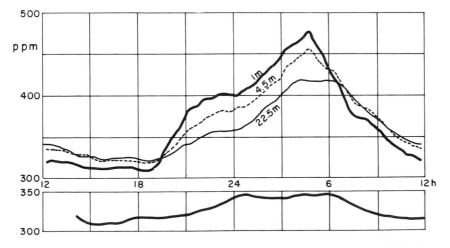

FIG. 5. Daily variation of CO_2 at 1, 4.5, and 22.5 meters above a wheat field during sunny weather (upper) and overcast weather (lower). In the latter case, the difference between the three heights was too small to be plotted (Huber, 1952).

In a more refined study, Monteith and Szeicz (1960) recently showed that the integrated fluxes of CO_2 over a field of sugar beets agreed fairly well with the measured growth rate of the beets. They determined the flux by measuring the wind speed and the CO_2 gradient over an interval of 25 cm above the leaves, and the agreement indicated that this simple method was a good approximation. They found gradients up to -3 ppm/25 cm during the day and up to $+76$ ppm/25 cm during nights with stable stratifications. Parallel measurements of the radiation demonstrated how closely the vertical CO_2 gradient is correlated with the intensity of assimilation, i.e., with the daily variation of radiation.

Needless to say, the consumption of fuel in highly populated or industrial areas constitutes a considerable source of CO_2. Except for these, the sources and sinks of CO_2 over land are distributed in time and space in such a way that net results are minimized. This is different over the sea. Here large areas act either as a sink or source and can thus have a profound influence on the CO_2 content of air masses. The concentration $[CO_2]$ in air over water is controlled by the concentration $[H_2CO_3]$ of the undissociated CO_2 or H_2CO_3 in water, which in turn is in dissociation equilibrium with bicarbonate HCO_3^- and carbonate $CO_3^=$ ions (see Section 4.2.1). The total dissolved CO_2 in ocean water is strongly dependent on the pH value, the temperature, and the salinity. Buch in his basic studies of the CO_2 in the oceans (summarized by Harvey, 1955), gave tables to calculate the total dissolved CO_2, but the agreement with observed values is not satisfactory because of the extreme sensitivity with respect to pH and temperature. Kanwisher (1960) recently made experimental measurements of the temperature dependence of $[CO_2]$ over sea water and found a linear increase of 4.5% per °C, if the total CO_2 fo the system air-water remains constant. A 0.02 unit change in pH will result in a 10% change of $[CO_2]$. The over-all effect of these relations is a larger $[CO_2]$ over the warm ocean water in lower latitudes, and a lower partial pressure in high latitudes. Unfortunately, there are not very many measurements of the CO_2 concentration in air over the oceans and parallel determinations of the equilibrium partial pressure $[CO_2]$ of sea water. Eriksson (1959 a) discussed these data in a recent survey. He calculates CO_2 partial pressures over the tropical oceans of 400 to 800 ppm, and a few observed air analyses in the same areas yield values which are only 30 to 70 ppm lower. Over the Atlantic at 40°N, Buch found that the CO_2 concentration in air was 20-40 ppm higher than the $[CO_2]$ of the sea and found the latter as low as 100 ppm in arctic waters. Thus, the tropical oceans act as a uniform source, and the waters in higher latitudes act as a huge sink of atmospheric CO_2. The resulting flux of CO_2 in the atmosphere from low to high latitudes must be counterbalanced by a corresponding flux in the ocean when arctic waters sink and spread to low latitudes.

Kanwisher (1960) points out that at least locally, the growth and decay of marine plankton can result in considerable changes of the [CO_2] of ocean water with a seasonal trend, but there are too few data to reveal any seasonal effects over sea water and to estimate the biological influence. Naturally, daily variations are small over the oceans.

1.3.2 The Distribution of Carbon Dioxide in the Atmosphere

The general features of the large-scale distribution of CO_2 in the atmosphere, and its seasonal variation, emerged only after an integrated effort had been made, during and after the IGY, under the direction of Keeling (1960). In the course of this program samples were taken at two Antarctic stations, two Arctic stations, at Mauna Loa Observatory in Hawaii, and during flights and cruises over the North and South Pacific. Recording stations were maintained in Antarctica, Hawaii, and California. The relative accuracy of the data is approximately ± 0.3 ppm.

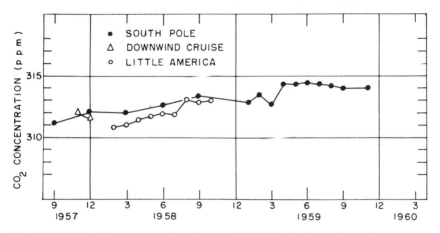

FIG. 6. Variation in concentration of atmospheric CO_2 in the southern hemisphere, 1957-1960 (Keeling, 1960).

If obviously local contaminations, either anthropogenic or natural, are excluded, and only representative data are used, the distribution demonstrated in Figs. 6 and 7 is observed. There is almost no seasonal variation in the southern hemisphere and the regional differences are surprisingly small, as indicated by the excellent agreement between the Antarctic data and those obtained during the Downwind Cruise between 0° and 50°S latitude. The South Pole data indicate a constant increase in CO_2 of 1.3 ppm annually.

In the North Pacific and in the Arctic, on the other hand, the CO_2 content shows a marked seasonal variation with an amplitude of about 5 ppm (Fig. 7). The maximum occurs in spring at the onset of the growing season and the minimum occurs in fall when plant growth has ceased. This strongly suggests that the variation is caused by the biological cycle of the terrestrial biosphere in temperate latitudes. The explanation is supported by the observation that the isotopic ratio C^{13}/C^{12} varies in a way which is to be expected if fractionation by assimilation is involved (Keeling, 1958).

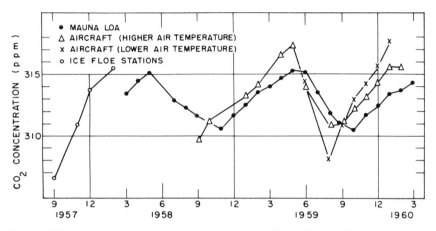

FIG. 7. Variation in concentration of atmospheric CO_2 in the northern hemisphere, 1957-1960 (Keeling, 1960).

The absence of a seasonal variation in the southern hemisphere is in line with this interpretation because here the wooded areas are concentrated in the tropical latitudes with no annual cycle, and those in temperate latitudes are rather small. A damping influence of the large ocean areas cannot be very marked because the exchange time of CO_2 between atmosphere and ocean is about 5 years and thus is long compared with the seasonal cycle. These observations seem to indicate also that mixing between the two hemispheres must be rather slow or otherwise the variation of the northern hemisphere would penetrate into the southern hemisphere. Calculations show that the mixing rate must be longer than 1 per year.

The slight increase of CO_2 in the southern hemisphere reflects the consumption of fossil fuel. A similar increase occurs in the northern hemisphere, but is difficult to determine accurately because of the large seasonal fluctuations.

The data in Figs. 6 and 7 were selected in such a way that the influence of local sources or sinks is avoided. Usually, ground observations of CO_2 are affected by local biological and anthropogenic activities, and the seasonal variations can be expected to exhibit geographical differences. Persistent source and sink areas must result in persistent horizontal gradients of the CO_2 content. This is indeed observed and the measurements of the Scandinavian CO_2 network offer a substantial material for a detailed study. The latest review of these data given by Bischof (1960) is concerned with 19 stations operated since 1955. It should be noted that the observations are made only three times a month at noon when turbulence has reduced local effects to a minimum. In general, there is a minimum in summer and a maximum in winter in agreement with Fig. 7, but there are considerable deviations. In the years 1955 to 1957, for example, there was a summer minimum, but it became successively narrower and in 1957 was enclosed between two maxima in May-June and September. In 1958 and 1959 the yearly fluctuations were very irregular. There is a striking difference in the behavior of the data from Finland and Scandinavia, the former showing markedly higher yearly averages by 10 to 20 ppm, and a summer maximum, particularly in the early years. One has the impression that whereas Scandinavia is climatologically part of the Atlantic region, Finland is linked to a continental Eurasian system. Other, scattered, data from Vienna and Central Europe seem to show a broad minimum in summer and a maximum in winter, in phase with the general pattern of the northern hemisphere.

Little need be said about the large-scale vertical distribution of CO_2. It is now generally accepted that mixing in the atmosphere up to about 80-km altitude is intense enough to inhibit any gravitational separation of gases. Hagemann et al. (1959) confirmed a constant mixing ratio of 311 ± 2 ppm up to 30 km altitude. This fact is used to determine the volume of collected air samples in connection with the measurement of other constituents (see, e.g., Barclay et al., 1960).

1.3.3 The Secular Increase of Carbon Dioxide

Based on a survey of available CO_2 measurements, Callendar (1940) came to the conclusion that the amount of CO_2 has increased by about 10% since the turn of the century and he suggested that this was due to the burning of fossil fuel by man. Estimates indicated that the amount of coal, oil, etc., burnt since the middle of the last century is only slightly higher than the observed increase of total atmospheric CO_2. Since then this subject has been discussed in various papers (e. g., Slocum, 1955). The following points were raised in these discussions:

(1) The available data are not numerous and consistent enough to prove that an increase really occurred. The data from the last century scatter considerably over such a range that it appears almost hopeless to draw any conclusions from them. In most cases they are too high. The accuracy of the data has been improving since the beginning of this century, but still there are some inconsistencies. It is understandable,

on the basis of our previous discussion, that the location, time of day, or sampling height may have a considerable systematic influence on the results. Since there is no long uniform series of measurements, one can only try to screen each set of available data carefully for reliability and select the most representative data. This procedure is certainly somewhat subjective and this is why the subject was debated. In a recent analysis of all the CO_2 data, Bray (1959) finds that the indicated increase is not always statistically significant. However, as of now, the general consensus is that the increase is real. We refer to the latest of a series of papers on this subject, that of Callendar in 1958, in which he very systematically selects the reliable sources and arrives at the conclusion that prior to 1900 the average CO_2 concentration in the northern hemisphere was 290 ppm and that since then there is proof of a fairly constant increase up to the present time. Figure 8

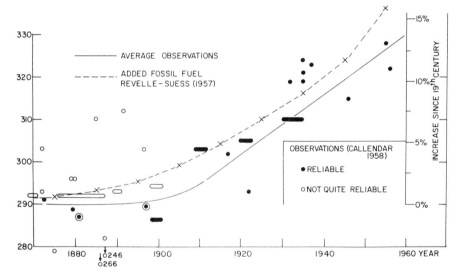

FIG. 8. The secular increase of CO_2, according to Callendar (1958). The solid line represents the average of the observations and the dashed line the expected increase by fossil fuel consumption since the middle of the last century, according to Revelle and Suess (1957). The right-hand scale gives the per cent increase since 1870. The left-hand scale gives ppm CO_2.

represents his data and the estimate of total fossil fuel burnt (Revelle and Suess, 1957) as a function of time. It appears that both sets of data agree fairly well and that the total observed increase in CO_2, as of now, is about 13%.

(2) The ocean is a huge reservoir of CO_2 in exchange with the atmosphere, and a considerable portion of the artificially produced CO_2 should have been absorbed by the ocean, leaving only a fraction in the

atmosphere. If this proved to be the case, it would be necessary to invoke additional sources of CO_2 such as changes in the amounts of carbon stored in the biosphere, a slight increase of ocean surface temperature, or similar possibilities. At the moment it looks as if indeed most of the CO_2 produced by man has remained in the atmosphere due to a peculiar buffer mechanism of sea water, and that Callendar's original suggestion is correct (Bolin and Eriksson, 1959), as will be discussed in more detail in the next section.

(3) It was argued that if all the artificially produced CO_2 that contains no C^{14} had remained in the atmosphere, one should expect the decrease in the C^{14}/C^{12} ratio to be equivalent to the CO_2 increase. However, the observed decrease of the C^{14}/C^{12} ratio, sometimes referred to as the Suess effect, is only about 2 to 3% (Revelle and Suess, 1957). The explanation is that the partitioning of the C^{14} between atmosphere and ocean is not affected by the buffering mechanism, so that the two quantities do not have to be the same. However, quantitative agreement has not yet been reached on this point.

Since most of these questions are closely related to the carbon cycle, we shall discuss them in more detail in the next section.

1.3.4 The Carbon Dioxide Cycle

The importance of CO_2 for life aroused early interest in the cycle of carbon on earth. The most important part of this cycle is the exchange of CO_2 between the atmosphere on the one hand, and the oceans and the terrestrial biosphere on the other. The oceans themselves do not represent a uniformly mixed reservoir and contain carbon in a variety of forms. For quantitative considerations, it proved useful to subdivide the ocean into two layers, one a shallow layer above the thermocline and the other, the deep sea. The upper layer has an average depth of 50 to 100 meters (Craig, 1957), is well mixed by the action of wind and waves, and contains most of the marine life. The deep sea moves slowly with an overturn time of the order of several hundred years.

The terrestrial biosphere consists of the living material of plants and the dead material of humus deposits. A schematic diagram of the size of the various reservoirs and of the carbon cycle is given in Fig. 9; it was first presented in this form by Craig (1957) and is now widely accepted.

A slower cycle is superimposed on this relatively fast cycle. It involves rock weathering and the dissolution or precipitation of carbonates in the ocean and is estimated to result in an overturn of marine carbon once in 10^5 years (Brown, 1957). This slow cycle is of importance for geology and geochemistry but can be disregarded for our discussions.

The amounts of carbon stored in the various reservoirs
(Fig. 9) are usually expressed in terms of average grams per square cen-
timeter of the earth, or in units of atmospheric carbon. It is apparent that
the deep sea contains by far most of the carbon of the "fast" cycle and that
the other reservoirs are comparable to each other in size. In turn, the carbon content of the sediments is several orders of magnitude larger than
that of the deep sea.

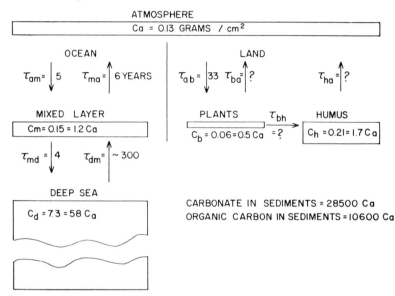

FIG. 9. Carbon cycle of the atmosphere and the ocean, essentially according
to Craig (1957). C denotes the global average carbon density in g/cm^2 for
the various reservoirs, atmosphere (a), mixed layer (m), deep sea (d), plants
on land (b), and humus (h). τ is the residence time in exchange with the respective reservoirs. The height of the columns is proportional to the carbon
density. Carbon in sediments, 28,500 C_a; organic carbon in sediments, 10,600 C_a.

The carbon cycle is an outstanding example of the successful application of isotopic methods to geophysical problems. There were
earlier estimates of the exchange times between the reservoirs, but reliable
values were obtained only after C^{14} measurements became available. Our
present knowledge is based on a series of papers by Craig (1957), Revelle
and Suess (1957), and Arnold and Anderson (1957). These studies were
concerned mainly with the exchange time τ_{am} of the CO_2 between the atmosphere and the ocean. Three different methods were used to determine
this quantity:

(1) Consideration of the steady state C^{14} balance relative
to cosmic-ray production, physical removal, and decay in the atmosphere
(Craig).

(2) Consideration of the steady state material balance of C^{14} in the ocean (Craig, Revelle and Suess, Arnold and Anderson).

(3) The dilution of C^{14} in the atmosphere (Suess effect) by the production of CO_2 from coal and other fossil fuels (Revelle and Suess, Arnold and Anderson).

The first two methods are not independent because both make use of the important value of the radiocarbon concentration in ocean water relative to the atmosphere, corrected for fractionation by the C^{13}/C^{12} ratio in water and air. This C^{14} concentration gives the apparent age of the ocean water. Within reasonable limits all three methods arrive at similar values for τ_{am}, which indicates that the factors governing the carbon cycle are relatively well understood. It should be noted, however, that the application of the third method was recently re-examined by Bolin and Eriksson (1959) in a careful analysis and resulted in some modifications of the conclusions.

We will now discuss these problems in more detail. We denote

K $= 1/\tau =$ exchange rate; $\tau =$ residence time in years for C^{12}

N $=$ amount of C^{12}

$K^*, N^* =$ indicates the same for C^{14}

R $= N^*/N =$ relative concentration of C^{14}.

Subscripts a, m, m', b, h, s, w, and t refer to the atmosphere (a), the rapidly mixed layer above the thermocline (m), the effective mixed layer (m'), the terrestrial biosphere (b), humus (h), sea (s), woods (w), and total (t). The combination of subscripts am means "between atmosphere and mixed layer," etc.

Q $=$ production rate of C^{14}

λ $= 1/\tau_r =$ decay rate and life time of C^{14}; $\tau_r = 8030$ years

$\alpha_{s/a} = \alpha_{s/w}/\alpha_{a/w} =$ ratio of fractionation factors of carbon-14 in the sea and air to wood of the 19th century.

$\alpha_{s/a} = 1.049/1.037 = 1.012$

We assume that the internal mixing within the various ocean layers is fast as compared to τ_r, so that the concentrations within the reservoirs are sufficiently constant. Under steady state conditions, for the balance of C^{14} in the atmosphere [method (1)], we then have

$$K_{am}^* N_a^* - K_{ma}^* N_m^* = Q - \lambda(N_a^* + N_b^* + N_h^*)$$

because

$$N_a^*(K_{ab}^* + K_{ah}^*) - N_b^*K_{ba} - N_h^*K_{ha} = \lambda(N_b^* + N_h^*).$$

For C^{12} the steady state requires

$$K_{am} \cdot N_a = K_{am} \cdot N_m$$

and

$$K_{am}^*/K_{ma}^* = \alpha_{s/a} \cdot K_{am}/K_{ma} = \alpha_{s/a}N_m/N_a \cong N_m/N_a. \qquad (1)$$

Substitution results in

$$\tau_{am}^* = \frac{\tau_r(1 - R_m/R_a \cdot \alpha_{s/a})}{[Q/\lambda - (N_a^* + N_b^* + N_h^*)]/N_a^*} \qquad (2)$$

where

$$\theta = \tau_r(1 - R_m/R_a\alpha_{s/a}) \qquad (3)$$

is the apparent C^{14} age of the mixed ocean layer. The C^{14} content of various shells shows this value to be about 400 years, but since there may be some local dilution by C^{12} carbonates from rivers in the coastal waters where these shells grow, 300 years seems to be a reasonable figure (Revelle and Suess, 1957). Q/λ is equivalent to the average total amount of C^{14} per cm², and thus the denominator is the ratio of C^{14} in the sea to that in the atmosphere.

The quantities N_b^* and N_h^* can only be estimated, but they are comparatively small so that errors in these estimations amount to only a few per cent uncertainty in τ_{am}^*. Q is 2 atoms/cm² sec, or 4.0×10^{-23} gr/cm² sec. The greatest uncertainty in τ_{am}^* is introduced by that of Q, which is about 25%. With an absolute value of

$$R_a = 1.037 \times R_w = 1.037 \times 1.24 \times 10^{-12} = 1.29 \times 10^{-12}$$

yielding $N_a^* = 1.62 \times 10^{-13}$ gr/cm², and $\lambda = 3.92 \times 10^{-12}$/sec, we obtain

$$\tau_{am}^* = \alpha_{a/w} \cdot \tau_{am} \cong \tau_{am} = 5 \pm 2 \text{ years.}$$

In the second method Craig considers the material balance of C^{14} for the upper mixed layer in the ocean. Assuming that mixing within the ocean cannot result in fractionation, i.e., that $K^* = K$, we have

$$K_{am}^* \cdot N_a^* + K_{dm}N_d^* = N_m^*(K_{ma}^* + K_{md} + \lambda)$$

$$K_{md}N_m^* = N_d^*(K_{dm} + \lambda)$$

and

$$K_{md}N_m = K_{dm}N_d.$$

Substitution and consideration of (1) and (3) yields

$$\tau_{am}^* = \frac{\tau_r}{F}\left[\frac{R_a}{R_m} - \frac{1}{\alpha_{s/a}}\right] = \frac{\theta\,R_a}{F\,R_m} \tag{4}$$

and very approximately,

$$\tau_{am}^* \cong \theta/F$$

where

$$F = \left[N_m + N_d\left(\frac{K_{dm}}{K_{dm}+\lambda}\right)\right]/N_a = \left[N_m + N_d\left(\frac{\tau_r}{\tau_{dm}+\tau_r}\right)\right]/N_a.$$

For rapid mixing between the deep sea and the mixed layer, we have

$$F = (N_m + N_d)/N_a$$

and with very slow mixing $F = N_m/N_a$.

$$N_{m'} = N_m + N_d\left(\frac{K_{dm}}{K_{dm}+\lambda}\right)$$

can therefore be called the *effective* marine reservoir which takes part in the exchange with the atmosphere.

We see that the value of θ is important for both expressions (2) and (4) and that $\tau_{am}^* \cong \tau_{am}$. The estimates of N_m and N_d are fairly reliable, but little is known about K_{dm}. A few scattered data indicate a relative age of the deep sea as against the mixed layer, i.e., an approximate value of τ_{dm}, of a few hundred years, which is small compared with τ_r. If we put $N_m = 1.2\,N_a$, $N_d = 58\,N_a$, $\tau_r = 8030$ years, and if τ_{dm} ranges from 0 to 1000 years, τ_{am} varies between 5.0 and 5.6 years. Thus, uncertainties in τ_{dm} have very little influence on this second value of τ_{am}, which agrees favorably with the previous one. The effective reservoir $N_{m'}$ is 0.97 of the total ocean, which is significantly different from N_m.

Numerical values for τ_{ma} and τ_{md} can be obtained from our equations and are included in Fig. 9. An independent estimate by Hutchinson (1954) yields $\tau_{ab} = 33$ years, so that the total residence time of CO_2 in the atmosphere becomes

$$\tau_a = \left(\frac{1}{\tau_{am}} + \frac{1}{\tau_{ab}}\right)^{-1} = 4.3 \text{ years.}$$

Values for τ_{ba}, τ_{ha}, and τ_{bh} are not known.

These calculated values of the exchange times determine the carbon cycle fairly well under equilibrium conditions. Since the in-

dustrial revolution, this equilibrium no longer exists for C^{12} and since the
tests of thermonuclear bombs, the same is true for C^{14}. Table 8 gives figures
for the global production of CO_2 in the past and an extrapolation for the
future, based on the assumption that atomic power will not be developed

TABLE 8

ESTIMATED CUMULATIVE AMOUNTS OF CO_2 ADDED
TO THE ATMOSPHERE BY CONSUMPTION OF FOSSIL FUELS [a]

Decade	Assuming future requirements estimated by the U.N. (% atm. CO_2)	Assuming that fuel consumption remains constant at the 1955 rate (% atm. CO_2)
1950-59	15.6	15.6
1960-69	21.0	19.5
1970-79	28.5	23.4
1980-89	39.0	27.2
1990-99	53.3	31.1

[a] Revelle and Suess (1957).

to any degree. Up to 1955, the total production amounted to 17% of the
atmospheric CO_2 (Fig. 8). The impact of this CO_2 production on our atmosphere is already a matter of concern and will be even more so in the future.
Revelle and Suess (1957) state: "Human beings are now carrying out a
large scale geophysical experiment of a kind that could not have happened
in the past nor be reproduced in the future. Within a few centuries we are
returning to the atmosphere and oceans the concentrated organic carbon
stored in the sedimentary rocks over hundreds of millions of years. This
experiment, if adequately documented, may yield a far reaching insight
into the processes determining weather and climate."

If the CO_2 injected into the atmosphere remained there, in
1955 one would expect an increase in the CO_2 content of 17%, but the corresponding decrease of the C^{14}/C^{12} ratio would be smaller due to isotopic
exchange. As Fig. 8 shows, there has been an increase of about 13% since
the turn of the century. The decrease of the C^{14}/C^{12} ratio is much less. Revelle and Suess (1957) report an average decrease of only 1.7% in wood
from various parts of the world between 1940 and 1950, compared to wood
from the 19th century. Values given by other authors vary between 1.8

and 3% (see Bolin and Eriksson, 1959). Data later than 1953 are likely to be influenced by C^{14} produced in atomic tests.

If isotopic exchange between atmosphere and ocean is neglected, these figures suggest that only 2-3% of the total CO_2 production had remained in the atmosphere and that the rest was absorbed by the ocean. This would explain the size of the Suess effect, but makes it necessary to invoke additional sources to explain the observed increase of CO_2. The third method of determining τ_{am} was based on these considerations, and values of about 10 years were calculated (Revelle and Suess, 1957; Arnold and Anderson, 1957). It was pointed out, however, that the discrepancy may, in part, be due to the peculiar buffer mechanism of sea water by which a 1% increase in the CO_2 concentration of sea water results in an approximate 10% increase of the CO_2 partial pressure in air. The quantitative treatment of the problem, however, was not satisfactory and is superseded by the analysis of Bolin and Eriksson (1959), which we will discuss in more detail.

The CO_2 dissolved in the ocean is present in the following form:

Concentration of undissociated CO_2 or H_2CO_3	$[H_2CO_3]$ = 0.013	millimole per liter
Concentration of bicarbonate	$[HCO_3^-]$ = 1.900	millimole per liter
Concentration of carbonate	$[CO_3^=]$ = 0.235	millimole per liter
Total concentration	$\Sigma\,[CO_2]$ = 2.148	millimole per liter.

$[HCO_3^-]$ and $[CO_3^=]$ are controlled by $[H_2CO_3]$ and the hydrogen ion concentration $[H^+]$ through the following equations:

$$[HCO_3^-] \cdot [H^+] / [H_2CO_3] = K_1$$

$$[H^+] \times [CO_3^=] / [HCO_3^-] = K_2$$

where K_1 and K_2 are the first and second dissociation constants of H_2CO_3 in sea water. The equilibrium concentration $[CO_2]$ in air is proportional only to $[H_2CO_3]$:

$$[CO_2] = \beta_1[H_2CO_3].$$

An important condition for this system is the balance of charges by cations, which implies that $[cations] = [HCO_3^-] + 2[CO_3^=]$ remains constant, if the slow processes of dissolution or precipitaion of $CaCO_3$ are disregarded.

The above system of equations requires that with an increase of $[CO_2]$ and correspondingly of $[H_2CO_3]$, $[H^*]$ must also increase. The effect of this change in the pH value is a 1% increase of the total carbon dioxide content in sea water for every 12.5% increase in $[CO_2]$. Bolin and Eriksson apply these considerations to a similar but refined system of equations for the same two-layer ocean model of Craig and calculate the increase of C^{12} in the atmosphere due to fossil fuel consumption as a function of τ_{am} and τ_{dm}. It turns out that the increase varies but little with τ_{am} and increases only slightly, from 8 to 11.5%, if τ_{dm} is increased from 200 to 1000 years. It is also found that τ_{am} is quite insensitive to variations in the exact subdivision of the ocean into the two layers used in the model. For a τ_{dm} of 500 years and a τ_{am} of 5 years, the observed CO_2 increase is in satisfactory agreement with theory, perhaps a little higher.

The question now arises as to the change of the C^{14}/C^{12} ratio with this improved model. The calculations yield a less satisfactory result for the amount of the Suess effect. For $\tau_{am} = 5$ years and again a range of τ_{dm} from 200 to 1000 years, the decrease of C^{14}/C^{12} is 4-6%. This is larger than the observed values. A possible reason for this discrepancy may be a more rapid exchange with the terrestrial biosphere. As of now the relation between the observed increase of CO_2 and the observed Suess effect is an open question and will perhaps remain so until more numerous and precise C^{14} measurements become available. On the other hand, the fair agreement between the observed increase of total atmospheric CO_2 and the fossil fuel consumption makes it unnecessary to invoke other CO_2 sources as suggested by previous authors. There are a number of such processes which are of interest. Revelle and Suess (1957) pointed out and Kanwisher (1960) demonstrated that the CO_2 concentration of the atmosphere should be very sensitive to changes of the temperature of ocean surface waters. The same should be true for changes in the reservoir of carbon in the soil and in the amount of organic matter in the ocean. The estimates indicate that the increase in arable land since the middle of the 19th century might have resulted in a 4% increase of atmospheric CO_2, and that a 1% change in the concentration of organic material in the sea might have the same result. Based on measured variations of the C^{14}/C^{12} ratio in trees of known age, there are indications of CO_2 fluctuations in the atmosphere prior to 1850 which certainly must have other reasons than fossil fuel consumption. Generally, this value seems to have decreased since 1500 (De Vries, 1959), but it is difficult to give any explanations of these observations at the present time. These long-range fluctuations of the atmospheric CO_2 content may indicate how delicate and perhaps unstable the CO_2 budget of the earth is and that it is worth every effort to pursue these questions further.

1.4 Ozone

1.4.1 Historical Remarks

In contrast to water vapor and CO_2, ozone is chemically formed and destroyed *within* the atmosphere. The complicated process of ozone formation and distribution within the atmosphere is of importance for the terrestrial radiation in the ultraviolet region and for the heat budget of the mesopshere and thus created an early interest in ozone, so that now it is the most thoroughly investigated nonpermanent constituent of the atmosphere. In the past 20 years the subject of atmospheric ozone has expanded to such an extent that some aspects cannot be treated exhaustively within the framework of this monograph, and the reader must be referred to some of the comprehensive original papers for more detailed information (e.g., Paetzold, 1957). In our discussion, emphasis will be placed on the distribution of ozone in the atmosphere, particularly in the troposphere, in the light of the most recent data on vertical profiles and on its budget.

Ozone is a comparatively minor constituent of the atmosphere, with an average concentration of about 2 to 3 $\times$ 10^{-6} ppm if uniformly distributed. The unit ordinarily used to express the *total* amount of ozone in the atmosphere is the height of an equivalent column of ozone at standard temperature and pressure. Expressed in this unit, the total amount varies from about 0.16 to 0.4 cm.

In vertical profiles it is customary to use 10^{-3} cm STP ozone per kilometer altitude as a unit. This is a volume concentration equivalent to 21.4 $\mu g/m^3$ and is usually replaced by the volume mixing ratio if processes of vertical mixing or circulation are considered.

The investigation of atmospheric ozone began in the early part of this century with the discovery that the cutoff of the solar spectrum at 3000 Å is due to the presence of ozone in the atmosphere. In the twenties, Dobson and his associates investigated the horizontal distribution of total ozone using a network of six stations in Europe. Later this network was extended over a larger part of the globe. Exploration of the vertical distribution of ozone began in the thirties and, parallel to it, the theory of ozone formation was developed. Research has now reached the stage where the formation and the distribution of ozone within the atmosphere are fairly well known.

The important problem still to be solved is one of meteorology, namely, the explanation of those features of the ozone distribution which are not controlled by photochemical processes, i.e., those below 25 to 30 km. They can be caused by horizontal and vertical mass exchange, by large-scale circulation or, most likely, by a complex combination of these factors. The solution of this problem will not be a simple task and will undoubtedly require a considerable increase of systematic observations over large parts of the globe. The situation has been further complicated by results which have recently become available for other stratosphetic constituents, such as water vapor and fission products, and which tend to confuse rather than clarify the picture, at least at present.

1.4.2 The Theory of Ozone Formation

Theoretical considerations of ozone formation started essentially with a paper by Chapman (1930) in which he discussed the photochemistry involved and showed that the presence of ozone can be explained in terms of the action of the ultraviolet light on oxygen. In the years between 1933 and 1937, Wulf, partly in association with Deming, published several papers (e. g., Wulf and Deming, 1937) in which he developed this theory and by considerable simplification succeeded in calculating the vertical distribution of ozone for photochemical equilibrium. These results were in encouraging agreement with the few observations available at that time. Since then various investigators, e.g., Schöerr (1944), Dütsch (1946), and Craig (1950), have refined the theory considerably and better data have become available on physical parameters for numerical calculations. More recently, Paetzold re-examined the theoretical results and compared them with directly observed vertical profiles (1953 a, b, 1957).

The theoretical considerations had a twofold aim; first, to calculate the vertical distribution of ozone under conditions of photochemical equilibrium and to determine the extent to which it depends upon the various parameters involved, and, second, to calculate the rate of return to this equilibrium after a disturbance has been imposed. For all practical purposes, this goal has been reached and in the future only adjustments will be required as better numerical data become available for some of the physical parameters involved.

The number of reactions in which ozone is involved in a radiated, but pure, atmosphere is considerable. Fortunately, only four of them are important for quantitative considerations:

$$O_2 + h\nu \to O + O \qquad\qquad \text{rate} = f_1\,[O_2]$$

$$O_2 + O + M \to O_3 + M \qquad\qquad \text{rate} = k_1\,[O_2]\,[O]\,[M].$$

These two lead to the formation of atomic oxygen and ozone, with M being a neutral third body which for all practical purposes is N_2 and O_2; $[O_2]$, etc., are the concentrations of the constituents in particles/cm^3; f and k are rate constants. The formation of atomic oxygen occurs in the range of the Schumann-Runge bands between 1760 and 2030 Å and below 30 to 40 km primarily at 2100 m, the ozone-oxygen-window.

The ozone destruction is controlled by the following reactions:

$$O_3 + h\nu \rightarrow O_2 + O \qquad\qquad \text{rate} = f_2\,[O_3]$$

$$O_3 + O \rightarrow 2O_2{}^* \qquad\qquad \text{rate} = k_2\,[O_3]\,[O].$$

Ozone absorbs between 2000 and 3200 Å in the ultraviolet Hartley bands, between 4500 and 7000 Å in the Chappius bands of the visible light, and to a small degree in the infrared. Most important for ozone photolysis are the Hartley bands. The reaction

$$O + O + M \rightarrow O_2 + M$$

is unimportant because of the very low concentrations of O in the layers in question and the thermal destruction of ozone,

$$O_3 + O_3 \rightarrow 3O_2{}^*$$

$$O_3 + O_2 \rightarrow 2O_2 + O,$$

is too slow at the temperatures encountered in the atmosphere. Possible reactions resulting from the exited $O_2{}^*$ are negligible at the ozone concentrations observed. For equilibrium conditions, therefore, it is only necessary to consider the first four reactions which yield:

$$d[O_3]/dt \equiv 0 \equiv k_1[O_2]\,[O]\,[M] - k_2[O_3]\,[O] - f_2[O_3]$$

and

$$d[O_3]/dt \equiv 0 \equiv f_1[O_2] - k_2[O_3]\,[O].$$

Substitution of [O] obtained from the last equation into the first equation yields

$$f_2[O_3]^2 + f_1[O_3]\,[O_2] - f_1 k[O_2]^2[M] = 0; \qquad k = k_1/k_2.$$

[M] is proportional to $[N_2] + [O_2]$, i.e., $[M] = s[O_2]$ with s being constant. This gives

$$[O_3] = [O_2]\,\{-f_1 + \sqrt{f_1^2 + 4f_1 f_2 s k\,[O_2]}\}/2f_2$$

or, since

$$f_1^2 \ll 4f_1 f_2 k s\,[O_2] \qquad\qquad [O_3] = s^{1/2}[O_2]^{3/2}(k f_1/f_2)^{1/2}.$$

In this basic equation for the vertical distribution of ozone, $[O_2]$ is well known. k is temperature dependent, and decreases by a factor of about 1.5 for a 10°C increase in temperature. Of special importance is the ratio of the absorbed light for the formation of O and the destruction of O_3. This ratio changes in a complicated way when the radiation penetrates to deeper layers of the atmosphere.

It is

$$f_1 = \varphi_1 \int I(\lambda,\, h)\, \alpha_{O_2}\, (\lambda,\, p)\, d\lambda$$

and

$$f_2 = \varphi_2 \int I(\lambda,\, h)\, \alpha_{O_3}\, (\lambda)\, d\lambda$$

where

φ_i = quantum yields

I = intensity of radiation as a function of altitude and wavelength

α = respective absorption coefficients.

For O_2, α is partly pressure dependent, a fact which complicates the calculations considerably and introduces some uncertainty because this dependence is still not well known. f_1 must be integrated for wavelengths shorter than 2424 Å and f_2 must be integrated over all absorption bands of O_3, including the infrared. However, visible and infrared light contribute very little to ozone destruction.

Since the dependence of f_1/f_2 on altitude is complicated, it is impossible to obtain an analytical expression for O_3. Instead, the concentration has to be calculated numerically in steps, starting at a high altitude, with an estimated intensity of the solar spectrum, and progressing downward. In these calculations k, α_{O_3}, and φ_2 are fairly well known, whereas I (around 2100 Å), α_{O_2} (around 2100 Å), and φ_1 are still uncertain to some extent.

Numerical calculations for various combinations of reasonable assumptions about these ozone parameters indicate that the resulting concentration is not too sensitive and varies by a factor of about 2 to 3. The height of the ozone maximum is almost independent of the choice of the parameters and varies around 23 km (Paetzold, 1953 a). These results show that, although better knowledge of the physical parameters would be very desirable, the vertical distribution of ozone for photochemical equilibrium has been farily well established.

The influence of each of the external parameters, i.e., the stratospheric temperature distribution and the zenith angle of the sun, is of equal importance. Different possible vertical temperature profiles modify the ozone profiles in a manner similar to that of the ozone parameters, i.e., the total amounts vary somewhat, but the height of the maximum varies little. The same is also true of the zenith angle of the sun. The value of the ozone concentration decreases by a factor of 4 when the zenith angle changes from 0⁰ to 70⁰.

Correspondingly, the total amount of ozone should decrease by a factor of 3 to 4 from the equator to high latitudes. As we shall see in the next section, the observations show the opposite to be true, a first

indication that besides photochemistry, air movements must be important for the ozone distribution. We see from this discussion that neither
the total amount of ozone nor the height of the ozone maximum are useful
parameter for a quantitative check of the photochemical theory.

Dütsch (1946) showed that the expression

$$\tau = \frac{1}{4} \, (k[\mathrm{M}]/f_1 f_2)^{1/2}$$

is a good approximation of the time it takes for a deviation from the equilibrium to decrease to $1/e$ of its value. Since both f_1 and f_2 decrease in lower
layers, due to absorption, τ increases rapidly below the ozone maximum.
The lower energy available for the photochemical reactions at lower altitudes is the essential reason for this change of τ. The value of τ is not very
sensitive to fluctuations of the various physical parameters involved, except for altitudes above 40 km. Paetzold (1953 a) obtained the following
values:

Altitude =	15	20	25	30	35	40	km
τ =	10^4	10^3	10^2	16	2.2	0.6	days

Clearly these figures indicate that photochemical equilibrium
conditions are closely maintained above 30 km and that ozone is a quasi-
conservative property of air masses below 25 km. This result is of basic
importance for the interpretation of ozone data. Above 30 km the ozone
observations should be in agreement with the photochemical theory and
can be used to check the theory. Short-term variations of ultraviolet solar
radiation should have little effect below 40 km. On the other hand, slow
variations, especially the 11 year solar cycle, should affect large parts of
the ozone layer, but may be modified by simultaneous fluctuations of the
atmospheric circulation. Willet (1962) found indeed strong evidence for
a variation of total ozone with solar activity.

If no radiation is present, as at night or during the polar
night, equilibrium no longer exists and the formula for τ cannot be applied. By far the most important reaction which can occur under these
conditions is thermal decay according to

$$\mathrm{O_3 + O_2 \rightarrow 2O_2 + O}.$$

This reaction is not only slow but also forms atomic oxygen again, which in
turn forms new ozone. Hence, the decay of ozone in darkness is very slow
and daily variations of total ozone due to radiation can hardly be expected.
Little is known about the winter pole, but it is assumed that even there the
ozone decrease is small.

1.4.3 The Distribution of Total Ozone

Total ozone is measured from the ground with special spectrometers developed by Dobson. His network of stations provided considerable information on the horizontal distribution of total ozone and its variation with time and latitude. Craig (1950) gave a comprehensive survey of these data. Figure 10 presents these data in the form of isopleths (Dütsch, 1946). According to more recent results concerning the absorption coefficients, the values have to be multiplied by a factor of 1.33 (e.g., Dütsch, 1959). The values vary between 0.16 and 0.4 cm STP. The lowest values are found in the tropical regions where they vary but little over the year.

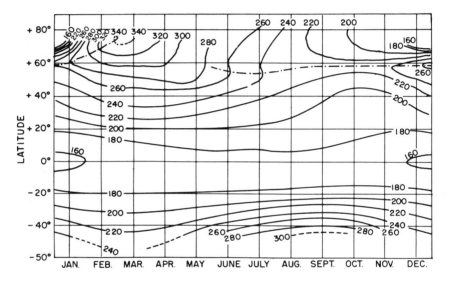

FIG. 10. Isopleths of total ozone in 10^{-3} cm STP (Dütsch, 1946). The values have to be multiplied by 1.33 according to improved values for absorption coefficients (Dütsch, 1959).

The values and their seasonal variation increase beyond about 25° latitude. In high latitudes there is a pronounced maximum in spring and a minimum during the fall (Fig. 11). Some evidence is available for low values over the winter pole so that a ridge of maximum values is formed at about 60° latitude for a considerable part of the year. Only during spring do the values tend to increase all the way to the pole. As we mentioned above, this distribution is not in agreement with the photochemical theory which predicts highest values at the equator and a maximum during the summer.

It soon became apparent that the daily fluctuations of total ozone are very pronounced and often exceed the yearly and latitudinal amplitudes. A strong correlation with weather is observed with high values in the rear of cyclones and low values in the rear of anticyclones or in the front of cyclones. These variations are suggested by the latitudinal ozone distribution, and the study of trajectories in the lower stratosphere shows that higher values occur with advection of polar air masses and viceversa. However, more detailed analysis suggests that advection alone cannot fully explain these weather-dependent variations. For example, it is observed that the amount of ozone in the rear of cyclones some 200-300 miles from the pressure center at the surface is higher than at any other latitude. Another indication is that the seasonal variation of these day-to-day fluctuations is not very pronounced, although the latitudinal gradient in middle latitudes is about 4 times greater in spring than in fall.

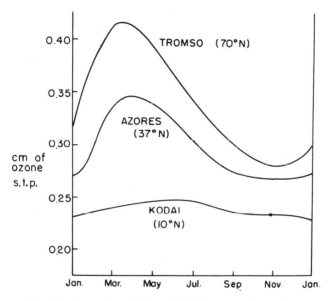

FIG. 11. Annual variation of total ozone at various latitudes (Brewer, 1960). (By courtesy of *Massachusetts Institute of Technology*.)

Vertical motions in the stratosphere are certainly involved in these ozone fluctuations, but again they can be only partly responsible for the phenomenon. The rate of ozone formation or destruction, indicated by the τ values above, is too slow below 35 km where most of the ozone is located to account for rapid changes in total ozone. Reed (1949) pointed out that vertical motions in the stratosphere are associated with considerable horizontal divergence or convergence. In upper troughs, which are displaced westward from the surface center of cyclones, air moves downward and converges horizontally. Computations show that this can account for about half of the observed increase of total ozone. The rest is due to advection and/or subsidence. The opposite occurs along the high pressure ridges in the rear of moving anticyclones. Other studies of vertical motions in the stratosphere agree with this interpretation and apparently the question of the daily changes of total ozone has been resolved (Craig, 1959).

1.4.4 The Vertical Distribution of Ozone

By far most of the ozone is found in the stratosphere and ozone research has become almost synonymous with stratospheric research. Information on the vertical distribution of ozone is crucial for its understanding but is difficult to obtain. Several methods have been developed for determining vertical profiles, some truly ingenious. Götz' *Umkehr* method is an indirect one based on ground measurements. It involves the measurement of scattered zenith light of two different wavelengths having different and suitable absorption coefficients for ozone. The usefulness of this method is demonstrated by a large series of valuable data from various latitudes; but it is not very accurate, particularly in the lower stratosphere, and gives only the main features (Götz, 1951). Another indirect method employs the distribution of light within the earth's shadow on the moon's surface. This distribution is influenced by ozone absorption and can be measured simultaneously for different earth latitudes during the same eclipse (e.g., Paetzold, 1952).

Very valuable and detailed information has been obtained by direct vertical soundings. Spectrographs were used by Regener (1934) and Paetzold (1953 a) on balloons and were also flown with rockets (e.g., Johnson *et al.*, 1952). These spectrographs record the total amount of ozone above the instrument, and considerable accuracy is required to derive the local concentration by differentiation. The most promising way for obtaining fine structure of the ozone distribution is to measure the local concentration directly by chemical means. Different methods have been used for aircraft and balloons by Ehmert (1941), Brewer (1960), and more recently by Regener (1960). The over-all agreement of all these methods is satisfactory when the limitations and accuracies are taken into consideration (see Brewer *et al.*, 1960).

In general, the ozone profiles plotted in terms of *concentration* show low tropospheric values of about 50 μg/m^3, which vary somewhat irregularly with altitude without showing systematic increase. Above the tropopause there is mostly a very pronounced increase of concentration with maxima between 13 and 27 km, depending on season and latitude, and with the main maximum between 20 and 25 km. Above 30 km the concentration decreases fairly regularly and somewhat faster than the air density. The profiles look entirely different when they are plotted in terms of ozone mixing ratio for considerations of vertical mixing and air movements

(Fig. 12). Here there is a rapid increase, with some fluctuations, up to about 25 km, and a subsequent slow but not quite regular decrease. The lower stratosphere is the layer with the most pronounced gradients of the vertical mixing ratio and hence it is also the region where vertical air movements, turbulent mixing, or convergence/divergence will have the profoundest effects on the vertical distribution and on the total amount of ozone, quite in agreement with the observations.

The variation of these profiles with season and latitude is most interesting and important for stratospheric meteorology. Since the number of balloon flights is still not large enough to give reliable average values for various seasons and latitudes, and since individual flights are quite variable, we have plotted idealized curves in Fig. 12 to represent the present state of knowledge, based primarily on Paetzold's (1953 b) data. The general features of these profiles have been confirmed by the more numerous but less accurate *Umkehr* data of various recent investigations (Dütsch, 1959; Ramanathan and Kulkarni, 1960).

In northern latitudes and in spring, ozone occupies most of the lower stratosphere in a broad layer which starts immediately above the tropopause and seems to result from the superposition of two maxima, one at about 23 km and another at 10 to 17 km. As the season progresses the lower maximum almost disappears. The yearly trend of total ozone, as e.g., shown in Fig. 11, is produced primarily by the pronounced seasonal variation of this additional ozone in the lower stratosphere. In lower latitudes the upper maximum does not change very much, whereas the ozone below 20 km decreases and disappears almost completely south of the subtropical jet stream. The mixing ratios ozone/air within the maxima are of the order ot 5 to 10 ppm. In higher altitudes the ozone distribution is such that 90% of total ozone is below 35 km, 99% below 45 km, and 99.9% below 55 km (Johnson *et al.*, 1952).

The hatched areas in Fig. 12 represent the theoretical calculations obtained for various assumptions regarding the parameters involved, as discussed previously. Above 25 to 30 km the agreement between the calculated and observed data is fairly good and within the expected limits. Below this altitude discrepancies are obvious and are not surprising because of the long adjustment times of the photochemical equilibrium. In high latitudes and in spring the lower stratosphere contains more ozone, represented by the secondary maximum, than is to be expected from photochemical theory. In low latitudes the opposite is observed. These deviations in the lower stratosphere cannot be explained by photochemical processes under any reasonable combination of assumptions. They must be the result of mixing and/or air movements.

As we know, ozone is photochemically a quasi-conservative property of the lower stratosphere and it is generally assumed that there

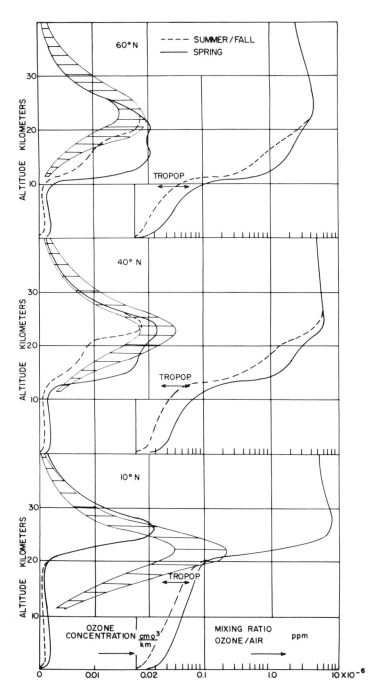

FIG. 12. Idealized ozone profiles based on data from various investigators, primarily Paetzold (1953 b). The profiles on the left-hand side are in terms of concentration. The shaded areas indicate the range of theoretical calculations when the physical parameters are varied within reasonable limits. On the right-hand side are the same profiles in terms of mixing ratio.

is no chemical destruction either. The variation with season and latitude in these layers must then be considered in terms of a reservoir whose ozone balance is controlled in a rather complex manner by the varying rates of influx and outflow. The source is obviously the layer above 25 km where ozone is readily formed. The sink is the troposphere where ozone is chemically destroyed. Up to the present time no attempt was made to explain the observed profile variations in quantitative terms.

The stratospheric distribution of ozone is generally explained by large-scale subsiding air movements over the polar region in late winter and early spring. The rather rapid rise of low stratospheric ozone in high latitudes is most likely related to the breakdown of the polar vortex and the explosive dynamic warmings observed in the polar stratosphere at this time of the year (Godson, 1960). During the summer the low stratospheric ozone reservoir becomes slowly depleted by exchange with the troposphere. The ozone which fills the low polar stratosphere is supposed to come from those equatorial regions where comparison with theory indicates a lack of ozone.

The only reliable data for vertical profiles in the tropical latitudes are the balloon soundings by Paetzold (1960) in Leopoldsville, Congo (see Fig. 12). They clearly show an ozone-free area of several kilometers depth above the tropical tropopause. This seems to support the concept of slowly ascending air motion across the tropical tropopause as suggested by Brewer (1949), but there is reluctance to accept such circulation on meteorological grounds and it is in disagreement with profiles of Sr^{90} and W^{185} (see section on artificial radioactivity).

Ramanathan and Kulkarni (1960) discuss a large number of *Umkehr* data over a wide range of latitudes. Their meridional cross sections for high and low total ozone contents (i.e., spring and autumn) confirm the profiles discussed above. In March, going northward, the ozone content in the lower stratosphere increases in a first step north of 30°, and in a second step north of 60° latitude, in conjunction with the sub tropical and polar jet streams. In July there is a weak latitudinal maximum in the layer of maximum ozone concentration between 50° and 70°N, which is also suggested in the total ozone distribution, Fig. 10. Otherwise, the differences with latitude disappear to a great extent during the summer. Variations above 30 km are very small throughout the year.

Figure 13 gives the seasonal variation of ozone concentration for different altitudes, based on balloon data (Paetzold, 1955). It demostrates that the total ozone measured at the ground is a rather complex net effect of the seasonal variations at different altitudes. The 15-20 and 20-25 km layers show the familiar spring maximum, which is somewhat delayed in the troposphere (see also Section 1.4.5 on tropospheric ozone). The 25-30 km layer does not show any systematic variation at all and above

30 km the seasonal variation is in phase with the zenith distance of the sun, as is to be expected from the photochemical ozone theory. Figure 13 indicates that the lower stratosphere is the dominant factor for the annual variation in agreement with the previous discussions and with the *Um-*

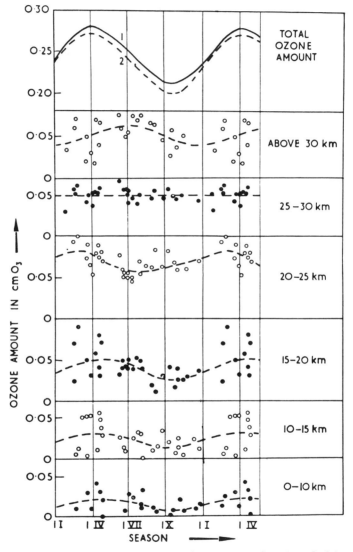

FIG. 13. The annual variation of ozone as a function of altitude. Curve 1 is the total amount of ozone from balloon data and curve 2 represents the same from Dobson's measurements in Arosa (Paetzold, 1955). (By courtesy of *Journal of Atmospheric and Terrestial Physics*.)

kehr measurements made by Dütsch (1959) in Arosa over a period of several years. These Arosa data also exhibit considerable differences from year to year, which seem to be correlated with large-scale fluctuations of the atmospheric circulation.

1.4.5 Tropospheric Ozone

Ozone research has been concerned primarily with the stratosphere, and the spectroscopic methods originally employed for the relatively high concentrations above the tropopause do not permit reliable determinations of the small concentrations in the troposphere. Thus, tropospheric ozone was not investigated properly until more sensitive chemical methods, in particular the potassium iodide method, became available (Ehmert, 1941). This method gives reliable values, except for polluted atmospheres with high concentrations of NO_2 and other oxidants (Bowen and Regener, 1951). Recently, Regener (1960) successfully employed chemical compounds which fluoresce on contact with ozone.

Regener (1941) was the first to advance the thesis that tropospheric ozone originates in the stratosphere. As suggested by Fig. 12, the downward flow of ozone is controlled by its concentration in the lower stratosphere, and by the air exchange mechanism across the tropopause or through the tropopause gaps. After its arrival in the troposphere, ozone is chemically destroyed in clouds, by gaseous and particulate trace substances and primarily by contact with the earth's surface. The ozone distribution in the troposphere resulting from these complictaed processes is still poorly understood. There is no evidence of tropospheric ozone sources, except for polluted areas, e.g., Los Angeles, and the profiles seem to be in qualitative agreement with Regener's concept that tropospheric ozone is exclusively of stratospheric origin.

The number of reliable tropospheric ozone profiles available is still very small. Data obtained by the spectroscopic ozone soundings or by the *Umkehr* method are too uncertain for any detailed study, and the same can be said about the data obtained by the chemical ozone sonde of Brewer (1960). A few profiles obtained with the more sensitive and very promising ozone sonde of Regener (1960) show a fairly constant *mixing ratio* up to the tropopause (Fig. 14). These profiles were obtained during the winter and spring of 1960-61 and are likely to reflect conditions of strong vertical mixing (Hering, 1961).

All the other fairly reliable tropospheric profiles were obtained by aircraft (Fig. 14). The average values of Kay (1953) and Brewer (1955) indicate a rather constant *concentration*, which means an increase of the mixing ratio with altitude. A constant concentration in the troposphere corresponds to an increase in mixing ratio by 2 at 5 km and by 4 at

10 km. Such an increase is to be expected under average conditions in order to allow for a downward flux of ozone.

The individual profiles of Kay (1953) show layers of higher and lower concentrations and agree in this respect with individual flights by other authors. Ozone-depleted layers reflect, perhaps, a stratification of destructive processes or materials, such as dust layers or clouds, but

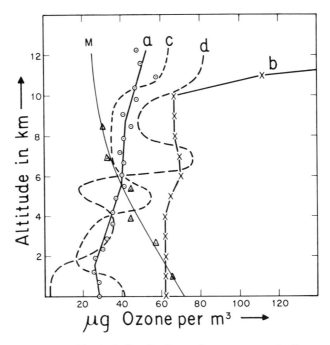

FIG. 14. Vertical distributions of ozone concentration in the troposphere. Curve *a* average of 13 flights over England October, 1952 to November, 1953 (after Kay, 1953). Curve *b*, average of 4 flights over Norway, June-July, 1955 (after Brewer, 1955). Curves *c* and *d*, individual flights of Kay. Curve *M*, constant mixing ratio and triangles representing average values of tropospheric ozone in Boston, Massachusetts, during winter-spring 1960-61 obtained with the Regener Ozone Sonde (after Hering, 1961).

can also represent surface air lifted upwards by cyclonic circulation or by large-scale convection. Kay's values may be too low in general, due to absorption of ozone in the intake tube (Brewer, 1955). Ehmert (1941) and Murgatroyd (1959) found relatively high values in subsiding air above inversion layers. Such large-scale downward transport of ozone and the stratified ozone structure suggest that small-scale turbulence is only of secondary importance for the vertical ozone flux in the troposphere. Therefore, it is questionable whether average eddy diffusion coefficients and average profiles can be used to obtain the vertical ozone transport.

A large number of measurements in ground air are available to study the behavior of tropospheric ozone in more detail and on a global scale. They show as a common phenomenon that the earth's surface is a sink for ozone. In stable air, with small eddy diffusion, ozone increases rapidly above ground indicating a downward flux. Regener (1957) measured ozone at 0.4, 1.6, 6.25, and 12.5 meters above the Great Plains in Nebraska. During days with moderate winds, the variation in ozone concentration over this altitude range was small, but after sunset, when the winds decreased rapidly, the ozone concentration dropped at 0.4 meter to about one-hald of its value at 12.5 meters. Parallel measurements of the wind profile and of the shearing stress at the surface enabled him to calculate the ozone flux density during the night hours for 2 days in August. The values were 1.2×10^{11} and 1.6×10^{11} molecules/cm² sec. This seems to be the only direct determination of the ozone flux density made up to the present time. A few earlier *estimates* based on considerations of stratospheric gradients gave the following values (molecules/cm² sec): Dütsch (1946): at 0° latitude, 7×10^{10}; at 45°, 3×10^9; at 90°, 0.4×10^9; Lettau (1951): 4×10^9; and Paetzold (1955): 2.5-5.0×10^{10}. All these estimates are smaller than Regener's value. They were expected to be equal or larger and cannot be considered very reliable.

Another set of ground air data was obtained by Teichert (1955). He recorded the ozone concentration on an 80-meter high radio tower and at ground level over a period of several months. His hourly means for different months are given in Table 9. The values at 80 meters are always higher than or equal to those at ground level. In September, when the thermal stratification of ground air is more stable and turbulence more suppressed, the diurnal variation is larger than in July, but at the same time the layer which shows a nocturnal decrease is much deeper. This may indicate that ozone is destroyed not only by contact with the ground, but also *within* the stable layer, perhaps by accumulated pollution. During daytime hours, when turbulence is well developed, there is almost no difference between the values at 80 meters and those at the surface. This is in agreement with Regener's finding and shows that fairly representative tropospheric ozone values can be obtained at the ground when the meteorological conditions are properly chosen.

Parallel measurements of surface ozone on the Pfaender (1060 meters) and at the Bodensee (400 meters above sea level), by Ehmert and Ehmert (1941), first demonstrated that the ozone content near the ground is much lower than at higher levels. On the shore of the Bodensee during calm weather, they found a diurnal variation with low values during the

TABLE 9

AVERAGE HOURLY CONCENTRATIONS OF OZONE ($\mu g/m^3$) [a]

June/July

Hour:	7-8	8-9	9-10	10-11	11-12	12-13	13-14	14-15	15-16	16-17	17-18	18-19	19-20
80 meters:	25	28	24	27	28	32	33	33	34	29	30	34	29
Ground:	18	19	21	25	28	30	31	29	33	26	30	29	26

September

Hour:	7-8	8-9	9-10	10-11	11-12	12-13	13-14	14-15	15-16	16-17	17-18	18-19
80 meters:	2	6	11	18	24	30	33	31	29	33	33	28
Ground:	2	5	9	17	24	28	33	28	28	34	28	26

[a] Teichert (1955).

night, a rapid rise in the morning, and maximum values on the afternoon. On the Pfaender, they did not observe diurnal variations and generally the fluctuations were smaller. Thus, the ozone destruction, at least at this location, must occur below the level of the mountain station, most likely in the stagnant air near the ground.

Regener (1957) recorded the ozone concentration simultaneously at various places in New Mexico, e.g., on Mt. Capillo (3070 meters) and near Albuquerque (1700 meters above sea level), at intervals over a 2-year period. On the average of 110 days, the concentration on the mountain was higher by about 40 $\mu g/m^3$. The values at the higher station showed little fluctuation.

Table 10 gives a survey of recent reliable and fairly representative measurements of tropospheric ozone. The values are not quite comparable because they refer to different methods, data selection, locations, and heights above the earth's surface, and different seasons. The influence of the ground is not always quite eliminated. Despite this, the mean and maxima values are surprisingly uniform. The maximum data should be most representative of tropospheric air. Mean maximum values above 90 $\mu g/m^3$ are already are. It seems to us that tropospheric ozone is a much more regular phenomenon than hitherto expected, if the ozone-depleted layers near the ground are excluded.

Götz and Volz (1951) measured the surface and total ozone for more than a year at Arosa, which is located in an Alpine valley at 1860 meters above sea level. In order to eliminate the ozone destruction near the ground and to obtain fairly representative values of ozone in the undisturbed troposphere, they selected only daily maximum values. Figure 15 shows these data together with the total amount of ozone. The average ozone concentration is about 50 $\mu g/m^3$ and varies approximately between 30 in winter and 60 in late spring. Extreme values are 19 and 80 $\mu g/m^3$. It is interesting to note that the maximum of the *total* ozone appears about one month earlier.

Price and Pales (1959) made similar observations in 1958 and 1959 at Mauna Loa Observatory in Hawaii. This is a unique place, at an elevation of more than 3000 meters, above the trade wind inversion, and remote from continents. If the daily maximum values are again selected as the most representative values and if they are compared with the Arosa data, one obtains Fig. 16 b. The similarity of the two average curves is striking. It implies that on a large scale the troposphere is very well mixed and that the tropospheric residence time of ozone must be of the order of 1 month or longer to allow for such uniform distribution. The daily variations are superimposed on these general curves and are certainly due to regional or local influences. The annual variation of the *total* ozone at Mauna Loa is only 0.25 to 0.29 cm, and, thus, the annual variation of

TABLE 10

CONCENTRATIONS OF TROPOSPHERIC OZONE AS GIVEN IN MORE RECENT AND EXTENSIVE STUDIES

Observer	Location, time, and remarks	Altitude	O_3 ($\mu g/m^3$)	
			Range [a]	Average [a]
Götz and Volz (1951)	Arosa, Switzerland, 1950-51, high valley, daily maxima values	1860 meters	19–90	50
Regener (1957)	Mt. Capillo, and Albuquerque, New Mexico, 1951-52	3100 meters	18–85	45
		1600 meters	3–120	36
Regener (1957)	O'Neil, Nebraska, 1953	12.5 meters above ground	30–100	60
Ehmert (1952)	Weissenau, Bodensee, Germany, 1952	20 meters above ground	0–90	35
			0–70	30
Teichert (1955)	Lindenberg Obs., Germany, 1953-54	80 meters above ground	0–50	30
			0–50	27
Kay (1953)	Farnborough, England, 1952-53	0-12,000 meters	26–50	38
Brewer (1955)	Tromsö, Norway, 1954	0-10,000 meters	60–70	65
Price and Pales (1959)	Mauna Loa Observatory, Hawaii	3000 meters	30–62	45
Wexler et al. (1960)	Little America Station, Antarctica	100 meters	20–60	45

[a] As interpreted from the published data. The values sometimes represent absolute maxima, sometimes mean maxima.

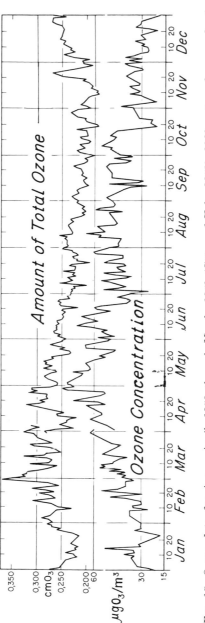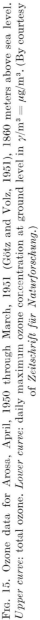

FIG. 15. Ozone data for Arosa, April, 1950 through March, 1951 (Götz and Volz, 1951), 1860 meters above sea level. *Upper curve:* total ozone. *Lower curve:* daily maximum ozone corcentration at ground level in $\gamma/m^3 = \mu g/m^3$. (By courtesy of *Zeitschrift für Naturforschung.*)

surface ozone in Hawaii must be controlled by mixing with the troposphere at higher latitudes or by the same source as for the latter, i.e., the low stratosphere in higher latitudes.

The small hemispheric differences in tropospheric ozone also imply that the destruction of ozone must be fairly uniformly distributed. Since the earth's surface seems to be the predominant sink, this does not appear unlikely. The time lack between total ozone (Fig. 15) and surface ozone can be interpreted as a result of the tropospheric destruction rate. We calculated from Fig. 10 the total stratospheric ozone burden of the stratosphere (which is for all practical purposes equal to the total atmospheric burden) and plotted it in Fig. 16 a. Again we see a time lack of about one month between stratosphere and troposphere. Figure 16 c demonstrates that the tropspheric ozone variations repeat themselves fairly regularly in subsequent years, at least in Arosa.

Such simple and general features encouraged an attempt to apply a simple model for the cycle and budget of tropospheric ozone (Junge, 1961). It is obvious from Fig. 16 that the total tropospheric ozone can be approximated by

$$\theta = a_1 + a_2 \sin\left[2\pi(t - a_3)\right] \text{ tons} \quad (\text{metric tons} = 10^3 \text{ kg}) \qquad (1)$$

where a_1, a_2, and a_3 are constants, and t is the time in years. We take 50 $\mu g/m^3$ as the average tropospheric surface concentration and assume an increase of the mixing ratio at the tropopause of $2:1$. This gives $a_1 = 2.6 \times 10^8$ tons O_3, and $a_2 = 0.79 \times 10^8$ tons O_3. We assume further that the destruction rate D of tropospheric ozone is such that

$$D = -c_0\,\theta \quad (\text{tons/year}) \qquad (2)$$

and that the rate of injection I of stratospheric ozone into the troposphere has the form

$$I = c_1 + c_2 \sin(2\pi t) \quad (\text{tons/year}), \qquad (3)$$

where c_0, c_1, and c_2 are constants. If most of the ozone is destroyed at the surface, (2) is a good approximation. Expression (3) can be justified on the basis that with (1) and (2), I must also have the form of a simple sine-function. The constant a_3 gives the time lack between I and θ, due to tropospheric destruction. We assume that it is equivalent to the time lack observed between the maximum of the stratospheric ozone burden and that of θ. The three constants c_0, c_1, and c_2 can be expressed by a_1, a_2, and a_3. Since a_3 is the least accurately known, the calculations were made for four different values. Table 11 shows the results.

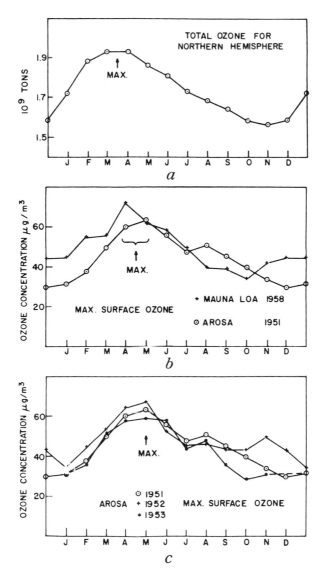

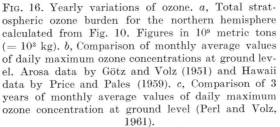

FIG. 16. Yearly variations of ozone. *a*, Total stratospheric ozone burden for the northern hemisphere calculated from Fig. 10. Figures in 10^9 metric tons (= 10^3 kg). *b*, Comparison of monthly average values of daily maximum ozone concentrations at ground level. Arosa data by Götz and Volz (1951) and Hawaii data by Price and Pales (1959). *c*, Comparison of 3 years of monthly average values of daily maximum ozone concentration at ground level (Perl and Volz, 1961).

TABLE 11

VARIOUS CALCULATED PARAMETERS FOR THE OZONE BUDGET

Parameter	Delay time a_3 (months)			
	0.5	1.0	1.5	2.0
c_0 (month^{-1})	1.8	0.9	0.5	0.3
Lifetime $\tau = 1/c_0$ of tropospheric ozone (months)	0.6	1.1	2.0	3.3
c_1 (tons/year)	5.7	2.9	1.5	0.94×10^9
c_2 (tons/year)	1.8	1.0	0.7	0.6×10^9
Average stratospheric residence time (years)	0.6	1.2	2.3	3.7
Ozone flux density (gr/m²sec)	4.0	2.0	1.0	0.65×10^{-7}
Molecules/cm²sec	5.0	2.5	1.25	0.81×10^{11}

With a_3 apparently between 1 and 1.5 months, we obtain a residence time for tropospheric ozone of 1.1 and 2.0 months, and a flux density close to that of Regener's calculations (1957). This agreement may be fortuitous since Regener's values can hardly be expected to be representative on a global scale. It indicates, however, that the conclusions drawn from this model are not unreasonable.

The rate of ozone destruction allows the calculation of stratospheric residence times, which turns out to be 1-2 years. This agrees favorably with similar residence times calculated for stratospheric fission products (see Chapter 3). It should be mentioned, however, that both ozone and fission products have a somewhat different stratospheric distribution, and that ozone is not a conservative property above 25 to 30 km. Unfortunately, all the calculated values are very sensitive to a_3, which is not too accurately known. Although this simple model of the tropospheric ozone budget can be considered only an approximation, it may be helpful for further studies.

Very little is known about the processes of ozone decomposition in the atmosphere. Volz (1952) observed an ozone decrease during the formation of orographic clouds and a rapid decomposition of ozone upon contact with various materials. Dillemuth et al. (1960) studied the decomposition of ozone by methane. The reaction constants are such that for natural concentrations of both ozone and methane, the reaction rate is too slow to be of any importance. According to Cadle (1960), H_2S destroys O_3 very rapidly at natural concentration levels. Estimates indicate that the total amount of H_2S released from the earth's surface per year is comparable with 0.1 the amount of ozone destroyed. Details on this reaction will be given in the discussion of H_2S.

It is now well established that considerable quantities of ozone are produced photochemically in Los Angeles, where concentrations up to 1000 $\mu g/m^3$ are found around noon (e.g., Renzetti, 1955). When exposed to sunlight, polluted atmospheres of similar composition will undoubtedly act as local sources of ozone. This is indicated by measurements made in Albuquerque (Regener, 1954), and in other places. It has also been suggested that point discharge at industrial installations or in the electrical field of the atmosphere are possible sources of tropospheric ozone (Cauer, 1951), but there is still no evidence of this.

1.5 Sulfur Dioxide and Hydrogen Sulfide

1.5.1 The Distribution of Sulfur In the Atmosphere

The role of sulfur in "polluted" atmospheres is well known and has been the subject of numerous studies for many years (see, e.g., Magill et al., 1956). The data on atmospheric sulfur in "unpolluted" areas on the other hand, are still very inadequate; the general features of the sulfur distribution in the atmosphere, its chemistry, cycle, and budget are just beginning to emerge. Interest in atmospheric sulfur has recently been stimulated by the discovery that sulfur pollution, like that of CO_2, has reached a continental and global scale and that sulfate is a world-wide constituent of atmospheric aerosols, even in the stratosphere. The difficulties in the studies of atmospheric sulfur are enhanced by the fact that sulfur is present in the atmosphere in at least three forms: as SO_2, H_2S, and as sulfate in aerosols.

The relationship between these three compounds and their abundance is of basic importance for an understanding of atmospheric sulfur. Several sets of data have recently become available on the ratio of gaseous to particulate sulfur and are summarized in Table 12 (Georgii, 1960). We see that sulfur over land is present primarily in gaseous form and that sulfur in aerosols does not amount to more than 10 to 20% of the total. Only in maritime areas remote from continents, as in Hawaii, the aerosol sulfate rises to more than 30%. Here the aerosol sulfate is part of the sea salt which can reach considerable concentrations independent of the gaseous sulfur components. From Table 11, we can conclude that measurements of *total* sulfur concentration over land can be listed as gaseous sulfur with good approximation, even if no attempt was made to separate particulate

TABLE 12

CONCENTRATION RATIO OF GASEOUS TO PARTICULATE SULFUR [a]

Location	Ratio	Author
Hawaii	~ 3	Junge
Florida	~15	Junge
St. Moritz	~ 8	Weber
London	8-11	Katz
London	14	Ellis
Frankfurt/M, summer	10	Georgii
Frankfurt/M, winter	25	Georgii

[a] Georgii (1960).

material. This fact facilitates considerably the interpretation of atmospheric sulfur data.

Very little is known about the ratio of SO_2 to H_2S. The only attempt to separate these two gases in relatively unpolluted air was made by Junge (1960). These measurements were made in Bedford, 15 miles northwest of Boston, Massachusetts, in the late fall (Table 13). The values

TABLE 13

SO_2 AND H_2S CONCENTRATIONS AT BEDFORD, MASSACHUSETTS

Winds	No. of measurements	Concentration ($\mu g/m^3$)		Ratio SO_2/H_2S
		SO_2	H_2S	
Northwest sector	12	17.5	8.3	2.12
Southeast sector	13	24.8	9.4	2.64
Indifferent	7	31.1	8.9	3.50
Total average	32	23.5	8.9	2.65

with northwest winds must be considered fairly representative of unpolluted air over the northeastern U.S., and the total SO_2 equivalent, 34 $\mu g/m^3$, is in agreement with values from other continental areas. The H_2S concentration is surprisingly constant for all wind directions so that the variation of the SO_2/H_2S ratio reflects mainly the variation of SO_2. The fluctuation of SO_2 clearly points to the influence of pollution from metropolitan Boston, with highest values in stagnant air.

It is interesting to compare these data with a similar unique set by Jacobs and others (1957) for such a highly polluted location as New York City. These authors made measurements almost daily over a period of 1 year and found surprisingly low and constant H_2S concentrations. The average was 3 $\mu g/m^3$, with an average maximum of 5.3 and an average minimum of 1.7 $\mu g/m^3$. The absolute maximum in 249 determinations was 7.5 $\mu g/m^3$. On the other hand, the SO_2 concentrations were rather high and varied between 0.1 and 0.5 ppm or between 280 and 1500 $\mu g/m^3$ (Greenburg and Jacobs, 1956).

Apparently, the H_2S level in New York City is slightly lower than in Bedford, indicating no net production. The data rather suggest that the H_2S in New York is of natural origin and is destroyed to some degree, perhaps by oxidation to SO_2. More information is needed on this interesting question before more general conclusions can be drawn, but we think that a mixture of SO_2 and H_2S must be expected in most areas and that H_2S may prevail in areas not affected by human activities.

Due to the lack of information on the SO_2/H_2S ratio, the gaseous sulfur or, as it may be, the total sulfur, is generally listed as SO_2. Our knowledge of the distribution of gaseous sulfur in the atmosphere is based on data on this "equivalent" SO_2. In some determinations of equivalent SO_2, or total sulfur, the H_2S may not have been completely oxydized and, therefore, these values should generally be considered minimum values.

Egnér and Eriksson (1955) obtained rather extensive data on the total sulfur concentration in Northern Europe. A selection of their results is given in Table 14. The values fluctuate considerably, between 0 and 40 $\mu g/m^3$, with a mean of about 10 $\mu g/m^3$. The general decrease of the SO_2 concentration from south (Alnarp) to north (Offer) suggests the influence of industrialized Central Europe. Perhaps only northern Scandinavia, with less than 10 $\mu g/m^3$, can be considered free of any pollution.

Sulfur pollution is indeed so widespread that a distinction between polluted and unpolluted areas becomes arbitrary. This is well demonstrated by a map of the average SO_2 concentration over England by Meetham (1959) (see Fig. 17). During winter, when conditions are favorable for the accumulation of pollution in the ground layers, values of 100 $\mu g/m^3$ and higher are found in and around populated or industrial areas and drop to 20 $\mu g/m^3$ in rural districts.

In Fig. 18 average concentrations of gaseous sulfur, calculated as SO_2, are compiled for various locations (Georgii, 1960). Compared with other trace gases, such as NO_2 or NH_3, SO_2 fluctuates over a wide range of concentrations, due to the pronounced anthropogenous influence. Concentrations of 59 $\mu g/m^3$ at the Kleiner Feldberg (Taunus) and of 47 $\mu g/m^3$

1. GASES

TABLE 14

MONTHLY AVERAGE CONCENTRATION OF SO₂ (μg/m³) FROM SOME STATIONS OF THE SWEDISH NETWORK CALCULATED FROM THE TOTAL SULFUR CONCENTRATION UNDER THE ASSUMPTION THAT SO₂ IS THE PREDOMINANT COMPONENT [a]

	Nov. 1954	Dec. 1954	Jan. 1955	Feb. 1955	Mar. 1955	Apr. 1955	May 1955	June 1955	July 1955	Aug. 1955	Sept. 1955	Oct. 1955
Offer	0.0	3.4	3.6	1.6	12.8	8.6	1.0	5.6	12.4	1.4	5.6	5.2
Erken	1.0	13.4	14.0	14.8	12.0	7.4	1.0	7.2	13.8	3.4	0.0	6.4
Farlsterbobruk	37.8	0.0	8.4	22.2	13.4	7.8	0.6	6.6	6.8	1.4	8.8	0.0
Alnarp	32.0	27.4	40.4	38.1	42.0	24.0	6.8	14.6	12.4	24.0	22.0	26.0
Average	17.7	11.1	16.6	19.3	20.1	11.9	2.3	8.5	11.3	7.5	9.1	6.0

[a] Egnér and Eriksson (1955).

at the Zugspitze represent values at 800 and 3000 meters above sea level. They are still fairly high and indicate the degree of pollution within the lower troposphere over Central Europe. The values were always higher at the foot of the mountains, particularly when temperature inversions below

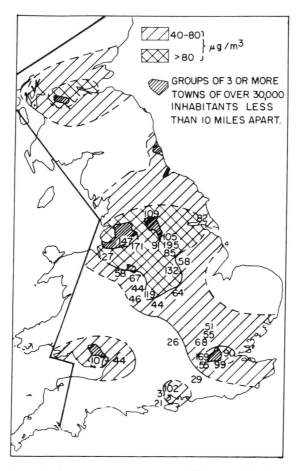

Fig. 17. Average concentration of SO_2 over England in winter (Meetham, 1959). Units: mg/1000 m³ $= \mu g/m^3$ (By courtesy of the *American Geophysical Union.*)

the top of the mountains prevented convection. Neuwirth (1958) observed an average SO_2 concentration of 40 $\mu g/m^3$ in Freiburg, in the upper Rhine Valley, and 20 $\mu g/m^3$ in the nearby Feldberg (Black Forest). These values are somewhat smaller than the previous ones, but the decrease with altitude depended in a similar way upon the thermal stability of the atmosphere.

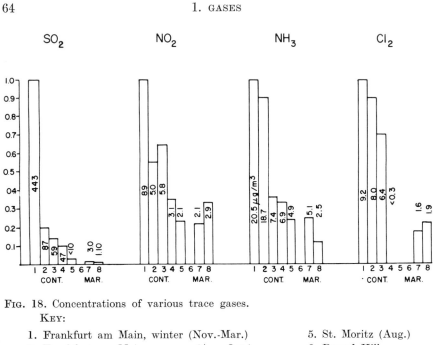

FIG. 18. Concentrations of various trace gases.
KEY:

1. Frankfurt am Main, winter (Nov.-Mar.)   5. St. Moritz (Aug.)
2. Frankfurt am Main, summer (Apr.-Oct.)   6. Round Hill
3. Kleiner Feldberg/Taunus (Nov.-Jan.)   7. Florida
4. Zugspitze (Aug.)   8. Hawaii

The heighth of the column is 1.0 for the winter values in Frankfurt. The absolute concentrations are given within the columns in $\mu g/m^3$. The stations are arranged in the order polluted-unpolluted maritime areas (Georgii, 1960).

The SO_2 concentrations at St. Moritz (Fig. 19), on the southern slopes of the Alps, seem to be much lower, perhaps because this area is somewhat separated from the polluted areas north of the Alps. Very

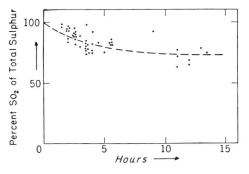

FIG. 19. Oxidation of SO_2 in a polluted atmosphere as a function of time according to Katz (1952).

low concentrations were observed in Florida and Hawaii (Junge, 1956). These measurements were made on the coast with winds predominantly from the sea and are fairly representative of pure maritime conditions. The mean values of 3 and 1 $\mu g/m^3$, respectively, for these locations are comparable to those of northern Sweden (Table 14) and indicate that traces of gaseous sulfur compounds are very widespread.

Except for the above data from mountains, no information is available on the decrease of sulfur with altitude. Recent measurements indicate that SO_4 plays an important role in the composition of *stratospheric* aerosols (Junge *et al.*, 1961). It is likely that these aerosols are formed by the oxidation of H_2S and SO_2 which penetrate into the stratosphere.

1.5.2 Sources and Sinks of Sulfur

Our knowledge of the sources of atmospheric SO_2 and H_2S is still very scanty. Apparently most natural sulfur enters the atmosphere as H_2S, produced in certain sea and land areas by the reduction of sulfate. This reduction occurs whenever there is excessive decay of organic material, which depletes the water, swamp, or soil of free oxygen. Under such conditions, sulfate is a source of oxygen and H_2S thus formed cannot be re-oxidized before it escapes into the air. Conway (1943) first suggested such a process on a global scale, on the basis of a careful study of the chemical development of the oceans. He came to the conclusion that a considerable amount of sulfate carried by the rivers into the ocean cannot be accounted for by weathering of sediments and rocks, but must be deposited by rain. If the sulfur cycle is a closed one, this sulfur must again escape from the oceans, most likely as H_2S. Conway suggests that this H_2S is produced in the blue reducing mud which covers most of the continental shelf area. However, there is the difficulty that the surface ocean water always contains dissolved oxygen, which readily oxidizes H_2S in solution before it escapes into the air. Another difficulty is the observation that sulfur concentrations are usually higher over the continents than over the oceans (Fig. 18).

Another important source of H_2S, suggested by Redfield (see Eriksson, 1959 b), is the release of H_2S from intertidal flats. Here the presence and decay of organic matter, the supply of sulfate from the sea, and the periodic exposure create ideal conditions for the escape of H_2S. Erikkson (1959 b) points out that the metabolic turnover of marine organic material may also contribute to the H_2S production. The marine biosphere is concentrated almost exclusively in the surface waters, and H_2S produced may have a chance to escape.

Swamp and shallow lakes, along the coast and inland, are well known sources of H_2S, the bottom mud being rich in reducing material. The lack of oxygen allows the development of sulfur bacteria which reduce the sulfate. Considerable amounts of H_2S can accumulate in such layers and can inhibit life. A famous example is the Black Sea with its very high H_2S concentrations in the deeper waters. We do not know the extent to which H_2S can penetrate the oxygen-containing surface layers and escape into the air, but the release of H_2S becomes obvious when the oxygen-depleted waters extend to the surface. In such cases, H_2S concentrations can reach the odor limit. Hydrogen sulfide concentrations of 100 to 1000 $\mu g/m^3$ have been observed (Gmelin, 1953) in Dutch cities with their systems of canals.

As in swamps, an adequate content of organic materials, sulfur, and moisture are expected to produce H_2S also in soils. Sulfur can be supplied either by sulfate or by the sulfur content of plant material, which is about $1^0/_{00}$ of the dry matter.

Volcanoes produce both H_2S and SO_2, but it is difficult to make global estimates of this source and to the best of our knowledge none are available.

In contrast to our lack of knowledge of the amounts produced by natural sources, emission of industrial SO_2 is known fairly accurately. World estimates show (Table 15) that most of the SO_2 comes from the com-

TABLE 15

WORLD SULFUR EMISSION TO THE ATMOSPHERE, PER YEAR, GIVEN AS SO_4 [a]

Year	Smelters (tons)	Crude oil (tons)	Coal (tons)	Total (tons)
1937	21.1×10^6	12.2×10^6	69.8×10^6	103.1×10^6
1943	25.4×10^6	13.5×10^6	77.2×10^6	116.1×10^6

[a] Magill *et al.* (1956).

bustion of coal (67%), oil (12%), and from copper smelters (13%) (Magill *et al.*, 1956).

Precipitation analyses suggest that the sulfur in rural areas (H_2S?) is of different origin than that of industrial areas (SO_2). In industrial areas, the highest values appear in winter due to increased coal consumption; but in rural areas the highest values appear in summer, probably because of the increased escape of H_2S from the soil (Eaton and Eaton, 1926).

The earth's surface acts not only as a source of gaseous sulfur compounds, but also as a sink. This was shown recently by Johansson (1959) and, in a discussion of some of his results by Eriksson (1959 b). Johansson measured the absorption of SO_2 by plants and soil in pots exposed downwind from a plant emitting SO_2. He determined the atmospheric concentration of SO_2 and the SO_4 deposit by rain over a period of years, and analysis of the pots gave the net direct uptake or loss of gaseous sulfur components (see Table 16). For most SO_2 concentrations, the amounts

TABLE 16

SULFUR UPTAKE OF SOIL AS A FUNCTION OF SULFUR CONCENTRATION IN THE AIR [a]

Sulfur dioxide content of air ($\mu g/m^3$)	Sulfur added by precipitation (kg/ha)	Sulfur added from the air (kg/ha)
156	38	260
90	20	100
86	12	74
46	12	24
24	7	10
20	4	7

[a] Johansson (1959).

deposited by rain are smaller than the amounts absorbed. In unpolluted areas with lower SO_2 concentrations than those indicated in Table 16, the ratio of absorption to rain deposit would of course be smaller. The figures also show that the uptake of SO_2 is not proportional to its concentration. This can have various causes. Eriksson suggests that Johansson's figures represent the net result of uptake and *loss*, and that this loss varies in such a way that the real uptake would be higher with low SO_2 concentrations.

Another set of experiments with plants in pots and increasing sulfur content of the soil seems to indicate a *net uptake* of sulfur when the soil has a *low* sulfur content and a *net loss* to the atmosphere by release of H_2S when the soil has a *high* sulfur content. Under average conditions, uptake and loss may approximately balance. Such a balance is also indicated by a comparison of maps of the sulfur run off in rivers and the sulfur deposit by precipitation over Scandinavia (Eriksson, 1959 b). Both maps agree within a factor of 2, which can be considered satisfactory. Thus run off and rain deposits almost balance each other, at least for Scandinavia and similar geographic areas, and consequently the same must the true of the direct exchange processes. However, Eriksson stresses that these conclusions are still very tentative and merely indicate the general trend. Absorption of SO_2 or H_2S must also be expected on the ocean surface.

Perhaps precipitation is the most efficient means of removing sulfur from the atmosphere. However, the solubility of both gases, SO_2 and H_2S is such that for liquid water contents of the order of 1 g/m³ in precipitating clouds, only negligible amounts can be removed by simple solution. Except over the sea, and perhaps in some arid regions over land, most of the sulfate in rain comes from oxidation of the gases. The universal presence of excess sulfate in rain, even in such remote places as the polar regions, testifies to the importance of this process. Sulfate is, for insatnce, by far the most predominant constituent in the center of the Greenland ice cap. Excess sulfate in rain water is determined by subtracting the SO_4 due to sea spray. This sea spray sulfate is calculated from the observed Cl or Na concentrations and the ratio SO_4:NaCl for sea water (see Chapter 4).

Our quantitative knowledge of these oxidation processes is still very unsatisfactory. The photochemical oxidation of SO_2 and SO_3 was the first process to be studied in more detail (Gerhard and Johnstone, 1955). They found that by irradiation of SO_2 in air by bright sunlight, the following reactions are likely ot occur:

$$SO_2 + h\nu \quad \rightarrow SO_3{}^*$$

$$SO_2{}^* + O_2 \quad \rightarrow SO_4$$

$$SO_4 + O_2 \quad \rightarrow SO_3 + O_3$$

$$SO_3 + H_2O \rightarrow H_2SO_4.$$

The reaction $SO_2 + O_3 \rightarrow SO_3 + O_2$ seems to be of minor importance. The net reaction is of the first order with a rate of $1\text{-}2 \times 10^{-3}$ per hour equivalent to a half-life for SO_2 of 30 to 15 days. The presence of nitric oxides, NaCl aerosols, and moisture up to 90% relative humidity had no effect on the rate of oxidation.

Tentative estimates of the half-life of industrial SO_2 in the atmosphere give no more than 4 days (Meetham, 1950; Junge, 1960). If this is correct, processes other than photochemical oxidation must be involved. As Cauer (1951) demonstrated, SO_4 always forms when water vapor condenses in the atmosphere. This formation of SO_4 in cloud and rain droplets can, e.g., be caused by traces of heavy metal ions such as Mn, Cu, Fe, etc. A preliminary quantitative study (Junge and Ryan, 1958) revealed that these ions are effective even in concentrations of 1 mg/liter. The SO_4 formation in solution does not continue indefinitely, but reaches a final value which depends upon the amount of catalyst present and which is proportional to the SO_2 partial pressure in air. The controlling factor is apparently the pH value of the solution, which stops the oxidation after dropping below a certain value. If the pH value is raised again, for instance by absorption of NH_3, oxidation is revived. Since the supply of atmospheric

NH_3 is rather limited, this process can explain why consistently only small fractions of the atmospheric SO_2 become oxidized, as indicated in Table 12 and demonstrated by Fig. 19. It is likely that other processes will support a limitation of aerosol sulfate in air. During smog, e.g., rather large particles form and sedimentation becomes important (Meetham, 1956).

The oxidation of SO_2 in solution, supported by small traces of NH_3, occurs in every cloud droplet. If a cloud droplet evaporates again, the pH value decreases rapidly, but will soon be raised again by the absorption of additional NH_3. In each condensation-evaporation cycle, additional SO_4 will thus accumulate. Estimates show that a nucleus goes through an average of 10 condensation cycles before it is removed by rain. If this nucleus contains chloride, as in the case of sea spray, HCl will be released and the Na/Cl ratio increased. Figure 18 shows the presence of gaseous Cl compounds, calculated as Cl_2, which may be generated this way.

In comparison to SO_2, we have but little information on the oxidation of H_2S, although this process is probably of great importance for the atmospheric sulfur cycle. There are several possibilities. H_2S can be oxidized after absorption on surfaces, e.g., on aerosol particles. In chemical literature it is further reported that H_2S is oxidized *photochemically in solution*, a process that would result in the fixation of the H_2S dissolved in cloud and rain droplets. However, H_2S seems to oxidize quite easily in solutions in the presence of dissolved oxygen, even without light, and of course cloud water is always saturated with oxygen. Unfortunately, we have no quantitative knowledge of these various possibilities. The only oxidation process for which such information is available is the reaction of H_2S with ozone (Cadle, 1960). The reaction seems to have the form

$$d(H_2S)/dt = k [O_3] [H_2S.]$$

At room temperature $k = 8 \times 10^{-6}$ $(\mu g/m^3)^{-1}$ $(min)^{-1}$ if the concentrations are given in $\mu g/m^3$. For tropospheric ozone concentrations of 50 $\mu g/m^3$, the lifetime of H_2S becomes $\tau = 1.7$ days. This is rather short and would seem to imply that very little H_2S should be able to penetrate to higher levels of the troposphere, even if no other H_2S oxidation processes occur. To clarify this question, it would be very desirable to have measurements of the concentration of both SO_2 and H_2S at various levels in the atmosphere.

Observations of particle formation indicate a direct oxidation of SO_2 and H_2S in air. Verzár and Evans (1959) showed that large numbers of Aitken nuclei are formed in outside air irradiated by sunlight and that this particle formation is enhanced by the addition of H_2S and NH_3. In presence of SO_2, particle formation can occur even in the dark. Such observations are of great interest for atmospheric aerosol studies, but should be repeated in extremely pure atmospheres to exclude the interference of other trace gases. We would like to conclude our discussion of the various oxidation processes with the remark that considerable work still remains to be done.

1.5.3 Sulfur Budget

Although some of the data on release and removal of atmospheric sulfur are still very vague, it seems worthwhile to attempt an estimate of the atmospheric sulfur budget (Fig. 20). The most reliable figures on sulfur release are those for industrial sulfur, which are given in Table 15.

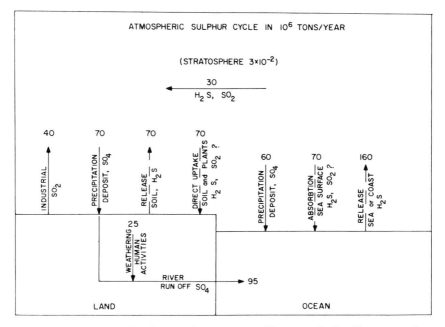

FIG. 20. Tentative cycle of atmospheric excess sulfur, i.e., of all sulfur except that which originates from sea spray particles. The dashed arrows represent the most uncertain estimates.

The best data on the removal of excess sulfur, which will be considered exclusively, are for precipitation and are given in Table 17 (Junge, 1950). According to these tables the total SO_4 deposit in rain is 390×10^6 tons and the total industrial SO_4 production 116×10^6. Industrial sulfur amounts, thus, to 30% of the rain deposit on a global basis. Since most of the SO_2 is produced in the northern hemisphere and since there is little exchange across the equator, this figure may be 50% for the northern temperate latitudes.

TABLE 17

WORLD ESTIMATE OF SULFUR DEPOSITION IN RAIN, PER YEAR, GIVEN AS SO_4 [a]

Area	Precipitation (tons)	Average $SO_4^=$ concentration (mg/liter)	$SO_4^=$ deposit (tons)
Land	10×10^{13}	2.2	220×10^6
Sea	34×10^{13}	0.5	170×10^6
Total	44×10^{13}	0.88	390×10^6

[a] Junge (1960).

Earlier estimates, based on less reliable data, give for industrial sulfur in rain 11% (Conway, 1943) and 20% (Eriksson, 1959 b). These are substantial fractions and are worthy of attention. Table 18 gives some interesting sulfur figures for the United States, which demonstrate the considerable quantities involved in the atmospheric budget. We see that the total amount of excess sulfur, which is only slightly higher over land than over sea, is almost equal to the total U.S. sulfur production or consumption. However, the total U.S. sulfur emission is two to three times this amount and only 35% is brought down again by rain within the country. The rest is transported to other parts of the northern hemisphere or is removed by means other than precipitation, e.g., by direct uptake.

TABLE 18

DATA ON SULFUR FOR THE UNITED STATES, CALCULATED AS $SO_4^=$ [a]

Average concentration of excess $SO_4^=$ in rain	2.22 mg/liter
Total amount of $SO_4^=$ brought down by rain, including sea spray	1.06×10^7 tons/year
Total amount of excess $SO_4^=$ brought down by rain	0.92×10^7 tons/year
Total U.S. estimated sulfur emission, 1957, calculated as $SO_4^=$ [b]	2.59×10^7 tons/year
Total U.S. sulfur consumption, 1957, calculated as $SO_4^=$ [b]	1.45×10^7 tons/year
Total U.S. sulfur production, 1957, calculated as $SO_4^=$ [b]	1.88×10^7 tons/year

[a] Junge (1960).
[b] Magill et al. (1956).

Figure 20 gives a very tentative picture of the global sulfur cycle. The solid arrows indicate those portions which are better known. According to Eriksson (1959 b), we assumed that the river run off in excess of weathering is equal to the deposit by precipitation, and that direct uptake by the soil and plants of gaseous sulfur is balanced by release from the soil. This requires a net influx within the atmosphere from sea to land of $30 - 10^6$ tons/year. This net influx, plus the release by industry, is deposited over land by precipitation and carried back to the ocean in river water. Over the ocean an absorption of 70×10^6 tons/year of gaseous sulfur was estimated and this, together with the other figures, then requires a total release of 160×10^6 tons/year over the ocean.

According to Fig. 20, the 40×10^7 tons/year industrial sulfur accumulate in the ocean and the sulfur cycle is no longer a closed one as would be expected under natural steady state conditions. The situation is, therefore, similar to the CO_2 cycle.

Closely related to the budget is the residence time of sulfur in the atmosphere, which can be estimated in various ways. The residence time of total sulfur it $\tau = S/R$, where S is the total atmospheric sulfur content and R the rate of removal. If we accept 6 $\mu g/m^3$ as average SO_2 concentration in the troposphere, $S = 4.3 \times 10^7$ tons of SO_4. The removal by precipitation alone, $R_p = 3.9 \times 10^8$ tons SO_4/year, gives $\tau = 40$ days, but the estimated total removal $R = 8.1 \times 10^8$ tons of SO_4/year shown in Fig. 20 yields $\tau = 19$ days. These values stand primarily for H_2S and may easily be in error by a factor of 2.

Meetham (1950) obtained a value of 11 hours for SO_2 based on a budget consideration of industrial SO_2 released and removed over England. Junge (1960) has re-examined this estimate and thinks it can be as much as 4 days. He also estimated a 7-day residence time for industrial sulfur in the U.S., based on the average speed of west wind circulation and the fact that 35% of the U.S. sulfur emission (Table 18) is removed by precipitation within the U.S. itself. If direct soil uptake is included, the value may be only 3-4 days. These τ values for SO_2 seem to be smaller than those of 20 to 40 days for total sulfur, and may indicate a longer residence time for H_2S. However, since H_2S seems to react quite rapidly with O_3, this difference should be small. Further studies are certainly necessary to obtain more reliable figures.

The presence of considerable quantities of industrial sulfur in the atmosphere raises the question whether there has been a secular increase of the sulfur concentration in the atmosphere since the turn of the century, as in the case of CO_2. Unfortunately, conclusions cannot be drawn from the few short series of measurements available.

There are a few older measurements for England, but these were made too close to cities of industrial areas to be sufficiently represen-

tative. Precipitation is stored for thousands of years in the ice cap of Greenland without modifications because the low average temperature of $-25^\circ C$
prevents melting, except for short periods during a few summers, so that
water cannot percolate through the ice. Measurements of the SO_4 concentration in a vertical profile in the central part of this ice cap back to 1915
did not reveal any increase (Junge, 1960). This is not surprising if SO_2
has a residence time of only a few days since most of the industrail SO_2
may already be washed out before the air masses from temperate latitudes
arrive in Greenland. Our figures of the sulfur budget in Fig. 20, however,
suggest that, at least in temperate latitudes of the northern hemisphere,
a measurable increase must have occurred, perhaps 30%, since most industries are located in the northern hemisphere and no exchange across
the equator can be expected.

The possibility cannot be excluded that this substantial increase in atmospheric sulfur has some effect on the climate. Sulfur is known
to be an important constituent of atmospheric condensation nuclei (see
Chapter 2), and the number and size distribution of atmospheric condensation nuclei are, in turn, important for the colloidal stability of clouds and
their ability to release rain, as recently demonstrated by Squires and Twomey (1960). An increase of sulfur may therefore render the clouds more
stable and increase the average cloud cover and cloud height, primarily
over oceanic regions. The average cloud cover, however, affects the radiation balance of the atmosphere.

One difficulty with the sulfur cycle given in Fig. 20 should
not be left unmentioned. A net flux from sea to land requires, on the average,
greater concentrations over sea. All data, however, i.e., the few direct
measurements of the SO_2 concentration in air and also the concentration
of excess sulfur in rain water, indicate the opposite. Even in land areas with
little industry and sparse population, the excess sulfur concentration in
rain seems to be higher than over sea. Perhaps part of this discrepancy is
due to higher concentrations of mineral dust or NH_3 over land, which favors
the conversion of sulfur to sulfate and thus the removal rate.

We will conclude our discussion with a remark about the
isotopic composition of atmospheric sulfur. Ostlund (1959) and more
recently Jensen and Nakai (1961) found that the S^{32}/S^{34} ratio of SO_4 in
rain water is rather constant around 22.1 and enriched in S^{32} by about 15
per mil with respect to sea water. This confirms the conclusions in this chapter (see, e.g., Table 18) and in Section 4.3.4 that over land the contribution
of sulfate from sea-salt particles is minor, or, in other words, that over land
excess sulfur plays the dominant role. Table 19 illustrates that the S^{32}/S^{34}
ratios for other possible sources of atmospheric sulfur are quite variable
and unfortunately cover the range found in rain water, so that it is difficult
to draw conclusions about the origin of the excess sulfur.

TABLE 19

RATIO OF S^{32}/S^{34} IN GEOCHEMISTRY [a]

Source	Sulfur compound	Range of S^{32}/S^{34}
Rain water	SO_4	22.15–22.26
Sea water	SO_4	21.88–22.19
Volcanos	SO_2	21.8–22.4
Volcanos	H_2S	22.2–22.4
Biosphere	S	21.7–22.5
Biosphere	H_2S	22.1–22.7

[a] Ault (1959), Östlund (1959).

According to Jensen and Nakai (1961) the values of rain water and sea water (by Östlund) should be corrected by subtracting 0.12.

It appears however, that the ratio found in H_2S produced in the biosphere by reduction of $SO_4^=$ is closest to the range observed in rain water.

1.6 Hydrogen and Helium

1.6.1 The Abundance of Hydrogen and Its Isotopes

It is a generally accepted concept that the presence of oxygen in the atmosphere is the result of photolysis of water and subsequent escape of hydrogen into space (Harteck and Jensen, 1948). A study of atmospheric hydrogen is therefore of special interest to geochemistry. The occurrence of HD and HT, and the relative abundance of these isotopes with respect to water, complicates the problem considerably but also makes it a very attractive and challenging field of research.

Due to the inherent experimental difficulties in determining the very small concentrations of hydrogen and its isotopes in air, the number of measurements is still small. In addition, the natural conditions for tritium have been severely disturbed since the testing of thermonuclear devices started and will remain so for a long time. Our knowledge about atmospheric hydrogen is, therefore, still very incomplete.

Table 20 presents a survey of important data available at the present time. The first approximate value of the hydrogen content, viz.,

TABLE 20

DATA ON ATMOSPHERIC HYDROGEN AND ITS ISOTOPES

	Author	Isotopic ratio	Mixing ratio in air
Hydrogen	Schuftan (1923) (see Paneth, 1937) Linde Company, Germany (see Harteck and Süss, 1949)		$5.0 \pm 0.5 \times 10^{-1}$ ppm $= 44$ $\mu g/m^3$ at STP
	Glueckauf and Kitt (1957), 11 samples		$3.7\text{-}10 \times 10^{-1}$ ppm av. 5.1×10^{-1} ppm
Deuterium	Harteck and Süss (1949), 2 samples taken in Hamburg, Germany	D/H = 25% higher than tap water	
	Begemann and Friedman (1959), 24 samples taken in Buffalo, New York and Hamburg and Nürnberg, Germany	D/H $= -16\%$ to $+ 6\%$ relative to water of D/H $= 1.48 \pm 0.02 \times 10^{-4}$ or D/H $= 1.2\text{-}1.6 \times 10^{-4}$	Since the ratio HD/H$_2$ $= 2 \times$ D/H the mixing ratio of HD in air is $1.2\text{-}1.6 \times 10^{-4}$ ppm
Natural tritium	Faltings and Harteck (1950), 1949 samples	T/H $= 3.8 \pm 1.2 \times 10^{-15}$	The mixing ratio of HT in air is 3.8×10^{-15} ppm
	Grosse et al. (1954), 1951 samples	T/H $= 16.6 \pm 1 \times 10^{-15}$	16.6×10^{-15} ppm

0.8 ppm, was obtained by Dewar in 1914. In 1923 Schuftan determined the H_2 content in various places in Germany and found no variation within the 10% limit of accuracy. This value was published in 1937 by Paneth. Harteck and Süss (1949) quote a similar value from essentially the same source.

The most recent determinations of the H_2 mixing ratio were published by Glueckauf and Kitt (1957), who analyzed two sets of samples. The first 17 samples were collected mostly in the laboratory at Harwell in 1951 and showed an average of 0.74 ppm with the extremes of 0.25 and 1.99 ppm. Another set of 11 samples taken outdoors in 1954 provided an average of 0.51 and limits of 0.37 and 1.0 ppm, with an accuracy of 10 to 20%. The laboratory values suggest local contamination. The outside samples were collected around noon, when turbulent mixing is strongest and local contamination is reduced to a minimum. Their average of 0.51 is close to Schuftan's value, which is now generally accepted. Paneth and Kitt feel that the fluctuations in the outdoor samples are real and related to weather.

The deuterium content of atmospheric hydrogen was first determined by Harteck and Süss (1949), who employed a relatively insensitive pycnometric method. They found the D/H ratio to be 25% higher than that of tap water. The only new and extensive data are those by Begemann and Friedman (1959), who made simultaneous measurements of the D/H and T/H ratio in 24 samples from the United States and Germany. They observed a D/H ratio somewhat less than that of Lake Michigan water. In comparison to ocean water, Lake Michigan water has a $\delta_{O^{18}} = - 6.1\%$ (see Section 1.1) and subsequently a $\delta_D = - 9 \times 6.1^0/_{00} = 5.5\%$. The D/H values of $- 16\%$ and $+ 6\%$ in Table 20 thus correspond to δ_D values of $- 21$ and $+ 1\%$ if ocean water is the standard. Atmospheric hydrogen compares, therefore, more with snow and is markedly lower in D than is the terrestrial water reservoir, which is practically equivalent to the oceans. It should be mentioned that the deuterium values have not been influenced by atomic tests.

Only two measurements of the *natural* tritium content of atmospheric hydrogen were made before the first thermonuclear device was fired in November 1952 (Ivy test) which released measurable quantities of tritium into the atmosphere. These values are about a thousand times higher than the T/H ratio in natural waters, a fact which is of importance with respect to the kinetics of hydrogen reactions in the atmosphere.

Since the Castle tests in 1954 and particularly since 1956, the T/H ratio of hydrogen has increased considerably and has reached a level about 30 times that of the natural background. This will be discussed later in connection with artificial radioactivity (Section 3.3).

1.6.2 Sources and Sinks of Hydrogen

The most likely sources of atmospheric hydrogen are the decomposition of organic matter and the photolysis of H_2O. In addition, there may be a small steady state concentration of hydrogen due to the influx of protons from the sun and the escape of hydrogen into space. According to Harteck and Süss (1949), hydrogen production by volcanoes and cosmic rays is negligible. We will discuss these sources in more detail.

The formation of H_2 by decomposition of organic matter under anaerobic conditions was suggested by various authors (e.g., Farkas *et al.*, 1934; Gonsior, 1959) without, however, giving any further information on the subject. Hoch *et al.* (1957) report the evolution of hydrogen from soybean root nodules together with N_2. They observed a higher rate of H_2 formation in the presence of O_2, i.e., under aerobic conditions. Cloud *et al.* (1958) found that bacteria from the Bahama banks produce a gas which contains 63% H_2, 26% CO_2, and smaller amounts of N_2 and O_2. The deuterium content is lower than that of sea water by a *factor* of 20! This is much more than the factor of 4, which one should expect from the thermodynamic exchange equilibrium

$$H_2 + HDO \rightleftharpoons HD + H_2O.$$

The deuterium depletion of this biological process is of interest in view of the relatively low D/H ratio found in atmospheric hydrogen. Hydrogen is also formed under certain conditions in the bacterial fermentation of carbohydrates (e.g., Buswell, 1954).

The production of H_2 by photolysis of water has been reasonably well established by laboratory experiments, the most recent of which are by Taylor and Chen (1957). Important for the reaction is the water vapor absorption between 1600 and 1800 Å, a radiation which occurs only at altitudes above 80 to 100 km. In the presence of O_2, however, the quantum yield of the reaction is rather low. This is due to the fact that the low concentration of H offers little chance to form H_2 by collision. Instead HO_2-radicals are formed which are finally transformed into H_2O and not into H_2. The photochemical formation of H_2 is further reduced by a rapid photooxidation of H_2 in the presence of O_2, as demonstrated by Volman (1956) and Barth and Suess (1960). The latter authors estimate the net quantum yield of H_2O photolysis in the presence of O_2 to be of the order of only 10^{-6}.

The photooxidation of H_2 in the presence of O_2 leads us to the sinks for atmospheric hydrogen. Many bacteria utilize hydrogen for the synthesis of protoplasm or to reduce nitrite and amino acids (e.g., Koffler and Wilson, 1951). Except for these processes in the biosphere, no sinks for hydrogen are known in the troposphere. The possibility of H_2 oxidation by O_3 in the stratosphere was discussed by Groth and Harteck (1938). They find that the thermal reaction with ozone is much too slow below 100°C. They also think that atomic oxygen is not very efficient in oxidizing H_2 to water. Atomic hydrogen, however, e.g., after its formation by photolysis of water, may be removed by reactions with ozone and atomic oxygen (McKinley and Garvin, 1955), a process which serves to reduce further the efficiency of water photolysis.

Another sink of atmospheric hydrogen is its escape into space (see e.g., Urey, 1959). The escape from the gravitational field occurs in the exosphere at altitudes of 500 to 1000 km and its rate of escape depends on the concentration of H_2 and the temperature in this layer. The concentration is determined by the upward flux of hydrogen. This flux of hydrogen in turn is affected by photooxidation or photolysis of water vapor in the lower layers. It seems most likely that the controlling factor for the net escape of hydrogen from the earth is the upward flux and not the temperature at the escape level, but our knowledge of the various parameters involved is so incomplete that at present quantitative considerations are fairly meaningless. It should be expected, however, that the D/H ratio for atmospheric hydrogen should increase due to slower diffusion and escape of deuterium.

There is a constant influx of protons from the sun. In equilibrium this influx must be balanced by a corresponding rate of escape of hydrogen which in turn requires a certain equilibrium concentration of hydrogen in the exosphere. It is not known if and to what degree this equilibrium mixing ratio can reach down into the troposphere across the layers in which hydrogen is photooxidized.

From our discussion, it is obvious that information about atmospheric hydrogen is still inconclusive. If photolysis of water vapor in the higher atmosphere is the major source of atmospheric hydrogen, one should expect a very constant mixing ratio in the troposphere and a very long hydrogen cycle, because of the low density of water vapor at the controlling level. The hydrogen fluctuations observed by Glueckauf and Kitt (1957) can hardly be explained on this basis. They point rather to production at the earth's surface.

The low D/H ratio of hydrogen also points to biological sources, but it is no argument against photolysis. The cold trap action of the tropopause should result in fairly low D/H ratios of water vaporin stratospheric air and a possible increase of this ratio due to fractionation during escape may not be sufficient to bring the ratio back to normal.

Begemann and Friedmann (1959) observed a positive correlation between the variation of the D/H and of the T/H ratios. They showed that it cannot be explained by exchange between hydrogen and water vapor because such a reaction is far too slow at normal temperatures to account for the observed variations. They suggest as an explanation local sources of hydrogen whose T/H ratio is similar to that of water, but whose D/H ratio is 20-30% lower. These sources may be due to biological processes which are not in thermal equilibrium with water or with industrial production.

The fact that the natural tritium content of hydrogen is about 1000 times higher than that of water was explained by Harteck (1954) in the following way: after T is formed by cosmic radiation, essentially it can undergo the following two primary reactions

$$T + O_2 + M \rightarrow TO_2 + M$$

$$T + H_2 \quad\quad \rightarrow H + HT.$$

Since the concentration of O_2 is so much larger than that of H_2, the formation of TO_2 is strongly favored; the TO_2, in turn, will finally, be transformed into HTO and not HT. Estimates show that the resulting HT/HTO ratio so calculated is several orders of magnitude lower than the observed ratios. Therefore, Harteck assumes that the radical TO_2 is decomposed photochemically, which assumption would favor the second reaction and may result in agreement with the facts.

1.6.3 Helium

On comparing observations from various parts of the world, Glueckauf (1951) found a very constant mixing ratio of 5.239 ± 0.002 ppm for helium. However, helium is not a permanent gas since considerable quantities are consistantly generated by radioactive decay in the earth's crust. It is composed of two isotopes, He^3 and He^4, which are produced by entirely different processes. The ratio He^3/He^4 is 1.2×10^{-6} (e.g., Damon and Kulp, 1958), i.e., almost all He is present as He^4. The total amounts of helium in the atmosphere are: for He^3, 2.4×10^7 m³ STP, and for He^4, 2.0×10^{13} m³ STP.

Helium-4 is produced in almost equal parts by the decay of U^{238} and Th^{232} and only about 2% is due to decay of U^{235}. The total production of the He^4 can be calculated from the total amounts of these mother elements in the lithosphere and the fraction of helium which escapes into the atmosphere. Both quantities are uncertain, especially the degree of degassing of the earth's crust. The total production of He^4 according to Damon and Kulp is, in the earth's crust, 7×10^6 m³ STP/year, and in the earth's mantle, 35×10^6 m³ STP/year. Leakage from the mantle is most unlikely. For complete leakage from the crust, the residence time of He^4 in the atmosphere is 3×10^6 years. Most likely the degassing will be incomplete, i.e., the He supply smaller and the residence time longer. Damon and Kulp estimate that only a few per cent of the helium now forming is being liberated, but their estimates are open to objections.

The age of the earth is about 3×10^9 years, i.e., considerably longer than the residence time of helium. The present concentration of He^4 thus must represent a steady state and forces to the conclusion that helium escapes into space. It is clear from our discussion in the introduction of this chapter and from Table I that for residence times of the order of 10^6 years time and space variations of helium in the atmosphere must be extremely small, in agreement with the observed constancy of its mixing ratio within 0.4%. Even measurements comparitively near the large helium sources of the United States did no show measurable deviations.

Helium-3 is produced in the atmosphere by cosmic-ray spallation reactions with N^{14} and also in the lithosphere by reactions with lithium and other elements. The highest He^3 content was found in lithium minerals, but the production of He^4 by radioactive decay is so much more profuse that as a consequence the lithospheric helium sources have lower HE^3/He^4 ratios than the atmosphere. The major source of the He^3 is cosmic radiation and the production rate is about twice that of tritium, i.e., 0.5 atom/cm³ sec = 4.0×10^2 m³ STP/year for the whole atmosphere. This gives a residence time of 6×10^4 years which can be assumed accurate within a factor of 2. Therefore, the concentration of the He^3 must also represent a steady state.

The escape of helium occurs in the exosphere, i.e., primarily between 500 and 1000 km. The calculation of the escape rate is still an open question (e.g., Bates and McDowell, 1959; Urey, 1959). Basically, the escape rate depends on the number of atoms which have a velocity higher than the escape velocity. This number is given by the concentration of the constituent and the temperature. If a static model is assumed for the atmosphere with complete mixing up to 120 km, the ground concentrations of He^3 and He^4 determine the concentration at the escape layer which in turn enables one to calculate the escape temperature. Invariably, both helium isotopes give different temperatures which is of course not possible. Most likely this discrepancy is due to the fact that the diffusion flux within the atmosphere is another controlling factor and modifies the vertical distribution of the constituent against the static model. The steady state requires that the *vertical flux* of He^3 and He^4 must be independent of altitude throughout the atmosphere and equal to the production and escape rates. This requirement determines the vertical distribution of He^3 and He^4 in the atmosphere, and the trend of the mixing ratio with altitude can be estimated. The general diffusion theory (e.g., Lettau, 1951) shows that the vertical flux of a constituent is composed of two terms: the first term is given by the product of the verticl gradient of the mixing ratio of the constituent times the sum of the eddy and molecular diffusion coefficient; the second term is independent of turbulent conditions and is given bt

$$F = \varrho v \mu d / H$$

where ϱ = density of helium
$\varrho(\text{He}^3) = 1.33 \times 10^{-4} \text{g/cm}^3$
$\varrho(\text{He}^4) = 1.78 \times 10^{-4} \text{g/cm}^3$

v = mixing ratio of He in air

$\mu = (m_{\text{air}} - m_{\text{He}})/m_{\text{air}};$
m = molecular weight
$\mu(\text{He}^3) = 0.90$
$\mu(\text{He}^4) = 0.86$

d = molecular diffusion coefficient of He in air,
$d(\text{He}^4) = 0.59 \text{ cm}^2/\text{sec}$ which is almost equal to that of He^3

H = scale height of the atmosphere = 8×10^5 cm.

For helium this flux is directed upward and has the following numerical values: He^3, $F = 6.7 \times 10^2$ m³ STP/year; and for He^4, $F = 5.4 \times 10^8$ m³ STP/year. In case of He^3, the calculated value is close to the observed value of 4.0×10^2 m³ STP/year. This is fortuitous and means that the mixing ratio of He^3 will be almost constant with altitude up to about 120 km, where diffusive separation starts. For He^4 the flux is larger than the estimated production rate and the mixing ratio has to increase with altitude, so that a downward turbulent flux will reduce the value. Since turbulent conditions in the upper atmosphere are still very uncertain, estimates of this increase are not possible. Because the production rate of He^3 is fairly well known and because its vertical distribution is not much affected by turbulence, this isotope seems to be best suited for calculation of the escape temperature.

1.7 Nitrogen Compounds

1.7.1 Nitrous Oxide

The following nitrogen oxides are known: N_2O (nitrous oxide), NO (nitric oxide), N_2O_3 (dinitrogen trioxide), NO_2 (nitrogen dioxide), N_2O_4 (dinitrogen tetraoxide), N_2O_5 (dinitrogen pentoxide), NO_3 (nitrogen trioxide), and N_2O_6 (dinitrogen hexoxide).

At normal temperatures and with small partial pressures, as in the atmosphere, the following oxides are completely dissociated:

$$N_2O_3 \rightarrow NO + NO_2$$
$$N_2O_4 \rightarrow 2NO_2$$
$$N_2O_5 \rightarrow N_2O_3 + O_2.$$

For example, at room temperatures and with an NO_2 concentration of 10 $\mu g/m^3$, the equilibrium is displaced so far toward the right that only 10^{-6} $\mu g/m^3$ of N_2O_4 are present (Bodenstein, 1922). Since the rate of dissociation of these three oxides is independent of pressure, the equilibrium adjusts fairly rapidly, even at the low partial pressures in the atmosphere. Some nitrogen oxides, i.e., NO_3 and N_2O_6, cannot exist in the atmosphere under normal conditions. The presence of NO is assumed and is likely for the high atmosphere. Only N_2O and NO_2 have been verified by measurements. Since no attempt has been made to separate NO_2 and N_2O_3, the data on NO_2 may refer to a mixture of NO_2 and N_2O_3.

Nitrous oxide, which we will discuss first, was discovered in the solar spectrum in 1939 by Adel (1939). Since then, its existence has frequently been confirmed by the identification of additional absorption bands (e.g., at 3.9, 4.5, 7.8, and 8.6 μ), which are quite well suited for quantitative determinations. Adel (1951) gives an average total N_2O of 0.3 cm STP. More recent measurements, summarized by Miller (1956), indicate a total of 0.4 to 0.5 cm STP, corresponding to a uniform mixing ratio of 0.5 ppm. Goody and Walshaw (1953), made spectroscopic measurements from an airplane which are compatible with a constant mixing ratio of 0.27 ± 0.08 ppm above altitudes of 3 to 10 km. Using mass spectroscopy, Slobod and Krogh (1950) found mixing ratios between 0.25 and 0.65 ppm near the ground in Texas. Birkeland *et al.* (1957) obtained 3 values between 0.39 and 0.57 ppm by spectroscopy in horizontal light paths. Newer data by Shaw (1959), based on a total of 36 samples of ground air in Columbus, Ohio, July 1958 to February 1959, again give a somewhat lower average of 0.28 ± 0.04 ppm. He thinks that the scatter of his data is due primarily to experimental errors and that no variation of the N_2O content with the time of year is suggested. He also made measurements in barns (sheep, swine, cattle) and in greenhouses (tomatoes, flowers) after they were closed overnight and found higher concentrations around 0.33 ppm. This points to biological processes as an important source.

It is quite possible that the differences indicated in all these data are real and that the mixing ratio may indeed vary in time and space between 0.25 and 0.60 ppm, with an approximate average of 0.40 ppm. The respective concentration values are 500, 1200, and 800 $\mu g/m^3$. These concentrations are quite high compared to those of many other trace substances.

Information on the vertical distribution is important. Earlier data (Adel, 1951) and the data of Goody and Walshaw (1953) suggest a fairly uniform mixing ratio. The most careful investigation of this question was made by Goldberg and Mueller (1953). They measured the variation of the N_2O absorption in the solar spectrum with the height of the sun and compared the observations with computed fluctuations for various assumed vertical distributions of NO_2. The agreement was best in the case of a constant vertical mixing ratio.

Chemically, N_2O is a very stable and inert gas and is unlikely to be destroyed within the lower atmosphere. Photodissociation occurs in radiation below 2100 Å, which can penetrate to the ozone layer. Bates and Witherspoon (1952) computed this process for various levels of the atmosphere and obtained the following values for the lifetime of N_2O: at a height of 10 km, 4000 days; at 20 km, 800 days; at 30 km, 50 days; at 40 km, 20 days. As a consequence of these figures, a fairly constant mixing ratio up to altitudes of about 20 km is to be expected, which is in agreement with Goldberg and Mueller's results. By photochemical reactions, Goody and Walshaw estimated the total rate of N_2O destruction to be 8×10^{10} molecules/cm² sec, or 6×10^{-12} g/cm² sec, as a mean value for the atmosphere. For a total amount of N_2O of 0.4 cm STP, this results in a residence time of about 4 years. This residence time is of the same order as that of CO_2 and one should, therefore, expect similar amplitudes of fluctuation, particularly if N_2O is produced at the ground. This seems to be borne out by the observations.

Under equilibrium conditions an equivalent source must be available. Two views regarding the origin of N_2O have been advanced:

(1) N_2O is produced by soil bacteria upon the decomposition of nitrogen compounds.

(2) N_2O is formed photochemically in the stratosphere.

Adel was the first to consider the soil bacteria process (1946, 1951), and more recent investigations (Goody and Walshaw, 1953) indicate that this is by far the most probable source. In detailed experiments, Arnold (1954) examined the bacterial transformation of NH_4^+ or NO_3^- ions in the soil into N_2O and, in part, into N_2. The amount of N_2O produced increases strongly with poor aeration of the soil, e.g., with high water content. Under average conditions, the entire amount of fixed nitrogen in the soil is transformed in about 100 to 1000 days. Using this value and the best data available for soil area, depth, and average fixed nitrogen content, Goody and Walshaw obtained an average world-wide N_2O production value of $1.6\text{-}16 \times 10^{10}$ molecules/cm² sec. This magnitude is similar to that of N_2O dissociation given above and shows that the soil can actually supply the main quantity of N_2O.

As for the photochemical production of N_2O, Bates and Witherspoon (1952) think that the reaction $N_2O_3 \rightarrow N_2O + O_2$ is most promising and should be able to balance the N_2O dissociation. However, by a rough experimental check, Goody and Walshaw (1953) found that this reaction can account for only 2.5% of the photochemical destruction and thus seems to be of little importance.

Harteck and Dondes (1954 a, b), considered the formation of N_2O by the reaction

$$N_2 + O_3^* \rightarrow N_2O + O_2$$

for the ozone layer and by

$$N_2 + O + M \rightarrow N_2O + M$$

for higher layers with larger atomic oxygen concentrations. The rate of these reactions is likely to be small but constant and since the reactions occur in higher layers they cannot explain any time and space variation of tropospheric N_2O. It must be concluded that photochemical production of N_2O is of minor importance. Most of the N_2O is released from the ground and destroyed in the stratosphere.

1.7.2 Nitric Oxide and Nitrogen Dioxide

No attempt has been made to separate NO and N_2O_3 from NO_2 in the atmosphere. If present, they are included in analyses generally interpreted as NO_2.

The existence of NO has been discussed in a number of papers, mostly with reference to high altitudes, but definite conclusions have not been reached. Recently, Barth (1961) made very elaborate calculations of all reactions and reaction products involving atomic oxygen and nitrogen above 60 km. For NO and NO_2, he arrived at mixing ratios of the order of 10^{-2} and 10^{-6} ppm, which increase somewhat with altitude and show no daily variation. If the NO mixing ratio of 10^{-2} extends below 60 km, it can be important for tropospheric considerations. The ionization in the D-layers and the night afterglow may indicate the presence of NO at altitudes higher than 80 km. By spectroscopic measurements, Migeotte and Neven (1952) showed that no more than 0.02 cm STP NO can be present in the atmosphere. This would correspond to a uniform mixing ratio of 2.5×10^{-2} ppm or a concentration of 33.5 $\mu g/m^3$ at STP, an upper limit that is still fairly high compared to that of other trace gases.

Since NO_2 has been found in the troposphere, the equilibrium $2NO + O_2 \rightleftharpoons 2NO_2$ is of interest. Bodenstein (1922) made a careful study of this reaction. The high partial pressure of O_2 shifts the equilibrium so far to the right that less than 10^{-5} $\mu g/m^3$ of NO will be present for an NO_2 concentration of 10 $\mu g/m^3$. However, since it is a second-order reaction, its rate decreases rapidly with the partial pressure of NO. If we assume an initial NO concentration of 10 $\mu g/m^3$, only 10% would be transformed after 10^3 days. Thus, if sources were present, equilibrium could never be reached and NO would be found in the atmosphere.

Traces of NO_2 were suggested long ago by the presence of nitrates in rain, but we still have only few direct measurements of the NO_2 content of air. Recent data indicate that the NO_2 concentrations are considerably higher than those of nitrates in aerosols, as is the case with the SO_2/SO_4 ratio (Table 21). Except for polluted areas, the ratio is about

TABLE 21

RATIO OF NO_2 TO NO_3 IN AEROSOLS (EXPRESSED AS NO_2) [a]

Location	Ratio	Observer
Frankfurt/M, winter	3	Georgii
Frankfurt/M, summer	5	Georgii
Zugspitze (3000 meters)	9	Georgii
Florida	10	Junge
St. Moritz	11	Weber
Hawaii	63	Junge

[a] Georgii (1960).

10 or higher. Therefore, determinations of total nitrate by bubbling air through wash bottles can be interpreted, with good approximation, as NO_2 in an unpolluted atmosphere.

Reynolds (1930) obtained some early values of the NO_2 concentration at distances of 8 and 23 km from the center of London. At 23 km, the NO_2 content had dropped to about one sixth of its average of 16 $\mu g/m^3$ at 8 km. He concluded that NO_2 is predominantly a component of urban air. Edgar and Paneth (1941) separated NO_2 from O_3 by adsorption on silica gel and by fractional distillation. They found 15 $\mu g/m^3$ in London and 1-6 $\mu g/m^3$ in a suburb, i.e., values similar to those of Reynolds.

Figure 18 contains more recent data for different locations, ranging from polluted areas to such remote places as Hawaii. The values in Frankfurt are similar to those in London. In clean air they drop to a few $\mu g/m^3$, but not in quite such a pronounced manner as SO_2. Table 19 contains more detailed information for unpolluted areas. Clearly, NO_2 is produced by human activities, but there is also a fairly uniform natural background, with an average of about 2-3 $\mu g/m^3$. A comparison of the data from Kleiner Felderg (800 meters), St. Moritz (1800 meters), and the Zugspitze (3000 meters) seems to indicate that there is no decrease of NO_2 with altitude if mixing ratios are considered; but these values do not represent a true vertical profile and conclusions can scarcely be drawn from them. However, Gerogii (1960) observed that the NO_2 concentrations at the Zugspitze were higher when turbulent conditions favored exchange with lower layers. This and the time and space fluctuations point to the earth's surface as the most likely source of NO_2 and to a fairly short lifetime of the order of 2 months. The suggestion that the soil is the major source of NO_2 is supported by the observation that NO_2 is formed under anaerobic conditions in silos containing corn, alfalfa, and cabbage (Altshuller, 1958). The presence of NO_2 in silos constitutes a serious agricultural occupational hazard and indicates the intensity of the production (e. g. Schuman, 1960). The NO_2 in this case probably results from oxidation of NO, which in turn is generated by bacterial reduction of nitrates to nitrites. Under acid conditions (pH $\leq$ 5) NO is formed from HNO_2 and this process occurs also in soils (Allison, 1955). Losses at higher pH values are not important. The lack of stability of HNO_2 is doubtless one of the main reasons for the negative nitrogen balance in acid soils. Microorganisms contribute to the NO and NO_2 formation, primarily through the formation of HNO_2, but seem to produce little NO directly. Considerable quantities of nitrogen are lost from the soil also in form of N_2 and N_2O by the activity of bacteria.

The question often arises whether lightning is of any importance in producing atmospheric NO_2. At present, the consensus of opinion is that the evidence is marginal (Viemeister, 1960). Reiter and Reiter (1958) think that the higher nitrate values in precipitation on a mountain (1780 meters) can be explained by electrical discharges.

On a global basis electrical processes cannot explain the presence of NO_2. Except for the soil, all other sources, such as, e.g., photochemical oxidation in higher altitudes and oxidation of NH_3, are doubtful and further investigations are needed to solve the question of the NO_2 origin.

Hoering (1957) measured the N^{15}/N^{14} ratio of NH_4^+ and NO_3^- in rain water and found it higher than that of atmospheric N_2. The values of the N^{15} enrichment in NH_4^+ and NO_3^- showed a strong positive correlation and this led him to suspect that the nitrate is produced by oxidation of ammonia. The fact that N^{15} is enriched excludes the formation of NO_2 and subsequently NO_3^- by direct fixation of atmospheric N_2, but the correlation between NH_4^+ and NO_3^- is no proof for oxidation of NH_3. Eriksson (1958) points out that both NH_3 and NO_2 are present as gases and that only a fraction of them is fixed in each rainfall. The process of fixation can result in a similar fractionation and enrichment of N^{15} for both constituents and this may explain the observations. Further studies of nitrogen isotopes in atmospheric compounds will certainly be of interest.

1.7.3 Ammonia

Atmospheric ammonia was detected very early in rain water. As in the case of SO_2 and NO_2, it has only recently been established that the gas phase predominates. Table 22 gives some data. Determination of total NH_3 in bubble tubes can therefore be regarded as a good approximation of the gas concentraion.

TABLE 22

RATIO OF NH_3 TO NH_4 IN AEROSOLS [a]

Location	Ratio	Observer
Frankfurt/M, winter	4	Georgii
Frankfurt/M, summer	6	Georgii
St. Moritz	10	Weber
Florida	42	Junge
Hawaii	52	Junge
Zugspitze (3000 meters)	57	Georgii
Mauna Kea (3200 meters)	360	Junge

[a] Georgii (1960).

Spectroscopic evidence of NH_3 in the atmosphere is uncertain. Mohler et al. (1948) believed that they had found it; but Migeotte and Chapman (1949) were able to show on the basis of better data that the total NH_3 must be below the limit of spectroscopic detection, 0.013 cm STP, which is equivalent to a uniform mixing ratio of 1.6×10^{-2} ppm or to a concentration of 10 $\mu g/m^3$ near the ground.

Quite a number of NH_3 determinations were made in the second half of the last century. During this period, the importance of fixed nitrogen compounds for the biological cycle was recognized, and interest was aroused in the content of nitrogen compounds in the atmosphere (see, e.g., Gmelin, 1934-1936). These old values obtained in various locations in Western Europe are rather high compared with more recent data. The lowest values at the ground were around 20 $\mu g/m^3$. In some cases local pollution might be suggested; however, values from the Pic du Midi (2800 meters) for the year 1880 fluctuate between 7 and 30 $\mu g/m^3$, with a mean value of 13 $\mu g/m^3$. With the turn of the century the interest in direct measurements of atmospheric ammonia ceased almost completely, and it was not until quite recently that new data became available.

In 1953, Egnér and Eriksson (1955) created a network of sampling stations in Scandinavia. Small amounts of air were continuously sucked through absorption solutions at these stations in order to obtain monthly average values for different trace substances, e.g., NH_3. This network has been extended through other parts of Europe, avoiding chemically disturbed areas if possible. Table 23 gives data for the same four stations as Table 14; the listings are from north to south. Despite noticeable fluctuations, the general level for all stations lies between 20 to 5 $\mu g/m^3$. On the whole, this indicates a rather uniform distribution. Most stations show annual variations of the ammonia concentration with maxima in summer and fall. This suggests production by the soil. A more careful evaluation of these observations would be of interest.

Table 24 gives NH_3 data for the southeast coast of Florida, for the east coast in Massachusetts, and for the windward side of the Island of Hawaii. In these measurements, filters were used to remove the aerosols and it may be that the values are too low by about 20% due to gas absorption in these filters. The values of Hawaii are representative for the center of the Pacific. They are lower by a factor of about 2 to 3 than the values in Florida, which are fairly representative for the subtropical Atlantic. But, both sets of data agree well with those from Sweden.

Figure 18 compares these results with some newer values from Central Europe. The NH_3 concentrations in Frankfurt are markedly higher than those from the surrounding areas (Kleiner Feldberg, 25 km north of Frankfurt, and 860 meters above sea level). In contrast to SO_2 and NO_2, the summer values for NH_3 are almost as high as the winter values. This suggests anthropogenic production in this highly populated area, but not by combustion of fuel as, e.g., in the case of SO_2. It is likely that NH_3 in Frankfurt is generated by special industries because corresponding data on the rain water composition from Berlin (Table 57) do not indicate considerable NH_3 pollution compared with SO_4 or the other constituents listed.

The NH_3 concentration above the trade wind inversion in Hawaii (Mauna Kea in Table 24) is markedly lower than at sea level. This points to the ocean as a source of NH_3 in agreement with the relatively small differences between pure maritime and continental air. But simultaneous measurements of the pH value and the NH_4^+ concentration of sea water near Hawaii indicate that the equilibrium concentration of NH_3 in the air above the ocean surface should be 1 to 2 $\mu g/m^3$. This value is smaller than 2.5 and seems to ecxlude the sea water as a source if it is assumed that the few observations are sufficiently representative. The role of the sea as a source or a sink for NH_3 is not quite clear. The ammonia concentration in temperate and tropical oceans decreases generally from about 0.03 at the surface to 0.01 mg/liter at a depth of 100 meters (see Eriksson, 1952).

TABLE 23

MONTHLY AVERAGE VALUES OF THE TOTAL NH$_3$ FROM SOME STATIONS OF THE SWEDISH NETWORK[a]

	Nov. 1954	Dec. 1954	Jan. 1955	Feb. 1955	Mar. 1955	Apr. 1955	May 1955	June 1955	July 1955	Aug. 1955	Sept. 1955	Oct. 1955
Offer	1.4	2.0	2.6	2.2	3.0	4.2	4.0	4.1	5.9	4.9	4.2	2.1
Erken	0.6	2.3	1.1	2.2	1.4	1.2	1.3	1.0	2.2	2.2	0.1	3.6
Falsterbobruk	2.2	1.0	1.3	3.8	1.3	2.2	1.8	1.9	2.9	4.0	2.9	3.4
Alnarp	3.8	2.2	3.4	3.4	4.0	4.5	3.5	6.0	9.4	9.4	5.0	4.8
Average	2.0	1.9	2.1	2.9	2.4	3.0	2.6	3.2	5.1	5.1	3.0	3.5

[a] Egnér and Eriksson (1955). Data represent predominantly the gas phase.

TABLE 24

CONCENTRATION OF NO_2 AND NH_3 IN UNPOLLUTED ATMOSPHERES ($\mu g/m^3$) [a]

Location	Remarks	NO_2		NH_3	
		Range	Average	Range	Average
Florida	Trade winds, southeast coast, 13 values, July-Aug., 1954	1.1–3.7	1.8	2.2–8.0	5.1
Hawaii	East coast Island of Hawaii, 14 values, Nov., 1954	1.5–3.2	2.6	1.1–3.9	2.5
Hawaii	Mauna Kea, 3200 meters above the trade-wind inversion, 4 night values, Nov., 1954	1.6–2.3 [b]	1.9 [b]	0.7–1.3 [b]	1.1 [b]
Ipswich, Massachusetts	9 values, Dec.-Jan., 1954-55	0.6–3.8	2.6	3.3–13.9	6.1

[a] Junge (1956).

[b] Reduced to sea-level pressure.

This seems to indicate a downward flux of NH_3, i.e., absorption of NH_3 at the ocean surface, as we found in Hawaii. The NO_3^- concentration in sea water shows the opposite trend with depth. The NH_4^+ is apparently formed by reduction of NO_3^- by plankton which proceeds in the surface layers until lack of NO_3^- becomes the controlling factor, whereas in deeper layers light is the limiting factor. This seems to indicate that, after all, the sea may act to some extent as a source. It is, however, possible that the main NH_3 source is not the sea water itself, but the organic films observed on the sea surface. This possibility would eliminate the apparent discrepancies.

All the data on NH_3 concentrations in air are rather consistent with each other if it is assumed that the land is a more important source than the ocean and that over land the soil is more important than pollution. Other land sources, such as volcanos or natural gases escaping from the earth's surface, can be neglected, and there are no other processes known which can form NH_3 *in* the atmosphere. The observations are also consistent with Migeotto's upper limit, even for the earlier high values in France, since it must be expected that they will be restricted to the lower troposphere.

The soil can be the source *and* the sink for NH_3, depending on the pH value (see Allison, 1955). Alkaline soils always favor the release of NH_3. The loss of NH_3 starts at a pH of 6 to 7 and increases markedly with increasing pH. The rate of exhalation is a complicated function of several factors such as soil condition and production rate of NH_3. The NH_3 loss is small in soils of high water content and high in soils with a low capacity in ion exchange or in soils that contain much decomposing organic material, even if they are acid, because the NH_3 generated can raise the pH locally. However, no quantitative data for the rate of release from soils seem to be available.

There are several studies which deal with the formation and role of NH_3 in soils (see Gmelin, 1934-1936). The main source for NH_3 is the biologically fixed nitrogen of the amino acids which are decomposed by bacterial activity. This explains the maximum of production in the warmer seasons. The discussion of NH_4^+ in rain water in Section 4.3.4 will provide further evidence for the origin of atmospheric NH_3.

1.8 Halogens

The halogens chlorine and iodine have been identified as gaseous constituents of air. Cauer (1951) analyzed air at various places in Europe by means of his condensation method and found that the ratios Cl/Na and Cl/Mg were lower in air than in sea water. This result is now confirmed on a large scale by various observers (see, e.g., Rossby and Egnér, 1955) who studied rain water over continents. Cauer concluded that Cl escapes from sea-salt droplets by reaction with ozone. More recently, Eriksson (1959 b) suggested that the formation of SO_4 by oxidation of SO_2 in cloud or aerosol droplets containing NaCl will result in a release of HCl by the reaction

$$2NaCl + H_2SO_4 \rightarrow Na_2SO_4 + 2HCl.$$

In order to pursue this question, Junge (1956, 1957) looked for gaseous Cl components in the atmosphere in Florida, Hawaii, and Massachusetts (Ipswich). In these measurements, the aerosols were carefully removed by filters and the gaseous character of the Cl component was verified. Table 25 contains the mean values obtained and also the simultaneous concentrations of Cl^- in aerosols. The true values of the gaseous Cl may be higher by 30% due to some absorption in the filters.

TABLE 25

AVERAGE CHLORINE CONCENTRATIONS ($\mu g/m^3$) OF PARTICULATE AND GASEOUS MATTER AT DIFFERENT LOCALITIES [a]

Location	Remarks	Concentration of total aerosol ($\mu g/m^3$)	Gas
Florida	All data	1.54 (13) [b]	1.57 (13) [b]
	Land breeze	0.56 (6)	0.80 (6)
	Sea breeze	2.39 (7)	2.23 (7)
Hawaii	All data	5.09 (10)	1.92 (14)
Ipswich, Massachusetts	All data	—	4.40 (9)

[a] Junge (1956, 1957).

[b] Figures in parentheses indicate the number of individual measurements.

These data provide strong evidence for an apparently widely distributed gaseous chlorine component. Nothing is known about its composition; most likely it is HCl or Cl_2. Table 25 shows that the concentrations for Cl_2 and Cl^- in aerosols are not very different. There was a positive correlation between both concentrations for the individual days in Florida.

More recent measurements by Georgii (1960), included in Fig. 18, indicate that chlorine is also produced by anthropogenic sources in quantitities similar to those of NH_3 and NO_2. Nothing is known about their chemical nature.

Measurements of the iodine content of the air were, in part, inspired by the interest in nutritional physiology and have been made almost exclusively in Europe by Fellenberg (1926) and Cauer (1939). They found a mean value of about 0.5 $\mu g/m^3$ as representative for Central Europe up to 1933, with higher concentrations in the western part of Europe and lower ones in its eastern regions. The individual values fluctuated considerably by about two orders of magnitude, indicating source regions of rather limited geographical extent.

After the year 1933, the I_2 concentration decreased considerably in Central Europe to about 0.05 $\mu g/m^3$. This coincided with a decline of the West European iodine industry, due to increased importation of iodine from Chile. The decrease of the iodine concentration occurred more slowly in Southern Germany than in Northern Germany. Iodine was produced primarily in Brittany, Scotland, and, to a lesser extent, in Scandinavia and Spain. The iodine industry continued in Brittany after 1934, but on a much reduced scale. Iodine was obtained by a fairly inefficient method of burning seaweed and considerable portions of iodine escaped into the air, raising the local iodine levels by three orders of magnitude (Cauer, 1939).

There is no real proof that iodine was and is present as a gas. Most of the iodine released by burning seaweed was certainly present in gaseous form. Studies by Chamberlain et al. (Chamberlain and Wiffen, 1959; Chamberlain, 1959) with radioactive I^{131} have shown, however, that gaseous iodine is readily absorbed on aerosols. This absorption seems to be fairly complete if the aerosol concentration is about a thousand times larger than that of iodine. When the ratio of iodine to aerosol concentration increases, considerable fractions of iodine are present as gas, as indicated by a rapid increase of its diffusion coefficient. If we apply these findings to the observed iodine concentrations in the atmosphere, we must conclude that the absorption of iodine on natural aerosols with concentrations of the order of 100 $\mu g/m^3$ must be more or less complete. The results of Chamberlain et al. for iodine are fairly fundamental for air chemistry and may apply to other gases as well, e.g., Cl_2.

According to Cauer, the anthropogenic contamination of the atmosphere by iodine in Europe had reached a continental scale, at least prior to 1934. We know now that the same is true for a number of other constituents. The reason it became evident so early and so clearly for iodine was the low natural concentration in connection with the simultaneous break down of most artificial sources in an unintended large-scale experiment.

Very little is known about iodine sources other than the West European iodine industry. According to Fellenberg, part of the iodine may come from the soil. Fuel also contains about $5 \times 10^{-4}\%$ iodine and may contribute to the iodine content of air in polluted areas.

Recently Bolin (1959) pointed out that considerable amounts of iodine may come from the ocean, but that very little iodine is carried back by river water to the sea. On the basis of deposition velocities for iodine found by Chamberlain (1959), Bolin concludes that the soil and the plants must exchange considerable fractions of iodine directly, i.e., in gaseous form. He thinks that the net transfer of iodine from the atmosphere to the land surface is several orders of magnitude smaller than the gross exchange. As we saw, a similar process was suggested for the H_2S and SO_2 exchange.

1.9 Methane, Carbon Monoxide, and Formaldehyde

1.9.1 Methane

Methane was discovered in the spectrum of the sun by Migeotte (1948). More recent spectroscopic determinations give a fairly reliable value of 1.2 cm STP of total CH_4 (Goldberg, 1951; Goldberg and Mueller, 1953), which is equivalent to a uniform mixing ratio of 1.5 ppm or to a concentration of 1100 $\mu g/m^3$ near the ground. By chemical methods, Glueckauf (1951) found a mixing ratio of 1.2 ppm.

Studies of infrared spectra of long horizontal path length in Ohio by Shaw (1959) indicated that mixing ratios in ground air were not higher than 2.4 ppm.

The CH_4 content of the atmosphere is rather high, compared to other trace gases. On the basis of spectroscopic observations at various heights of the sun, Goldberg and Mueller (1953) concluded that the mixing ratio of CH_4 is constant with altitude, and that CH_4 is uniformly distributed over the globe, except perhaps for local variations near the earth's surface.

There are many sources of CH_4 in the biosphere. Methane is the predominant hydrocarbon produced in all anaerobic bacterial decomposition of organic matter in swamps, lakes, marshes, and sewage (Buswell and Mueller, 1952; Dzens-Litovskiy, 1945). Together with mineral oils and lignins, CH_4 itself is immune to bacterial attack. Hutchinson (1954) thinks that animal sources are more important. He estimates a total CH_4 production of 10^7 to 10^8 tons/year.

Natural gas contains 40-97% methane and considerable quantities still escape to the atmosphere all over the world, although it is more and more utilized as fuel.

It is clear from this brief discussion that the earth's surface is the source area of methane. Its sinks, on the other hand, are at high altitudes.

Laboratory experiments, most recently by Dillemuth *et al.* (1960), showed that methane is destroyed by ozone. The rate of the first-order reaction is given by

$$d[O_3]/dt = 0.1 \; [O_3] \; [CH_4] \quad \text{moles/cm}^3 \text{ sec};$$

it decreases by a factor of about 10 for a decrease in temperature by 25°C. The concentrations of O_3, even in the stratosphere, are such that the half-lifes for both constituents are over 10^3 years. The reaction thus is of no importance for air chemistry.

A reaction of CH_4 with atomic oxygen is still doubtful and can only occur at altitudes above the ozone layer. It is possible that the reaction occurs only in the presence of atomic hydrogen, which may be formed in the atmosphere by photolysis of water. The various possible reactions with atomic hydrogen were recently discussed by Altshuller (1958), but it is impossible at the present time to make any estimates of the net destruction rate by atomic oxygen with and without the presence of atomic hydrogen. Probably it will be small, due to the low concentrations involved.

We think that CH_4 is predominantly destroyed by radiation below 1450 Å (see Noyes and Leighton, 1941) in high altitudes. This radiation does not penetrate much below 70 km. The possible reaction products are numerous, some of them may reform methane, and their final composition cannot be predicted.

Production of methane at the surface and destruction in high altitudes requires a decrease in mixing ratio with altitude which is, however, small since the lifetime of CH_4 is likely to be fairly long. The production rate of 10^7 to 10^8 tons/year by Hutchinson (1954) gives a lifetime of the order of 100 years. This is in agreement with C^{14} measurements in CH^4 which gave a specific activity comparable to that of biogenic methane and places an upper limit of about 200 years on the mean lifetime (Glueckauf, 1951).

Methane contains tritium and it was found that on a global basis this tritium content increases rapidly with time due to artificial production. Details will be discussed in Section 3.4.5.

It is possible that other hydrocarbons are present in the atmosphere in low concentrations. Plants, e.g., produce, among other hydrocarbons, small quantities of ethylene. Goldberg and Mueller (1953) showed that spectroscopic observations indicate for this gas an upper limit of 0.01 cm STP or 10^{-2} ppm for uniform mixing. The reaction of ethylene with ozone is about 10^6 times faster than that of CH^4 (Cadle and Schadt, 1952). This would indicate lifetimes for ethylene of the range of hours and would indeed point to very low equilibrium concentrations.

Natural gas seems to be a minor source of atmospheric CH_4 and it is therefore likely that other constituents found in natural gas, such as ethane, propane, and butane are also present in the atmosphere in only very minute concentrations. Went (1960) observed haze formation by terpenes in the presence of ozone and estimated that 10^8 tons of terpene-like-hydrocarbons are produced each year by plants. The oxidation products of this material could explain the presence of organic matter in rain, even in very remote places (see Section 4.3.2).

1.9.2 Carbon Monoxide and Formaldehyde

Like methane, atmospheric carbon monoxide was discovered only very recently in the solar spectrum by Migeotte and Neven (1952). It has since been observed at various places and the more reliable data are compiled in Table 26. They show that CO is a world-wide constituent of the atmosphere of considerable concentration compared to other trace substances. It is present at higher altitudes above the Jungfraujoch where local industrial contamination is excluded, and its total amount varies considerably with time and space. This immediately indicates that the lifetime cannot be very long. Benesch and Migeotte (1953), e.g., observed that total CO at the Jungfraujoch dropped from 0.065 to 0.045 cm within 4 hours and that the lower concentration lasted for at least another day, excluding daily variations. However, they were not able to correlate the fluctuations with trajectories of air masses or other meteorological parameters.

The data in Table 26 seem to indicate that CO is fairly uniformly distributed within the atmosphere. However, the Jungfraujoch data, after correction to sea level under the assumption of a constant mixing ratio, have a tendency to be lower than those obtained near sea level in Ottawa and Ohio. Is should be mentioned that systematic differences between the various observers and methods are not excluded. The mixing ratio obtained in ground air by Shaw (1959) is of special interest, despite the fact that its accuracy is not better than 20 to 50%. The value is definitely higher than those mixing ratios calculated from the observations of the solar spectrum on the assumption of a constant mixing ratio. All this seems to indicate somewhat higher mixing ratios in the lower tropospheric layers.

Our knowledge about the sources and sinks of CO are still very unsatisfactory. The biosphere does not produce CO and it is practically not present in natural or volcanic gases (Altshuller, 1958). Bates and Witherspoon (1952) discuss in great detail the possibilities of its formation and destruction. The dissociation of CO_2 into CO is appreciable only above 100 km. This source can hardly explain the quantities required and the fluctuations observed. However, considerable quantities of CO are produced in all combustion processes. It is shown in Section 5.2 that CO is the most abundant gaseous pollutant if we disregard CO_2. The production of CO in populated areas is also well illustrated by the following figures of the CO content (ppm) in polluted air: busy streets, 100; cities, 5; urban areas, 0.2; unpolluted areas, 0.08.

Bates and Witherspoon estimate a production rate of 4×10^{-4} gr/cm² year. For a total CO content of 0.1 cm STP we obtain a residence time of 0.3 year, a value which seems reasonable in view of the observed variations and the vertical distribution.

TABLE 26

OBSERVATIONS OF ATMOSPHERIC CO

Observer	Location	Total amount (cm STP)	Mixing ratio (ppm)
Migeotte and Neven (1952)	Jungfraujoch, 3580 meters	0.01-0.16 [a] Corrected for sea level: 0.015-0.23	0.19-0.29 [b]
Benesch and Migeotte (1953)	Jungfraujoch, 3580 meters 6 days, Aug. 1950-Sept. 1951	0.017-0.075 [a] Corrected for sea level: 0.025-0.11	0.031-0.14 [b]
Locke and Herzberg (1953)	Ottawa, 14 days, June 1952-Oct. 1952	0.09-0.18 [a]	0.11-0.22 [b]
	Ohio	0.15 [a,c]	0.19 [b]
	Jungfraujoch	0.12 [a,c]	0.15 [b]
	Mt. Wilson	0.13 [a,c]	0.16 [b]
Shaw (1959)	Ohio	0.1 [a]	0.13 [b]
Shaw (1959)	Ohio	0.32-1.75 [b]	0.4-2.2; 1.1 av. [d]

[a] Measurement in solar spectrum.
[b] Calculated from the observed data, assuming uniform mixing ratio with altitude.
[c] Recalculated for sea level from other data.
[d] Observed spectroscopically in ground air.

Very little is known about the destruction of CO. Bates and Witherspoon point out that no direct oxidation of CO by O_2 in sunlight was ever observed. Atomic oxygen is too low in concentration to be of importance. Ozone oxidizes CO easily, but the rates are too small for the concentrations in the atmosphere. For a residence time of the order of a year, the destruction in layers beyond the middle stratosphere cannot be of great importance. Another possibility is the earth's surface, where bacterial activities are known to oxidize CO. However, it is difficult to estimate global destruction rates on the basis of laboratory experiments. The process of CO removal from the atmosphere cannot, at the present time, be identified with certainty.

Dhar and Ram (1939) found formaldehyde in rain water and dew in amounts ranging from 0.1 to 1.0 mg/liter, with a mean concentration of 0.5 mg/liter. They observed no relationship with thunderstorms and the concentration in dew was higher than in rain water. With a liquid water content of raining clouds of 1 g/m^3, it can be estimated that the formaldehyde concentration in air had the magnitude of 1 $\mu g/m^3$. In Europe, Cauer (1951) measured concentrations of 0 to 16 $\mu g/m^3$ with a mean of 0.5 $\mu g/m^3$.

Cauer thinks that the observed CH_2O was generated by incomplete combustion and is of anthropogenic origin. According to Dhar and Ram, it is formed through the action of sunlight on solutions of organic substances in water. There is the possibility of CH_2O formation above 70 km as a result of photochemical dissociation of CO_2 and CH_4 and of secondary reactions among the products.

Formaldehyde is photolyzed by radiation below 3600 Å and is thus destroyed in the atmosphere down to the ground. No quantitative considerations of these various processes have been made.

List of Symbols

$a_{1,2,3}$ = constants
$c_{1,2,3}$ = constants
d = molecular diffusion coefficient
D = destruction rate of ozone; eddy diffusion coefficient
E = enrichment factor
f = fraction of phase
$f_{1,2}$ = reaction rate constants
F = formation rate; flux of helium; mathematically defined quantity
h = altitude
H = scale height of atmosphere
I = intensity of radiation; injection rate
k = $1/\tau$ exchange rate; ratio of reaction rates
$k_{1,2}$ = reaction rate constants
$K_{1,2}$ = ion equilibrium constants; exchange rates
m = water vapor mixing ratio; molecular weight
M = total amount of gas in a reservoir
N = amount of carbon in reservoir
p = pressure of air; rate of precipitation
Q = production rate of C^{14}
R = relative isotope concentration; removal rate
s = factor
S = salinity; total sulfur content in atmosphere
z = altitude
α = absorption coefficient; fractionation factor
β_1 = solubility constant of CO_2
δ = enrichment factor in per cent or per mill
$\varphi_{1,2}$ = quantum yields of photoreaction
λ = radioactive decay rate; wavelength
μ = relative molecular weight difference
ν = mixing ratio of He
θ = total tropospheric ozone; apparent C^{14} age of mixed ocean layer
τ = residence time
ϱ = density of helium

Subscripts:

a = air
b = biosphere
d = deep ocean
h = humus
l = liquid
m = mixed ocean layer
s = sea
t = total
v = vapor
w = wood
$*$ = C^{14}

REFERENCES

ADEL, A. (1939). Note on the atmospheric oxides of nitrogen. *Astrophys. J.* **90**, 627.

ADEL, A. (1946). A possible source of atmospheric N_2O. *Science* **103**, 280.

ADEL, A. (1951). Atmospheric nitrous oxide and the nitrogen cycle. *Science* **113**, 624-625.

ALLISON, F. E. (1955). The enigma of soil nitrogen balance sheets. *Advances in Agron.* **7**, 213-250.

ALTSHULLER, A. P. (1958). Natural sources of gaseous pollutants in the atmosphere. *Tellus* **10**, 479-492.

ARNOLD, J. R., and ANDERSON, E. C. (1957). The distribution of carbon-14 in nature. *Tellus* **4**, 28-32.

ARNOLD, P. W. (1954). Losses of nitrous oxide from soil. *J. Soil Sci.* **5**, 116-128.

AULT, W. V. (1959). Isotopic fractionation of sulfur in geochemical processes. *Researches in Geochem.* pp. 241-259.

BANNON, J. K., and STEELE, L. P. (1957). Average water-vapour content of the air. *Meteorol. Research Papers Air Ministry London No.* **1075**, 1-18.

BARCLAY, F. R., ELLIOTT, M. J. W., GOLDSMITH, P., and JELLY, J. V. (1960). A direct measurement of the humidity in the stratosphere using a cooled-vapour trap. *Quart. J. Roy. Meteorol. Soc.* **86**, 259-264.

BARRETT, E. W., HERNDON, L. R., and CARTER, H. J. (1950). Some measurements of the distribution of water vapor in the stratosphere. *Tellus* **2**, 302-311.

BARTH, C. A. (1961). Nitrogen and oxygen atomic reactions in the chemosphere. International Symposium on Chemical Reactions in the Lower and Upper Atmosphere. San Francisco, California, 1961.

BARTH, C. A., and SUESS, H. E. (1960). The formation of molecular hydrogen through photolysis of water vapor in the presence of oxygen. *Z. Physik* **158**, 85-95.

BATES, D. R., and McDOWELL, M. R. C. (1959). *J. Atmospheric and Terrest. Phys.* **16**, 293.

BATES, D. R., and WITHERSPOON, A. E. (1952). The photochemistry of some minor constituents of the earth's atmosphere. *Monthly Notices Roy. Astron. Soc.* **112**, 101-124.

BEGEMANN, F. (1961). Der "natürliche" Tritiumgehalt der Erde und die Frage seiner zeitlichen Variation. *Chimia* **16**, 1-15.

BEGEMANN, F., and FRIEDMAN, I. (1959). Tritium and deuterium content of atmospheric hydrogen. *Z. Naturforsch.* **14a**, 1024-1031.

BENESCH, W., and MIGEOTTE, M. (1953). Investigation of atmospheric CO at the Jungfraujoch. *J. Opt. Soc. Am.* **43**, 1119-1123.

BIRKELAND, J. W., BURCH, D. E., and SHAW, J. H. (1957). Some comments on two articles by Taylor and Yates. *J. Opt. Soc. Am.* **47**, 441.

BISCHOF, W. (1960). Periodical variations of the atmospheric CO_2-content in Scandinavia. *Tellus* 12, 216-226.

BISHOP, K. F., DELAFIELD, H. J., EGGLETON, A. E. J., PEABODY, C. O., and TAYLOR, B. T. (1961). The tritium content of atmospheric methane. Symposium on the Detection and Use of Tritium in the Physical and Biological Sciences, Vienna, 1961, Paper No. TTS/79.

BODENSTEIN, M. (1922). Bildung und Zersetzung der höheren Stickoxyde. *Z. Physik. Chem.* 100, 68-123.

BOLIN, B. (1959). Note on the eschange of iodine between the atmosphere, land and sea. *Intern. J. Air Pollution* 2, 127-131,

BOLIN, B., and ERIKSSON, E. (1959). Changes in the carbon dioxide content of the atmosphere and sea due to fossil fuel combustion. *In* "The Rossby Memorial Volume" (B. Bolin, ed.), pp. 130-142. Rockefeller Inst. Press, New York.

BOWEN, I. G., and REGENER, V. H. (1951). On the automatic chemical determination of atmospheric ozone. *J. Geophys. Research* 56, 307-324.

BRASEFIELD, C. J. (1954). Measurement of atmospheric humidity up to 35 kilometers. *J. Meteorol.* 11, 412-416.

BRAY, J. B. (1959). An analysis of the possible recent change in atmospheric carbon dioxide concentration. *Tellus* 11, 220-230.

BREWER, A. W. (1949). Evidence for a world circulation provided by the measurements of helium and water vapor distribution in the stratosphere. *Quart. J. Roy. Meteorol. Soc.* 75, 351-363.

BREWER, A. W. (1955). Ozone concentration measurements from an aircraft in N. Norway. *Meteorol. Research Papers No.* 946, Meteorol. Research Comm., London.

BREWER, A. W. (1960). The transfer of atmospheric ozone into the troposphere. *Mass. Inst. Technol. Dept. Meteorol.* pp. 1-15.

BREWER, A. W., DÜTSCH, H. V., MILFORD, J. R., MIGEOTTE, M., PAETZOLD, H. K., PISCALOR, F., and VIGROUX, E. (1960). Distribution verticale de l'ozone atmosphérique. Comparaison de diverses methodes. *Contribs. inst. astrophys. Paris Ser. B No.* 198, 1-27.

BRIDGE, H. S., DILWORTH, C., LAZARUS, A. J., LYON, E. F., ROSSI, B., and SCHERB, F. (1961). Paper presented at the Conference on Cosmic Rays, Kyoto, Sept. 4-15. To be published.

BROWN, F., GOLDSMITH, P., GREEN, H. F., HOLT, A., and PARHAM, A. G. (1961). Measurements of the water vapour, tritium and carbon-14 content of the middle stratosphere over southern England. *Tellus* 13, 40-416.

BROWN, H. (1957). The carbon cycle in nature. *In* "Fortschritte der Chemie organischer Naturstoffe" (L. Zechmeister, ed.), Vol. 14, pp. 317-333. Springer, Wien.

BUSWELL, A. M. (1954). *In* "Industrial Fermentations" (Underkofler and Hickey, eds.), Vol. II, pp. 518-551. Chemical Publ., New York.

BUSWELL, A. M., and MUELLER, H. F. (1952). Mechanics of methane fermentation. *Ind. Eng. Chem.* 44, 550-552.

CADLE, R. C., and SCHADT, S. (1952). Kinetics of the gas phase reaction of olefins with ozone. *J. Am. Chem. Soc.* **74**, 6002-6004.

CADLE, R. D. (1960). Personal communication.

CALLENDAR, G. S. (1940). Variations of the amount of carbon dioxide in different air currents. *Quart. J. Roy. Meteorol. Soc.* **66**, 395-400.

CALLENDAR, G. S. (1958). On the amount of carbon dioxide in the atmosphere. *Tellus* **10**, 243-248.

CAUER, H. (1939). Schwankungen der Jodmenge der Luft in Mitteleuropa, deren Ursache und deren Bedeutung für den Jodgehalt unserer Nahrung. *Angew. Chem.* **52**, 625-628.

CAUER, H. (1951). Some problems of atmospheric chemistry. *Compendium Meteorol.* pp. 1126-1138.

CHAMBERLAIN, A. C. (1959). Deposition of iodine in northern England in October 1957. *Quart. J. Roy. Meteorol. Soc.* **85**, 350-361.

CHAMBERLAIN, A. C., and WIFFEN, R. C. (1959). Some observations on the behavior of radioiodine vapor in the atmosphere. *Geofis. pura e appl.* **42**, 42-48.

CHAPMAN, S. (1930). On ozone and atomic oxygen in the upper atmosphere. *Phil. Mag.* **10**, 369-383.

CLOUD, P. E., FRIEDMAN, I., and SISLER, F. D. (1958). Microbiological fractionation of the hydrogen isotopes. *Science* **127**, 1394-1395.

CONWAY, E. J. (1943). Mean geochemical data in relation to oceanic evolution. *Proc. Roy. Irish Acad.* **A48**, 119-159.

CRAIG, H. (1956). Isotopic tracer technique for measurement of physical processes in the sea and the atmosphere. *Contrib. Scripps Inst. Oceanog.* [N. S.] *No.* **7**.

CRAIG, H. (1957). The natural distribution of radiocarbon and the exchange time of carbon dioxide between atmosphere and sea. *Tellus* **9**, 1-17.

CRAIG, H., and BOATO, G. (1955). Isotopes. *Ann. Rev. Phys. Chem.* **6**, 403-432.

CRAIG, H., and LAL, D. (1961). The production rate of natural tritium. *Tellus* **13**, 85-105.

CRAIG, R. A. (1950). The observations and photochemistry of atmospheric ozone and their meteorological significance. *Meteorol. Monographs* **1** (2), 1-50.

CUNNINGHAM, R. M. (1952). Distribution and growth of hydrometeors around a deep cyclone. *Mass. Inst. Technol. Dept. Meteorol. Tech. Rept.* **18**.

DAMON, P. E., and KULP, J. L. (1958). Inert gases and the evolution of the atmosphere. *Geochim. et Cosmochim. Acta* **13**, 280-292.

DANSGAARD, W. (1953). The abundance of O^{18} in atmospheric water and water vapor. *Tellus* **5**, 461-469.

DE BARY, E., and MÖLLER, F. (1960). Die mittlere vertikale Verteilung von Wolken in Abhängigkeit von der Wetterlage. *Ber. deut. Wetterdienstes No.* 67, 1-27.

DE TURVILLE, C. M. (1961). Terrestrial accreation from the solar wind. *Nature* **190**, 156.

DE VRIES, H. (1959). Measurement and use of natural radiocarbon. *Researches in Geophys.* pp. 169-189.

DHAR, N. R., and RAM, A. (1939). Formaldehyde in rain and dew. *J. Indian Chem. Soc.* 10, 287-298.

DILLEMUTH, F. J., SKIDMORE, D. R., and SCHUBERT, C. C. (1960). The reaction of ozone with methane. *J. Phys. Chem.* 64, 1496-1499.

DOLE, M., LANE, G. A., RUDD, D. P., and ZANKELIES, F. A. (1954). Isotopic composition of atmospheric oxygen and nitrogen. *Geochim. et Cosmochim. Acta* 6, 65-78.

DÜTSCH, H. V. (1946). Photochemische Theorie des atmosphärischen Ozons unter Berücksichtigung von Nichtgleichgewichtszuständen und Luftbewegungen. Doktor-Thesis, Universität Zürich.

DÜTSCH, H. V. (1959). Vertical ozone distribution over Arosa. Final Report, Cambridge Air Force Research Center, Contract AF 61 (514)-905, pp. 1-24.

DZENS-LITOVSKIY, A. I. (1945). Natural gases of bottom deposits of mineral lakes. *Compt. rend acad. sci. U.R.S.S.* 48, 491-493.

EATON, S. V., and EATON, J. H. (1926). Sulphur in rain. *Plant Physiol.* 1, 77-87.

EDGAR, J. L., and PANETH, F. A. (1941). The determination of ozone and nitrogen dioxide in the atmosphere. *J. Chem. Soc.* 144, 511-519.

EGNÉR, H., and ERIKSSON, E. (1955). Current data on the chemical composition of air and precipitation. *Tellus* 7, 134-139 and subsequent issues.

EHMERT, A. (1941). Über den Ozongehalt der unteren Atmosphäre bei winterlichem Hochdruckwetter nach Messungen. *Ber. deut. Wetterdienstes US-Zone No.* 11, 1949, 63-66.

EHMERT, A. (1952). Über örtliche Einflüsse auf den Ozongehalt der Luft. *Ber. deut. Wetterdienstes US-Zone* 37, 283-285.

EHMERT, A., and EHMERT, H. (1941). Über den Tagesgang des bodennahen Ozons. *Ber. deut. Wetterdienstes US-Zone No.* 11, 1949, 58-62.

EPSTEIN, S. (1959). The variation of the O^{18}/O^{16} ratio in nature and some geological implications. *Researches in Geochem.* pp. 217-240.

EPSTEIN, S., and MAYEDA, T. K. (1953). Variation of O^{18} content of waters from natural sources. *Geochim. et Cosmochim. Acta* 4, 213-224.

EPSTEIN, S., and SHARP, R. P. (1959). Oxygen isotopes studies. *Trans. Am. Geophys. Union* 40, 81-84.

ERIKSSON, E. (1952). Composition of atmospheric precipitation I. Nitrogen compounds. *Tellus* 4, 215-232.

ERIKSSON, E. (1958). On the isotopic composition of the ammonia and the nitrate ion in rain. *Geochim. et Cosmochim. Acta* 15, 153.

ERIKSSON, E. (1959 a). The circulation of some atmospheric constituents in the sea. *In* "The Rossby Memorial Volume" (B. Bolin, ed.), pp. 147-157. Rockefeller Inst. Press, New York

ERIKSSON, E. (1959 b). The yearly circulation of chloride and sulfur in nature; meteorological, geochemical and pedological implications. Part I. *Tellus* 11, 375-403, Part II *Tellus* 12, 63-109.

FALTINGS, V., and HARTECK, P. (1950). Der Tritiumgehalt der Atmosphäre, *Z. Naturforsch.* **5a**, 438-439.

FARKAS, A., FARKAS, L., and YUDKIN, J. (1934). The decomposition of sodium formate by bacterium coli in the presence of heavy water. *Proc. Roy. Soc.* **115**, 373-379.

FELLENBERG, T. V. (1926). Das Vorkommen, der Kreislauf und der Stoffwechsel des Jods. *Ergeb. Physiol.* **25**, 176-363.

FRIEDMAN, I. (1953). Deuterium content of natural waters and other substances. *Geochim. et Cosmochim. Acta* **4**, 89-103.

GATES, D. M., MUCRAY, D. C., and SHAW, C. C. (1958). Near infrared solar radiation measurements by balloon to an altitude of 100,000 feet. *J. Opt. Soc. Am.* **48**, 1010-1016.

GEORGII, H. W. (1960). Untersuchungen über atmosphärische Spurenstoffe und ihre Bedeutung für die Chemie der Niederschläge. *Geofis. pura e appl.* **47**, 155-171.

GERHARD, E. R., and JOHNSTONE, H. F. (1955). Photochemical oxidation of sulfur dioxide in air. *Ind. Eng. Chem.* **47**, 972-976.

GLUECKAUF, E. (1951). The composition of atmospheric air. *Compendium Meteorol.* pp. 3-12.

GLUECKAUF, E., and KITT, G. P. (1957). The hydrogen content of atmospheric air at ground level. *Quart. J. Roy. Meteorol. Soc.* **83**, 522-528.

GMELIN, L., ed. (1934-1936). "Handbuch der anorganischen Chemie," 8th ed., System 4 (Nitrogen), p. 16 ff. Verlag Chemie, Berlin.

GMELIN, L., ed. (1953). "Handbuch der anorganischen Chemie," 8th ed., System 9, Section B 1 (Sulfur), p. 46 ff. Verlag Chemie, Berlin.

GODSON, W. L. (1960). Total ozone and the middle stratosphere over arctic and subarctic areas in winter and spring. *Quart. J. Roy. Meteorol. Soc.* **86**, 301-317.

GÖTZ, F. W. (1951). Ozone in the atmosphere. *Compendium Meteorol.* pp. 275-291.

GÖTZ, F. W. P., and VOLZ, F. (1951). Aroser Messungen des Ozongehaltes der unteren Troposphäre und sein Jahresgang. *Z. Naturforsch.* **6a**, 634-639.

GOLDBERG, L. (1951). The abundance and vertical distribution of methane in the earth's atmosphere. *Astrophys. J.* **113**, 567-582.

GOLDBERG, L., and MUELLER, E. A. (1953). The vertical distribution of nitrous oxide and methane in the earth's atmosphere. *J. Opt. Soc. Am.* **43**, 1033-1036.

GONSIOR, B. (1959). Tritium-Anstieg im atmosphärischen Wasserstoff. *Naturwissenschaften* **46**, 201-202.

GOODY, R. M., and Walshaw, C. D. (1953). The origin of atmospheric nitrous oxide. *Quart. J. Roy. Meteorol. Soc.* **79**, 496-500.

GREENBURG, L., and JACOBS, M. B. (1956). Sulfur dioxide in New York City atmosphere. *Ind. Eng. Chem.* **48**, 1517-1521.

GROSSE, A. V., JOHNSTON, R. L., WOLFGANG, R. L., and LIBBY, W. F. (1951). Tritium in nature. *Science* **113**, 1-2.

GROSSE, A. V., KIRSCHENBAUM, A. D., KULP, J. L., and BROECKER, W. S. (1954). The natural tritium content of atmospheric hydrogen. *Phys. Rev.* **93**, 250-251.

GROTH, W., and HARTECK, P. (1938). Photochemische Untersuchungen im Schumann-ultraviolett. *Z. Elektrochem.* **44**, 621-627.

HAGEMANN, F., GRAY, J., Jr,, MACHTA, L., and TURKEVICH, A. (1959). Stratospheric carbon-14, carbon dioxide, and tritium. *Science* **130**, 542-552.

HARE, F. K. (1960). The disturbed circulation of the arctic stratosphere. *J. Meteorol.* **17**, 36-51.

HARE, F. K., and ORVIG, S. (1958). The arctic circulation. *McGill Univ. Montreal, Publ. Meteorol. No.* **12**, 1-209.

HARTECK, P. (1954). The relative abundance of HT and HTO in the atmosphere. *J. Chem. Phys.* **22**, 1746-1751.

HARTECK, P., and DONDES, S. (1954 a). Origin of nitrous oxide in the atmosphere. *Phys. Rev.* **95**, 320.

HARTECK, P., and DONDES, S. (1954 b). The oxidation of nitrogen by ozone to form nitrous oxide. *J. Chem. Phys.* **22**, 758.

HARTECK, P., and JENSEN, J. H. D. (1948). Über den Sauerstoffgehalt der Atmosphäre. *Z. Naturforsch.* **3a**, 591-595.

HARTECK, P., and SÜSS, H. (1949). Deuteriumgehalt des freien Wasserstoffs in der Erdatmosphäre. *Naturwissenschaften* **36**, 218.

HARVEY, H. W. (1955) "The Chemistry and Fertility of Sea Waters." Cambridge Univ. Press, London and New York.

HELLIWELL, N. C., and Mackenzie, J. K. (1957). Observations of humidity, temperature and wind at Idris 23rd May-2nd June, 1956. *Meteorol. Research Papers Air Ministry London No.* **1024**, 1-38.

HERING, W. (1961). Personal communication.

HESSTVEDT, E. (1959). Mother of pearl clouds in Norway. *Geofys. Publikasjoner Norske Videnskaps-Akad. Oslo* **20**, 1-29.

HOCH, G. E., LITTLE, H. N., and BURRIS, R. H. (1957). Hydrogen evolution from soybean root modules. *Nature* **179**, 430-431.

HOERING, T. (1957). The isotopic composition of the ammonia and the nitrate ion in rain. *Geochim. et Cosmochim. Acta* **12**, 97-102.

HOUGHTON, J. T., and SEELEY, J. S. (1960). Spectroscopic observations of the water-vapour content of the stratosphere. *Quart. J. Roy. Meteorol. Soc.* **86**, 358-370.

HOUGHTON, J. T., MOSS, T. S., SEELY, J. S., and HAWKINS, T. D. F. (1957). Some observations of the infrared solar spectrum from a high flying aircraft. *Nature* **180**, 1187-1188.

HUBER, B. (1952). Der Einfluss der Vegetation auf die Schwankungen des CO_3-Gehaltes der Atmosphäre. *Arch. Meteorol. Geophys. u. Bioklimatol. Ser. B* **4**, 154-167.

HUTCHISON, G. E. (1954). The biochemistry of the terrestrial atmosphere. *In* "The Earth as a Planet" (G. P. Kuiper, ed.), pp. 371-433, Univ. Chicago Press, Chicago, Illinois.

JACOBS, M. B., BRAVERMAN, M. M., and HOCHHEISER, S. (1957). Ultramicro determination of sulfides in air. *Anal. Chem.* **29**, 1349-1351.

JENSEN, M. L., and NAKAI, N. (1961). Sources and isotopic composition of atmospheric sulfur. *Science* **134**, 2102-2104.

JOHANSSON, O. (1959). On the sulfur problem in Swedish agriculture. *Ann. Roy. Agr. Coll. Sweden* **25**, 57-169.

JOHNSON, F. S., PURCELL, J. D., TOUSEY, R., and WATANABE, K. (1952). Direct measurements of the vertical distribution of atmospheric ozone to 70 kilometers altitude. *J. Geophys. Research* **57**, 157-176.

JUNGE, C. E. (1956). Recent investigations in air chemistry. *Tellus* **8**, 127-139.

JUNGE, C. E. (1957). Chemical analysis of aerosol particles and of gas traces on the island of Hawaii, *Tellus* **9**, 528-537.

JUNGE, C. E. (1960). Sulfur in the atmosphere. *J. Geophys. Research* **65**, 227-237.

JUNGE, C. E. (1961). Considerations about the ozone budget. Unpublished material.

JUNGE, C. E., and RYAN, T. G. (1958). Study of the SO_2 oxidation in solution and its role in atmospheric chemistry. *Quart. J. Roy. Meteorol. Soc.* **84**, 46-55.

JUNGE, C. E., CHAGNON, C. W., and MANSON, J. E. (1961). Stratospheric aerosols. *J. Meteorol.* **18**, 81-108.

KANWISHER, J. (1960). P_{CO_2} in sea water and its effect on the movement of CO_2 in nature. *Tellus* **12**, 207-215.

KAPLAN, L. D. (1960). The influence of carbon dioxide variations on the atmospheric heat balance. *Tellus* **12**, 204-208.

KATZ, M. (1952). The photoelectric determination of atmospheric sulphur dioxide by dilute starch-iodine solutions. *In* "Air Pollution; Proceedings of the United States Technical Conference on Air Pollution" (L. C. McCabe, ed.), pp. 580-595. McGraw-Hill, New York.

KAY, R. H. (1953). An interim report on the measurement of the vertical distribution of atmospheric ozone by a chemical method, to heights of 12 km, from aircraft. *Meteorol. Research Papers No.* **817**, 1-15. Meteorol. Research Comm., London.

KEELING, C. D. (1958). The concentration and isotopic abundances of atmospheric carbon dioxide in rural areas. *Geochim. et Cosmochim. Acta* **13**, 322-334.

KEELING, C. D. (1960). The concentration and isotopic abundances of carbon dioxide in the atmosphere. *Tellus* **12**, 200-203.

KIRSCHENBAUM, I. (1951), "Physical Properties and Analysis of Heavy Water," pp. 24-30, McGraw-Hill, New York.

KOFFLER, H., and Wilson, P. W. (1951). *In* "Bacterial Physiology" (C. H. Werkman and P. W. Wilson, eds.), pp. 517-530. Academic Press, New York.

LANE, G. A., and Dole, M. (1956). Fractionation of oxygen isotopes during respiration. *Science* **123**, 574-576.

LETTAU, H. (1951). Diffusion in the upper atmosphere. *Compendium Meteorol.* pp. 320-333.

LETTAU, H. (1954). A study of the mass, momentum, and energy budget of the atmosphere, *Arch. Meteorol. Geophys, u. Bioklimatol.* A **7**, 133-157.

LIBBY, W. F. (1959). Tritium in hydrology and meteorology. *Researches in Geochem.*, pp. 151-168.

LOCKE, J. L., and HERZBERG, G. (1953). The absorption due to CO in the infrared spectrum. *Can. J. Phys.* **31**, 504-516.

LUNDEGARDH, H. (1924). "Der Kreislauf der Kohlensäure in der Natur," 308 pp. Fischer, Jena.

LUNDEGARDH, H. (1954). "Klima und Boden." Fischer, Jena.

McKINLEY, J. D., Jr., and GARVIN, D. (1955). The reactions of atomic hydrogen with ozone and oxygen. *J. Am. Chem. Soc.* **77**, 5802-5805.

MAGILL, P. L., HOLDEN, F. R., and ACKLEY, C., ed. (1956). "Air Pollution Handbook," pp. 2-45. McGraw-Hill, New York.

MASTENBROOK, H. J., and DINGER, J. H. (1960). The measurement of water-vapor distribution in the stratosphere. *NRL-Rept. No.* **5551**, 1-36.

MEETHAM, A. R. (1950). Natural removal of pollution from the atmosphere. *Quart. J. Roy. Meteorol. Sco.* **76**, 359-371.

MEETHAM, A. R. (1956). "Atmospheric Pollution," 2nd ed. Pergamon, New York.

MEETHAM, A. R. (1959). The behavior of sulphur dioxide in the atmosphere. *In* "Atmospheric Chemistry of Chloride and Sulfur Compounds" (J. P. Lodge ed.), pp. 115-121. Geophysical Monograph No. 3. Am. Geophys. Union and Natl. Acad. Sci.

MIGEOTTE, M. V. (1948). Spectroscopic evidence of methane in the earth's atmosphere. *Phys. Rev.* **73**, 519-520.

MIGEOTTE, M. V., and CHAPMAN, R. M. (1949). On the question of atmospheric ammonia. *Phys. Rev.* **75**, 1611.

MIGEOTTE, M. V., and NEVEN, L. (1952). Recent progress in the observation of solar infrared spectrum at Jungfraujoch (Switzerland). *Mem. soc. roy. sci. Liège* **12**, 165-178.

MILLER, L. E. (1956). The chemistry and vertical distribution of the oxides of nitrogen in the atmosphere. *Geophys. Research Paper* **39**, 1-135.

MOHLER, O. C., GOLDBERG, L., and McMATH, R. R. (1948). Spectroscopic evidence for ammonia in the earth's atmosphere. *Phys. Rev.* **74**, 352-353.

MONTEITH, J. L., and SZEICZ, G. (1960). The carbon-dioxide flux over a field of sugar beet. *Quart. J. Roy. Meteorol. Soc.* **86**, 205-214.

MURCRAY, D. G., MURCRAY, F. H., WILLIAMS, W. J., and LESLIE, F. E. (1960). Water vapor distribution above 90,000 feet. Scientific Report No. 5, Contract AF 19 (604)-2069, Air Force Cambridge Research Center, AFCRC-TN-60-452, pp. 1-15.

MURGATROYD, R. J. (1959). Some recent measurements of ozone concentrations from a Canberra aircraft up to 15 km. Symposium on Atmospheric Ozone, UGGI, Monograph No. 3, p. 5.

NEUWIRTH, R. (1958). Einige Resultate luftchemischer Untersuchungen im Zusammenhang mit der atmosphärischen Turbulenz. *Meteorol. Rundschau* 11, 137-141.

NOYES, W. A., Jr., and LEIGHTON, P. A. (1941). "The Photochemistry of Gases." Reinhold, New York.

ÖSTLUND, G. (1959). Isotopic composition of sulfur in precipitation and sea-water. *Tellus* 11, 478-480.

PAETZOLD, H. K. (1952). Determination of vertical ozone distribution at various latitudes during eclipses of the moon. *J. Atmospheric and Terrest. Phys.* 2, 183-188.

PAETZOLD, H. K. (1953 a). Die vertikale Verteilung des atmopshärischen Ozons nach dem photochemischen Gleichgewicht. *Geofis. pura e appl.* 24, 1-14.

PAETZOLD, H. K. (1953 b). Versuch einer Analyse der gemittelten vertikalen Ozonverteilung in verschiedenen geographischen Breiten. *Geofis. pura e appl.* 24, 1-14.

PAETZOLD, H. K. (1955). New experimental and theoretical investigation on the atmospheric ozone layer, *J. Atmospheric and Terrest. Phys.* 7, 128-140.

PAETZOLD, H. K. (1957). Ozone in der Erdatmosphäre. In "Handbuch der Physik" (S. Flügge, ed.), Vol. 48, pp. 370-426. Springer, Berlin.

PAETZOLD, H. K. (1960). Paper presented at the International Symposium of the UGGI, Helsinki, 1960.

PANETH, F. A. (1937). The chemical composition of the atmosphere. *Quart. J. Roy. Meteorol. Soc.* 63, 433-438.

PERL, E., and VOLZ, F. (1961). Personal communication.

PRICE, S., and PALES, J. C. (1959). Some observations of ozone at Mauna Loa Observatory, Hawaii. Symposium on Atmospheric Ozone, UGGI, Monogrpah No. 3, p. 37.

RAMANATHAN, K. R., and KULKARNI, R. N. (1960). Mean meridional distributions of ozone in different seasons calculated from Umkehr observations and probable vertical transport mechanisms. *Quart. J. Roy. Meteorol. Soc.* 86, 144-155.

REED, R. J. (1949). The effects of atmospheric circulation on ozone distribution and variations. Mass. Inst. Technol. Ph.D. Thesis.

REGENER, E. (1934). Aufnahmen des ultravioletten Sonnenspektrums in der Stratosphäre und die vertikale Ozonverteilung. *Physik. Z.* 35, 788-793.

REGENER, E. (1941). Ozonschicht und atmosphärische Turbulenz. *Ber. deut. Wetterdienstes US-Zone No.* 11, 1949, 45-57.

REGENER, V. H. (1954). Recordings of surface ozone in New Mexico, Scientific Report No. 5, pp. 1-24. Contract AF 19 (122)-381, Air Force Cambridge Research Center, Bedford, Massachusetts.

REGENER, V. H. (1957). Vertical flux of atmospheric ozone. *J. Geophys. Research* 62, 221-228.

REGENER, V. H. (1960). On a sensitive method for the recording of atmospheric ozone. *J. Geophys. Research* 12, 3975-3977.

REITER, R., and REITER, M. (1958). Relations between the contents of nitrate and nitrate ions in precipitations and simultaneous atmospheric electric processes. *In* "Recent Advances in Atmospheric Electricity" (L. G. Smith, ed.), pp. 175-194. Pergamon, New York.

RENZETTI, N. A. (1955). An aerometric survey of the Los Angeles Basin, August-November, 1954, Rept. No. 9, pp. 1-333. Air Pollution Foundation, Los Angeles, California.

REVELLE, R., and SUESS, H. E. (1957). Carbon dioxide exchange between atmosphere and ocean, and the question of an increase of atmospheric CO_2 during the past decades. *Tellus* **9**, 18-27.

REYNOLDS, W. C. (1930). Notes on London and suburban air. *J. Soc. Chem. Ind. (London)* **49**, 168 T-172 T.

ROSSBY, C. G., and EGNÉR, H. (1955). On the chemical climate and its variation with the atmospheric circulation pattern. *Tellus* **7**, 118-133.

SCHRÖER, E. (1944). Theorie der Entstehung, Zersetzung und Verteilung des atmosphärischen Ozons. *Ber. deut. Wetterdienstes US-Zone* **11**, 1949, 13-23.

SCHUMAN, L. M. (1960). Nitrogen dioxide poisoning in silo atmospheres (silo filler's disease). Paper presented at the Third National Air Pollution Research Seminar, New Orleans, Louisiana, 1960.

SHAW, J. H. (1959). A determination of the abundance of nitrous oxide, carbon monoxide, and methane in ground level air at several locations near Columbus, Ohio. Scientific Report No. 1, Contract No. AF 19 (604)-2259, Air Force Cambridge Research Center, pp. 1-38.

SLOBOD, R. L., and Krogh, M. E. (1950). Nitrous oxide as a constituent of the atmosphere. *J. Am. Chem. Soc.* **72**, 1175-1177.

SLOCUM, G. (1955). Has the amount of carbon dioxide in the atmosphere changed significantly since the beginning of the twentieth century? *Monthly Weather Rev.* **83**, 225-231.

SQUIRES, P., and TWOMEY, S. (1960). The relation between cloud droplet spectra and the spectrum of cloud nuclei. *In* "Physics of Precipitation," Monograph No. 5, NAS/NRC No. 746, pp. 211-219. Am. Geophys. Union, Washington, D.C.

STOERMER, C. (1940). Height of mother of pearl clouds observed in southern Norway during 1926-1934. *Nature* **145**, 221-222.

TAYLOR, H. A., and CHEN, M. C. (1957). The photolysis of water vapor. *In* "The Threshold of Space" (M. Zelikoff, ed.), pp. 111-115. Pergamon, New York.

TEICHERT, F. (1955). Vergleichende Messung des Ozongehaltes der Luft am Erdboden und in 80 m Höhe. *Z. Meteorol.* **9**, 21-27.

TUCKER, G. B. (1957). An analysis of humidity measurements in the upper troposphere and lower stratosphere over southern England. *Meteorol. Research Papers. Air Ministry, London No.* **1052**, 1-31.

UREY, H. C. (1959). The atmospheres of the planets. *In* "Handbuch der Physik" (S. Flügge, ed.), Vol. 52, pp. 375-383. Springer, Berlin.

VERZÁR, F., and EVANS, H. S. (1959). Production of atmospheric condensation nuclei by sunrays. *Geofis. pura e appl.* **43**, 259-268.

VIEMEISTER, P. E. (1960). Lightning and the origin of nitrates found in precipitation. *J. Meteorol.* **17**, 681-683.

VOLMAN, D. H. (1956). Photochemical oxygen-hydrogen reaction at 1849 A. *J. Chem. Phys.* **25**, 288-292.

VOLZ, F. (1952). Über die Zersetzung des Ozons in der Troposphäre. *Ber. deut. Wetterdienstes US-Zone* **35**, 257-259.

WENT, F. W. (1960). Organic matter in the atmosphere, and its possible relation to petroleum formation. *Proc. Natl. Acad. Sci. U.S.* **46** (2), 212-221.

WEXLER, H., MORELAND, W., and WEYANT, W. S. (1960). A preliminary report on ozone observations at Little America, Antarctica. *Monthly Weather Rev.* **88**, (2), 43-54.

WILLET, H. C. (1962). The relationship of total atmospheric ozone to the sunspot cycle. *J. Geophys. Research,* **67**, 661-670

WULF, O. R., and Deming, L. S. (1937). The distribution of atmospheric ozone in equilibrum with solar radiation and the rate of maintenance of the distribution. *Terrestrial Magnetism Atmospheric Elec.* **42**, 195-202.

2.   *Aerosols*

2.1 Introduction

Although atmospheric aerosols have concentrations which are generally much smaller than those of gases, they are of special importance for various branches of meteorology. For a better understanding of their complex chemical nature, we will start with a survey of their physical properties.

Aerosols are defined as dispersed solid or liquid matter in a gaseous medium, in our case, air. The particle size in the atmosphere ranges from clusters of a few molecules to particles of about 20 μ radius, if we disregard cloud, fog, and rain drops, and consider only dry air. Particles of about 5×10^{-3} μ radius and smaller have very short lifetimes because they become rapidly attached to the larger aerosol particles and can exist in considerable concentrations only if they are produced constantly. Reaction products of gas reactions, small ions, or "primary" particles produced by cosmic radiation or decay of radon are examples. The small ions are produced in air by all ionizing radiation and are important for atmospheric electricity. They have radii of about 6×10^{-4} μ and consist of clusters of 10 to 30 molecules of oxygen and water, and perhaps trace gases, held together by the electrical charge (e.g., Przibram, 1933). Their average concentration of a few hundred per cm³ represents a mass concentration of about 10^{-7} $\mu g/m^3$, a value several orders of magnitude smaller than the corresponding value of all the other aerosols. Thus, they are of no importance for air chemistry. Separated from the smallest aerosol particles proper by a distinct gap in the size distribution, the small ions cease to exist when their charge is neutralized, in contrast to the aerosol particles which are held together by chemical forces.

The upper limit of aerosol particle size is due to sedimentation. Particles larger than 20 μ radius remain airborne for only a limited time and their occurrence is therefore restricted to the vicinity of their source.

The atmospheric aerosol thus defined forms a spectrum which extends over almost four orders of magnitude. For convenience, the size range is usually subdivided into three groups (Fig. 21). The smallest particles (≤ 0.1 μ radius) are called Aitken particles. They were discovered in 1875 by Coulier (Verzár, 1959), but were thoroughly studied for the first time by Aitken at the turn of the century and are recorded by the counter which bears his name. Aitken's numerous papers on this subject are still interesting to read (e.g., Aitken, 1923). The larger particles are classified as large (0.1 to 1.0 μ radius) and giant (> 1.0 μ radius). The giant particles escaped attention for a long time because of their very low concentration and only recently were studied more carefully in connection with their potential role in rain formation.

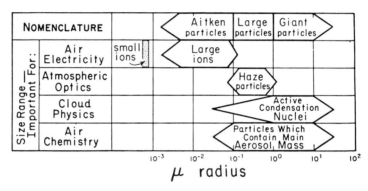

FIG. 21. Nomenclature of natural aerosols and the importance of particle sizes for various fields of meteorology.

In meteorology, the aerosol particles are often labeled condensation nuclei or just nuclei. This designation is fundamentally correct since all these particles can act as nuclei for water vapor condensation, irrespective of their physical and chemical properties, if the water vapor supersaturation is high enough (e. g., Junge, 1936). However, in the atmosphere, most of them will never act as such and, therefore, we prefer to speak generally of aerosol particles.

Aerosol particles can either bear an electrical charge or not. The charged particles are called large ions and are usually subdivided into the following groups (e.g., Israël and Schulz, 1932):

Small medium ions	radius $\leq 7 \times 10^{-3}$ μ
Large medium ions	7×10^{-3} $\mu \leq$ radius $\leq 2.5 \times 10^{-2}$ μ
Langevin ions	2.5×10^{-2} $\mu \leq$ radius $\leq 5.5 \times 10^{-2}$ μ
Ultra large ions	radius $\geq 5.5 \times 10^{-2}$ μ.

The range of the large ions is therefore practically identical with that of the Aitken particles.

As in the case of the spectrum of electromagnetic waves, different parts of the particle size spectrum are responsible for different phenomena in the atmosphere (Fig. 21). Aitken particles play a significant role in air electricity by affecting the air conductivity and subsequently other electrical parameters. The large particles are responsible for the scattering of visible light and thus control the visibility outside clouds and fog. The third example of is cloud formation. Since water vapor supersaturations in the atmosphere are always small, normally only the giant and large nuclei become activated as condensation nuclei, whereas the Aitken nuclei remain inactive. However, the line of separation between active and inactive nuclei varies considerably with the circumstances and is not sharp.

As the relative humidity increases, the aerosol particles gradually change both in size and physical properties, and finally become cloud and fog droplets, or ice particles. They pick up other material from the surrounding air by a variety of processes, and thus their composition and physical structure changes continually.

Unless otherwise stated, we will use $\mu g/m^3$ as the unit for concentration, which is represented, e.g., by a water droplet of 0.012 cm diameter in a cubic meter of air.

2.2 Physical Properties of Tropospheric Aerosols

2.2.1 Size Distribution

For a better understanding of the results of the size distribution measurements, we will discuss brifly the methods used in such investigations.

The well-known Aitken nuclei counter, which operates on the principle of the Wilson cloud chamber, determines only the total number of particles. The expansion ratio is adjusted to 1.25 to exclude small ions (see e.g., Landsberg, 1938). The numbers obtained with this counter in atmospheric air are practically identical with the numbers below 0.1 μ radius, because of the relatively small concentrations of the large and giant particles. This is the reason why particles smaller than 0.1 μ are referred to as Aitken particles, although the upper limit of the counter is larger and is determined by the sedimentation *within* the counter.

Information on the size distribution of particles smaller than 0.1 μ can be obtained by measuring the diffusion coefficient (e.g., (e.g., Nolan and Doherty, 1950), or the distribution of the electrical mobility of the charged particles (e.g., Israël and Schulz, 1932). The latter method permits a fairly accurate size resolution up to a radius of about

0.1 μ. To convert such an ion spectrum into an aerosol spectrum, one must know both the charge of the praticles, and the fraction of particles that carry a charge, as a function of praticle radius (Junge, 1955 a).

Size determinations based on measurements of diffusion and ion mobility are restricted to sizes below about 0.1 μ radius. The most difficult range for measuring particles is between 0.1 and 0.5 μ radius. It is, for instance, relatively easy to collect these particles with spider threads (Dessens, 1949), with impactors (May, 1945), or by electrical or thermal precipitation. However, these samples cannot be evaluated by the light microscope because of its limit of resolution at about 0.3 μ and because the electron microscope tends to modify the particles by partial evaporation through heating in the electron beam. Recently Götz and Preining (1960) designed a special particle centrifuge which allows reliable measurements above a tenth of a micron. Satisfactory results for radii larger than 0.3 μ have also been obtained through the use of light scattering devices (e.g., Green and Lane, 1957).

The light microscope is an ideal instrument for evaluating samples of *giant* particles. Woodcock (1952), for instance, collected sea-spray particles on small glass plates exposed from an aircraft and determined their size distribution as well-developed droplets at a constant, high relative humidity. Samples can also be collected by cascade impactors or by gravity on horizontally exposed plates (Woodcock, 1952; Junge, 1953). The latter collection method has the advantage of simplified evaluation because particles over a wide size range appear in about equal concentrations due to the opposite trends of particle concentration and fall speed. However, it gives only average values for time intervals of a day or so.

From this brief survey we see that several methods need to be used simultaneously to determine the entire size range. In view of the difficulties involved, very few measurements of the *complete* size distribution have been made to date. On the other hand, extensive data have been obtained with single instruments, e.g., the Aitken nuclei counter and various forms of impactors (e.g., the Owen's dust counter and the Zeiss conimeter). However, all these instruments cover only a limited and often poorly defined section of the total size distribution, and the measurements are therefore only of relative and limited value. A comparison of these methods was made by Kup (1942).

The independent use of these various instruments led to the view that the natural aerosols consist of fairly independent groups of particles, e.g., the hygroscopic condensation nuclei in contrast to the "dust" particles counted with the Owen's dust counter and similar instruments. This view prevailed for a long time and it has only recently been realized that the natural aerosols have an essentially coherent size distribution. This is of great importance for a proper understanding of the optical, electrical, and other properties of atmospheric aerosols (Junge, 1952 b).

Before we present the results of size distribution measurements, a few words about their appropriate representation will be helpful. It is a fundamental requirement for histograms or continuous distribution curves that the number of particles or any other quantity within a radius interval Δr or dr be represented by the *area* over this interval and not by the value of the ordinate. Unfortunately, this rule has not always been followed, so that comparison of values sometimes becomes difficult or even impossible.

Because of the wide range of particle sizes and concentrations, it is advisable to use logarithmic scales. The log radius-number distribution, which we will use mostly, is defined by

$$n(r) = dN/d \ (\log r) \ \mathrm{cm}^{-3}, \tag{1}$$

where N is the total concentration of aerosol particles of radius smaller than r. The number of particles ΔN between the limits of the interval $\Delta (\log r)$ is then obtained from these curves by

$$\Delta N = n(r) \ \Delta (\log r).$$

The corresponding log radius-surface (s) and log radius-volume (v) distributions are defined by

$$s(r) = dS/d \ (\log r) = 4\pi r^2 dN/d \ (\log r)$$

and

$$v(r) = dV/d \ (\log r) = \frac{4}{3} \pi r^3 dN/d \ (\log r).$$

If ϱ is the density of the aerosol particles, the log radius-mass distribution is

$$m(r) = \varrho v(r).$$

Little is known about ϱ, but chemical composition indicates values of 1 to 2 g/cm³ for most natural aerosols, depending on the relative humidity.

The best values for the size distribution of Aitken particles were obtained from ion spectra. Figure 22 shows typical examples of Israël and Schulz (1932) and the corresponding aerosol spectra (see Section 2.2.5). The particles exhibit a lower limit of about $4 \times 10^{-3} \ \mu$ and a distinct grouping at certain sizes. The cause of these "line spectra" is not known. Probably, the lines represent predominant local or aerial sources of particles. In this case they should vary with time and tend to disappear in aging aerosols, due to coagulation.

Figure 23 gives complete size distributions of atmospheric aerosols. The distributions were obtained in populated continental areas and represent mean values from which individual distributions can deviate considerably. For simplicity, the line spectra of the Aitken particles were converted to continuous distributions. The data exhibit the following main features: The lower limit of the particle size varies from day to day and is separated by a gap from the size of small ions. The upper limit of 10 μ for curve 2 is incorrect because the observational procedure precluded detection of the few still larger particles. Curve 5 places the true value in the neighborhood of 20 μ. The maximum of these log radius-number distri-

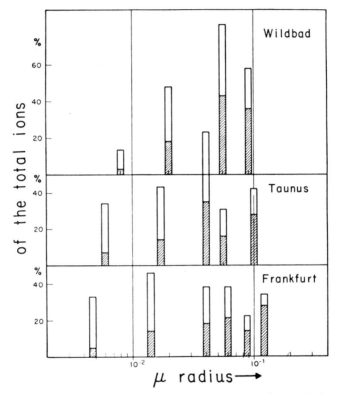

FIG. 22. Large ion spectrums at various places (hatched columns) according to Israël and Schulz (1932). The total height of the columns indicates the calculated size distribution of the corresponding aerosol spectrum (ions plus uncharged particles) in arbitrary units.

butions lies between 0.01 and 0.1 μ, usually at 0.03 μ radius. This has been confirmed repeatedly by Nolan and his co-workers (e.g., Nolan and Doherty, 1950) and by other investigators.

The most striking feature of these "continental" size distributions is the regular decrease in concentration above 0.1 μ, which can be approximated by

$$dN/d \ (\log r) = cr^{-\beta}$$

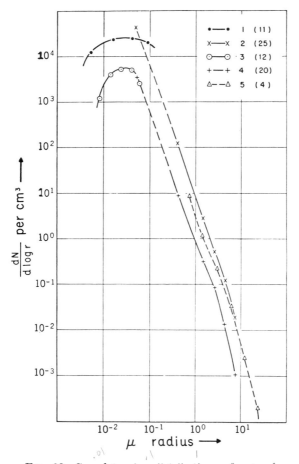

FIG. 23. Complete size distributions of natural aerosols, average data (Junge, 1953, 1955 a). Frankfurt/Main, curves 1, 2, and 5. Curve 1, ion counts converted to nuclei numbers. Curve 2, data from impactors. The point below 0.1 μ radius was obtained from the total Aitken nuclei number under the assumption that the radius interval of the Aitken nuclei is $\Delta \log r = 1.0$. Curve 5, average sedimentation data over a period of 11 days. Curves 1, 2, and 5 are *not* simultaneous. Curves 3 and 4 are simultaneous measurements at the Zugspitze, 3000 meters above s.l., and correspond to curves 1 and 2 for Frankfurt. The figures in parentheses give the number of individual measurements. The dashed curves between 8×10^{-2} and 4×10^{-1} μ are interpolated.

where β is about 3 and c is a constant. The corresponding radius-number distribution is

$$dN/dr = (c/2.30) \cdot r^{-(\beta+1)}$$

This size distribution yields a constant log radius-volume or log radius-mass distribution as shown in Fig. 24, which means that for continental atmospheric aerosols the mass of large particles and that of giant particles are about equal, and that both together represent the major part of the total aerosol mass. The Aitken particles, despite their large numbers, do not account for more than 10 to 20% of the aerosol substance. The distribution at an altitude of 3000 meters shows that the mean features of the size distribution are not restricted to tropospheric ground layers, although the concentrations are lower by one order of magnitude. There is an indication that the upper size limit decreases somewhat with altitude.

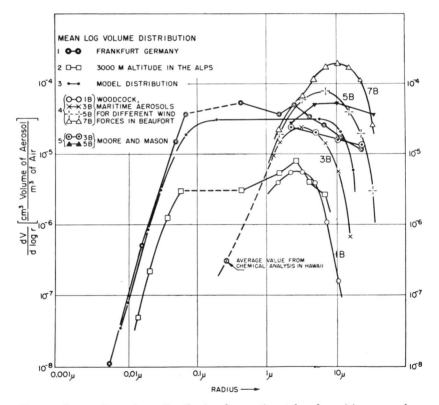

FIG. 24. Log radius-volume distribution for continental and maritime aerosols, (Woodcock, 1953; Moore and Mason, 1954; Junge, 1956). Curve 3B is extrapolated to a point determined by chemical analysis. The curve of Frankfurt is approximated by a " model " distribution, which is used for calculations in Fig. 28.

In Fig. 23, we intentionally suppressed the fact that the size spectrum in the Aitken range shows line structure. The tendency to form line spectra disappears for larger particles, in agreement with the concept that they are subject to considerable and continuous modifications in the atmosphere, smoothing out any orignal irregularities in the distributions. The observations give the impression that distributions like those in Fig. 23 represent the stable end product, or a semi-steady state reached after one or a few days. Junge (1952 b) and Georgii (1958) report cases where size distributions which were heavily disturbed after the influx of polar-maritime air masses readjusted themselves in a matter of days. There are unpublished data obtained by light scattering meters which show that for the range from about 0.2 to 0.8 μ, β is surprisingly constant and is usually around 3.

The number of direct complete measurements of the size distribution is still rather small and general conclusions can scarcely be drawn from them. However, for the range from about 0.08 to 0.6 μ radius, world-wide optical data provide strong evidence that on the average β is around 3. This will be discussed in more detail in Section 2.2.4.

Friedlander (1960) recently made an attempt to explain the size distribution as an interaction of coagulation and sedimentation. He assumes that the upper end of the size spectrum tends to approach a quasi-stationary state into which matter enters by coagulation from the Aitken range and from which matter is lost at the same rate by sedimentation. His estimated distribution curves are not in disagreement with the observations. However, we feel that the condensation and evaporation cycle of cloud and rain drops is another process which also has to be considered.

Figure 24 contains the log radius-mass distribution of continental and maritime aerosols, and it is obvious that the conditions over the *ocean* are fundamentally different (Junge, 1956). Unfortunately, most size distribution measurements in maritime air have been made for giant particles only. Woodcock (e.g., 1953 and subsequent papers) made a very detailed study of aerosol of this size range over the ocean and found that they consist of sea spray particles. Figure 24 shows that the total concentration of sea salt increases with increasing wind force, and that the peak of the mass distribution and the upper limit of the aerosol distributions shift to larger particle sizes. Below 2 μ radius, the mass distribution already begins to drop; chloride analyses made in Hawaii of the large particles confirmed this. This implies that for pure sea spray aerosols, the large particles must be less numerous by one or two orders of magnitude, than for continental aerosols, a fact which is qualitatively indicated by the larger range of visibility in maritime air. As we see from Table 27, the concentration of Aitken particles shows similar differences between continent and

TABLE 27

CONCENTRATION OF AITKEN PARTICLES PER CM³ IN DIFFERENT LOCALITIES [a]

Locality	Number of:		Average	Average	
	Places	Observat.		Max	Min
City	28	2500	147,000	379,000	49,100
Town	15	4700	34,300	114,000	5900
Country (inland)	25	3500	9500	66,500	1050
Country (sea shore)	21	7700	9500	33,400	1560
Mountain					
500-1000 meters	13	870	6000	36,000	1390
1000-2000 meters	16	1000	2130	9830	450
> 2000 meters	25	190	950	5300	160
Islands	7	480	9200	43,600	460
Ocean	21	600	940	4680	840

[a] Landsberg (1938).

ocean. Figures 24 and 25 indicate that for the radius interval between 2 and 10 μ and for average wind speeds the third-power law can also be applied to Wordcock's sea spray data. However, other analytical expressions seem to represent the giant sea-salt particles better (Eriksson, 1959).

Recent determinations of the size distribution of chloride particles in maritime air masses over Ireland by Metnieks (1958) extend the range to 0.07 μ radius for dry salt or 0.15 μ radius for a salt droplet at 80% relative humidity. Two of his curves are shown in Fig. 25. The particle concentration for the smaller particles was generally higher in Dublin than at the west coast of Ireland, but it is hard to estimate how representative this is because of the small number of measurements. The concentrations are considerably lower than those in Woodcock's data, particularly for radii between 0.7 and 5 μ in size. The peak of our extrapolated curve b agrees fairly well with the peak of Metnieks' curves. This peak in the distribution occurs at a size that is already close to the size at which the collection efficiency of Metnicks' cascade impactor starts to drop. However, Rau (1955) collected chloride particles in Germany with a thermal precipitator and found that the maxima occurred at about the same size. It can thus be expected that under normal conditions the maximum of the sea-spray particle distribution is in the vicinity of 0.25 μ radius at 80% relative humidity.

Chloride particles are apparently also formed by industrial activities and can thus not always be used over land as an indicator for maritime origin. The relatively high concentrations of small chloride par-

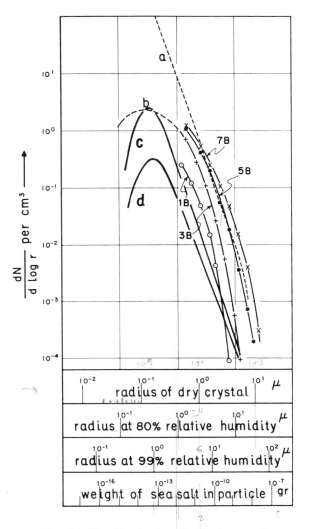

FIG. 25. Size distribution of sea-salt particles.
Curves 1B, 3B, 5B, and 7B, represent average
data of Woodcock (1953) for wind forces 1, 3,
5, and 7 Beaufort. Curve a represents a typical
continental distribution for comparison. Curve b
(dotted) is an extrapolation of curve 3B on the
basis of chloride analysis in correspondence to
Fig. 24. Curves c and d are individual distributions obtained by Metnieks (1958) for Dublin
and the west coast of Ireland.
The various scales at the bottom allow a conversion of the different units used in the literature
to indicate the size of the sea-spray particles.

ticles in Dublin (Metnieks, 1958) and in South West Germany (Rau, 1955) compared with the Irish West Coast may point in this direction. Recently Podzimek (1959, Podzimek and Cernoch, 1961) measured vertical profiles of chloride particles in Czechoslovakia and found the highest concentrations during winter, and anticyclonic conditions in the lowest layers, which strongly indicates continental origin.

The extrapolated curve for the mass distribution of sea spray particles in Fig. 24 is valid only for extremely pure maritime air. The presence of continental aerosols will always increase the mass and number concentration in the range of the large and Aitken particles and large scale horizontal mixing must produce a great variety of transitions between the continental distribution, represented, e.g., by the data from Frankfurt and the distribution of the sea spray component. This results in considerable fluctuations of the number concentrations of Aitken and large particles, particularly in coastal areas, whereas the concentration of the giant particles does not vary so much. The interpretation of aerosol data from coastal areas in terms of continental or maritime origin is thus difficult. It is not surprising that below 1 μ residues of continental aerosols are found to be present far out in the open sea, as for instance by Moore and Mason (1954) over the East Atlantic.

These general features of the size distribution of natural aerosols establish the framework within which the numerous individual observations of limited size ranges must by fitted. Table 27 contains data on Aitken particles compiled by Landsberg (1938) and shows a pronounced decrease in the concentrations from populated areas to the ocean. In entirely undisturbed maritime areas, the concentration drops to 100 to 200/cm³; in a few instances, e.g., in Greenland, the concentrations are below the limit of detection, i.e., less than about 20/cm³ (Fenn, 1960). Clearly, the Aitken particles are of continental and, to a certain degree, of anthropogenic origin. The low concentrations found over the ocean may be due to small local sources or to residual continental aerosols. No information is available for distinguishing between these two possibilities.

A large number of measurements within the range of the *large* particles were made in the past decades. The reported concentrations vary widely, between 10 and several 100 particles per cm³ (see, e.g., Effenberger, 1940). Higher values are often, but not always, associated with industries or cities. It must be expected from the steep slope of the size distribution curves that the values obtained with the various impactor-type instruments are very sensitive to the lower limit of the collection efficiency. This limit is usually around a few tenths of a micron, but varies with the type of instrument and the operating conditions (Kup, 1942). In the case of the Owen's "dust" counter, water condenses on the particles prior to collection, which lowers the limit below 0.1 μ.

The concentration of giant particles over the ocean (Woodcock, 1953) and continent (Junge, 1953) varies between about 0.1 and 1/cm³. Generally the giant particle concentrations fluctuate less than the concentrations of all smaller ones.

We have summarized our present knowledge about size distributions in Fig. 26, in which we have plotted two representative model distributions for land and ocean. The corresponding particle numbers are also given in Table 28. Such model distributions are quite useful for various

TABLE 28

PARTICLE CONCENTRATIONS PER CM³ FOR THE TWO MODEL SIZE DISTRIBUTIONS OF FIG. 26 AND FOR THE STRATOSPHERE

	Particle concentration of radius (μ):							Total number
	<0.01	0.01— 0.032	0.032— 0.10	0.10— 0.32	0.32— 1.0	1.0— 3.2	> 3.2	
Surface air								
Continent	1600	6800	5800	940	29	0.94	0.029	15,169
Ocean	3 [a]	83 [a]	105 [a]	14 [a]	2	0.47	0.029	207
Stratosphere								
1 km [b]	2 [a]	24 [a]	9.1 [a]	0.19	0.019	0.001	—	35
4 km [b]	0.08 [a]	3.4	1.7 [a]	0.06	0.006	0.0003	—	5.4

[a] These values are estimated from the total number of Aitken particles and the assumptions about the size distribution.

[b] Above tropopause.

quantitative considerations, but it should be emphasized that under specific conditions the concentrations can deviate considerably, and that all transitions between the two typical distributions are possible.

2.2.2 Sedimentation and Coagulation

Sedimentation and coagulation determine the properties of tropospheric aerosols to a considerable extent. Sedimentation controls the upper size limit; coagulation controls the lower size limit and the size distribution of the Aitken particles. A brief discussion of these processes, therefore, seems to be justified.

The basic parameters of the particles are the fall velocity v and the diffusion coefficient d. Analytical expressions for these quantities are well known. Two sets of expressions are available. One set applies to molecular sizes and is derived from the kinetic theory of gases (v_{sk} and d_{sk}). The other set is given by the Stokes-Cunningham formula (v_{sc} and d_{sc}). It can be shown that these two sets are identical within a certain size range when extrapolated to larger and smaller sizes, respectively, and thus together cover the entire range from molecular sizes to giant particles.

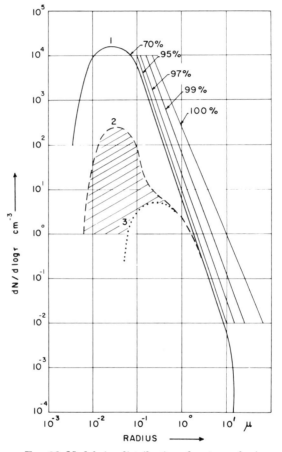

FIG. 26. Model size distributions for atmospheric aerosols. Curve 1, continent. Curve 2, ocean. The part of the curve below 1 μ is estimated. Curve 3, sea-spray component of the maritime aerosol. The hatched area between curves 2 and 3 represents the non-sea-spray component over the ocean.

The straight lines indicate the shift of the continental log radius-number distributions curve due to particle growth by humidity for mixed particles of about 20% soluble material.

Parameters v and d are both related to the particle mobility B, which is defined as the velocity per unit driving force:

$$v_s = m_s g B_s$$

$$d_s = kT B_s$$

where m_s = mass of the particle

g = gravity acceleration

k = Boltzmann's constant

T = absolute temperature.

The index s refers to quantities of the particles. The mobility B for *particles* is (Davis, 1945)

$$B_{sc} = (1 - \varrho/\varrho_s)\alpha/6\pi\eta r_s$$

where ϱ = density of air

ϱ_s = density of particle

α = $1 + \beta l/r_s$, Cunningham's slip correction factor

β = $1.26 + 0.40 \exp(-1.10 \, r_s/l)$;
β varies only slightly with l/r_s; it is 1.65 for $l/r_s > 10$ and 1.25 for $l/r_s < 0.1$.

l = mean free path length

r_s = particle radius

η = viscosity of air.

With

$$l/\eta = (1/n)\sqrt{\pi/mkT}$$

where m = mean mass of the air molecules

n = number of air molecules per cm^3,

and for $l/r_s \gg 1$, that is, for $r < \sim 10^{-2} \, \mu$,

$$v_{sc} = (\pi/mkT)^{1/2} \, 2 \, \beta \, r_s \, \varrho_s \, g/9n.$$

On the other hand, the general diffusion theory (see, e.g., Lettau, 1951) shows that the settling rate of molecular particles of the mass m_s is

$$v_{sk} = d_{sk}(m_s - m) \, g/kT$$

where

$$d_{sk} = 3[2kT \, (m + m_s)/\pi \, m \, m_s]^{1/2}/16 \, n(r + r_s)^2$$

is the diffusion coefficient given by the kinetic theory of gases and r the radius of the air molecules. With $m_s = 4\pi r_s^3 \varrho_s/3$ and for $r_s \gg r$, i.e., for $r_s > \sim 10^{-3}$, we obtain

$$v_{sk}/v_{sc} = 9/4\sqrt{2}\,\beta\,.$$

Since $\beta = 1.65$ for $1/r > 10$, it follows tnat

$$v_{sk}/v_{sc} \cong 1.$$

Thus, both the gas kinetic formula extrapolated to larger sizes and the Stokes-Cunningham formula are identical over the range of particle sizes between $\sim 10^{-3}$ and $\sim 10^{-2}\ \mu$. For $r_s > 10^{-2}\ \mu$, v_{sc} should be used; for $r_s < 10^{-3}\ \mu$, v_{sk} is valid.

The fall speed of particles is related to the diffusion coefficients by

$$v_{sc} = d_{sc} m_s\, g/kT$$

$$v_{sk} = d_{sk}\,(m_s - m)\, g/kT.$$

For the same range of r_s from $\sim 10^{-3}\ \mu$ to $\sim 10^{-2}\ \mu$, $d_{sk}/d_{sc} \cong v_{sk}/v_{sc} \cong 1$ and what was said about the expressions for v also holds true for those for d.

The given range of agreement for both formulas is good for a pressure of 1 atm. At lower pressures, the mean free path length increases and the upper limit of agreement, $r = 10^{-2}\ \mu$, increases correspondingly. By proper application of both expressions, all considerations about diffusion and sedimentation of particles are covered without a gap from molecular dimensions to giant particles.

Sedimentation is the controlling factor in limiting the upper end of the aerosol spectrum. It also has some influence on the vertical distribution of giant particles. For particles smaller than $1\ \mu$, the effect of gravity on tropospheric aerosols becomes negligible. The discussion of the previous section indicated that a radius of $20\ \mu$ can be considered a good average size for the upper limit of the size distribution over land and sea. We will try to confirm this by theory.

This limit is obviously determined by the ability of the eddy diffusion near the ground to carry particles to higher layers. If $n(r)_z$ is the concentration of particles of radius r at altitude z, this ability can be expressed by the ratio

$$\varepsilon = n(r)_z/n(r)_{z=0}\,.$$

Over the sea, conditions are ideal for calculating ε as a function of r for various altitudes and turbulent conditions. When winds are constant, the production of sea spray particles is very uniform over wide areas and steady state conditions can be assumed (Junge, 1955 b). Near the ground the eddy diffusion is given by

$$D = A/\varrho = u_5 k(z + b)$$

where A = Austausch coefficient (g/cm sec)

u_5 = wind speed at an altitude of 5 meters

k = Karman's constant, 0.4

z = altitude

b = roughness parameter of the surface

ϱ = density of air.

Observations indicate that over water, b is not very dependent on wind speed and wave height. For average conditions, 4 cm is a reasonable approximation. At higher altitudes, D tends to become more or less constant and we can approximate it by

$$D = \frac{A_\infty \, u_5 \, k(z + b)}{A_\infty + \varrho u_5 k \, (z + b)}$$

so that for $z \to \infty$, $D_\infty \to A_\infty/\varrho$.

Under steady state conditions, the rate of sedimentation $vn(r)_z$ equals the upward flux by turbulence:

$$\frac{\partial n(r)}{\partial t} \equiv 0 = \partial \left[D \frac{\partial n(r)}{\partial z} - vn(r) \right] / \partial z.$$

The expression for ε, which is a solution of this equation, is evaluated in Fig. 27 for the following ranges of the parameters involved: $b = 0.25$ to 4 cm; $u_5 = 5$ to 20 meters/sec; $A = 100$ to 400 g/cm/sec; $z = 10$ to 250 meters.

Figure 27 shows that despite considerable variations in these parameters, ε as a function of r does not vary much. The value of ε decreases fairly rapidly with increasing r so that the upper limit of particle size is rather sharp and constant. If we define this upper limit by a certain low value of ε, for instance 0.2, the calculated values are in satisfactory agreement with the observed values of 10 to 20 μ. It should be mentioned that the production of sea spray particles larger than 20 μ is established, so that the limit observed is not due to a cutoff in production.

Figure 27 also shows that the concentration for particles slightly smaller than the upper size limit decreases with altitude, but that this decrease becomes unimportant if r approaches 1 μ. Thus, a decrease in particle concentration with altitude in the troposphere for particles smaller than a few microns cannot be explained by an eddy diffusion-sedimentation equilibrium, except perhaps under very special conditions, as, e.g., for a strong inversion above ground with very little vertical mixing. However, observations in the troposphere indicate that the concentration of particles of all sizes down to the Aitken range decreases considerably with altitude and in a rather similar way. It will be shown later that this is due to a combined effect of washout and coagulation, or to non-steady state conditions.

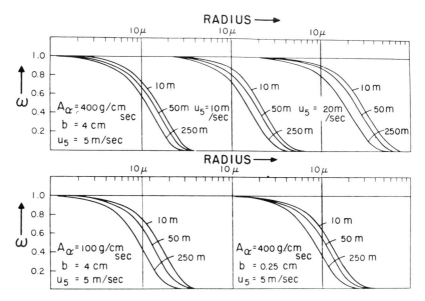

FIG. 27. Calculated value for ε of sea-spray particles as a function of radius at altitudes of 10, 50, and 250 meters. In the upper part of the figure the wind speed u_5 is varied, while A_∞ and b remain constant. In the lower part of the figure A_∞ and b are varied.

Conditions over land are much more complex than over water and less suitable for theoretical treatment. The surface is rougher and irregular, and the injection of particles is not uniform and often occurs at a certain altitude (stacks) and not at the ground. Estimates show that for these reasons one can expect the upper limit of praticle size to be somewhat higher, over land but that otherwise the difference will be small.

The upper size limit of the natural aerosols is a rather fundamental meteorological quantity. This is well demonstrated by the size of pollen grains and loess particles. The efficiency of pollen obviously depends on a fairly wide but still somewhat restricted distribution. The size of pollen grains should, therefore, represent very accurately the average upper limit of particles which can stay airborne. Indeed, the pollen of a large variety of plants is very uniform in size, close to 10 μ radius. About the same size is found to prevail in loess deposits (see, e.g., Krumbein and Sloss, 1951). Loess deposits form at a certain distance from the source area and indicate that the particles were able to stay airborne for quite a while but had a definite tendency to settle down again.

In contrast to sedimentation, coagulation is controlled by the diffusion coefficient of the particles and is thus important primarily for the smaller Aitken particles. Coagulation determines the lower limit of the aerosol distribution. The theory of coagulation was developed in 1918 by Smoluchowsky and extended by Müller (1928). Extensive laboratory studies have confirmed the theory (see, e.g., Whytlaw-Graw and Patterson, 1932), so that its application is well founded, at least for particles larger than about $5 \times 10^{-3} \mu$. We will discuss the effect of this coagulation on a given aerosol distribution.

The rate of coagulation between 2 groups of particles of different size within a population $n(r)$ is given by

$$dn(r_{1,2})/dt = - 4\pi(d_1 + d_2) (r_1 + r_2) n(r_1) n(r_2) dr_1 dr_2$$

where d, r, and $n(r)$ are the diffusion coefficient, the radius, and the concentration of the particles, respectively. Substitution of the previous expression for d results in

$$\frac{dn(r_{1,2})}{dt} = -\frac{2}{3} \frac{kT}{\eta} \left[\frac{1}{r_1} + \frac{1}{r_2} + l\beta \left(\frac{1}{r_1^2} + \frac{1}{r_2^2} \right) \right] (r_1 + r_2) n(r_1) n(r_2) dr_1 dr_2$$

$$\equiv k_0 f(r_1, r_2) n(r_1) n(r_2) dr_1 dr_2.$$

If the aerosol consists of droplets, the combination of an r_1 and r_2 particle results is a particle with

$$r = (r_1^3 + r_2^3)^{1/3}.$$

The largest particles, $r_1 = r_2$, which can participate in the formation of an r-particle are thus of size

$$r_1 = r/2^{1/3}.$$

The total number of r-particles *formed* during dt is then

$$I_1 = k_0 \int_{r_1=0}^{r_1=r/2^{1/3}} f(r_1, \sqrt[3]{r^3 - r_1^3}) n(r_1) n(\sqrt[3]{r^3 - r_1^3}) \frac{r^2 dr_1 dr dt}{\sqrt[3]{r^3 - r_1^3}}.$$

At the same time, the number of r-particles *decreases* by coagulation of r-particles with larger and smaller particles at the following rate:

$$I_2 = - k_0 \int_{r_1=0}^{r_1=\infty} f(r_1, r) n(r_1) n(r) dr_1 dr dt.$$

The total change, Δn, in numbers of r-particles over a time interval $t = 0$ to $t = t_1$ is thus

$$\Delta n(r) = \int_0^{t_1} (I_1 + I_2)\, dt.$$

Numerical calculations were made for artificial aerosols by Zebel (1958) and for natural aerosols by Junge (1955 b), in the latter case by using some approximations to reduce the amount of calculation involved. The upper part of Fig. 28 shows how a given model distribution of particles, which closely follows the data of Fig. 23, changes with time. The decrease in concentration of the small Aitken particle is rather rapid compared to meteorological processes, and results in a displacement of the maximum concentration toward larger particles. The increase in concentration of

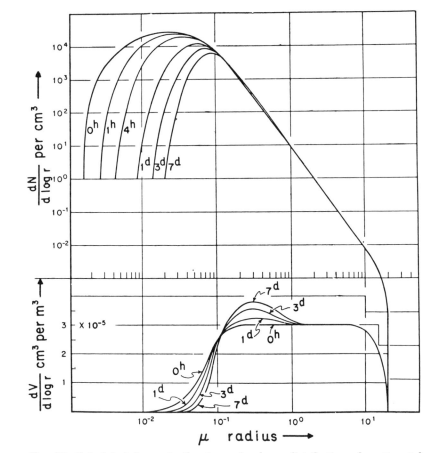

Fig. 28. Calculated change in the size and volume distribution of continental aerosols due to coagulation. The size distribution at the beginning, O^h, corresponds to the model distribution of Fig. 24. h = hours, d = days.

the large particles is very small and hardly visible in the figure. Figure 23 makes it very plausible that for natural aerosols the maximum of the numer distribution is always found between 0.01 and 0.1 μ radius, because any maximum below 0.01 will disappear very rapidly and the shift beyond 0.1 is very slow. It is apparent from these results that particles smaller than 5×10^{-3} μ can exist only for short periods and that the lower limit of the aerosol distribution is determined by the rate of coagulation.

The lower part of Fig. 28 shows the corresponding volume changes. Here the losses below 0.1 μ must balance the gains above 0.1 μ. It is seen that coagulation results in a steady flux of material from the Aitken particles into the size range of the large particles. This favors the formation of mixed particles in the affected range and suggests that the chemical composition of both size ranges is somewhat similar.

Table 29 gives some figures on the decrease in concentration and increase in mean particle size which correspond to the numerical calculations of Fig. 28. They are considered to be rather representative for conditions over populated continents.

TABLE 29

CHANGE OF TOTAL PARTICLE CONCENTRATION AND MEAN RADIUS
DUE TO COAGULATION [a]

Time (hours):	0	1	3	10	30	100
Concentration (cm^{-3}):	27,000	20,000	16,000	9800	5800	3500
Mean radius (10^{-2} μ):	3.2	4.0	4.7	6.0	7.7	10

[a] According to Fig. 28.

2.2.3 The Physical Constitution of Aerosol Particles and Their Role in Water Condensation

The physical constitution of aerosol particles in the atmosphere varies between such extremes as a dry insoluble dust particle and a clear droplet of salt solution. Dry dust particles come from aride soils or are formed by the activities of certain industries, and sea-salt particles represent clear droplets at relative humidities above 75%. Over wide areas, however, individual particles consist of mixtures of insoluble and soluble materials, and the composition can vary greatly with the geographical location and the history of the air masses. A mixed particle or nucleus is, therefore, the most general concept for an atmospheric aerosol particle.

A most important characteristic of mixed aerosol particles is the variation of size with relative humidity. The factors which determine this variation are the ratio of insoluble to soluble matter, the relative humidity at which the soluble fraction forms a saturated solution (often somewhat unclearly termed hygroscopicity), and the relative humidity of the air itself. Koehler (1936) was the first to consider the growth of salt droplets quantitatively. The vapor pressure, p, over a small droplet of a solution is raised by $+ \Delta p_1$ due to the Thomson effect of curvature, and lowered by $- \Delta p_2$ due to the dissolved salt

$$p = p_0 + \Delta p_1 - \Delta p_2 \tag{1}$$

where p_0 is the saturation pressure of a plane, pure water surface.

The quantity Δp_1 is given by Thomson's formula

$$\ln (1 + \Delta p_1/p_0) = \frac{2\,\sigma\,v}{RT} \cdot \frac{1}{r} \equiv c_1/r$$

where $\sigma =$ free surface energy

$v =$ mole volume of water

$R =$ gas constant

$T =$ absolute temperature

$r =$ droplet radius

$c_1 =$ a constant.

For $\Delta p_1/p_0 \ll 1$,

$$\Delta p_1 = p_0 c_1/r.$$

For high relative humidities, the solutions are fairly dilute and the vapor depression is proportional to the salt concentration (Raoult's law). This gives

$$\Delta p_2 = - p_0 c_2/(r^3 - r_0^3)$$

where $r_0 =$ radius of insoluble matter. By substitution, we obtain from (1)

$$p/p_0 = 1 + c_1/r - c_2/(r^3 - r_0^3) \tag{2}$$

for the relative humidity in equilibrium with the droplet. The term c_1/r is smaller than about 1% relative humidity for radii above 0.1 μ (Fig. 31, curve 5 a), and may thus be disregarded for approximate considerations of particle growth with humidity. Aerosol droplets of a salt solution then assume a size at which the concentration of the solution is in vapor-pressure equilibrium with its surroundings. This growth with humidity can be calculated accurately only when data are available for both the density of solution and the water vapor pressure above this solution as a function of the salt concentration. The application of Raoult's law, which gives a linear relationship between salt concentration and water vapor depression, is a good approximation for high relative humidities, i.e., for dilute solutions. The *relative* vapor pressure depression of most salt solutions is nearly independent of the temperature.

Figure 29 gives examples of growth curves for various substances and for mixed nuclei. An NaCl crystal, for instance, becomes a droplet at, or a little below, 75% relative humidity, which is the relative humidity of a saturated solution. However, with decreasing humidity, this droplet does not crystallize until about 40% r.h. is reached, i.e., until the solution becomes considerably supersaturated. A similar delay in the phase transition for decreasing humidities is observed for other salts (Junge, 1952 c). In other words, the relative humidity for the phase transition is

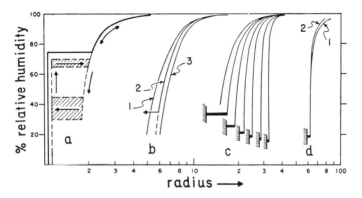

FIG. 29. Growth of aerosol particles with relative humidity. The curves are valid for the size range of the large particles, but are not very different for other sizes. With the logarithmic radius abscissa, the curves are almost independent of the absolute size of the particles.

a, NaCl. The solid curve is calculated. At 75% the crystal goes into solution, increasing the radius by a factor of about 2. The dashed lines represent observations made in the size range of the giant particles. With increasing humidity the crystal goes into solution somewhat earlier than the calculated value; with decreasing humidity a considerable salt supersaturation in the droplet delays the crystallization.

b, Calculated growth curves for various hygroscopic substances. Curve 1, HNO_3; curve 2, $CaCl_2$ (the arrow indicates the expected crystallization point); curve 3, H_2SO_4. The differences are small.

c, Calculated growth curves for mixed particles composed of a solid spherical core (indicated by the hatched areas) and of a liquid layer of H_2SO_4 of varying thickness (indicated by the length of the solid line).

d, Measured average growth curves of continental giant (curve 1) and Aitken (curves 2) particles. The hatched area indicates the size of the solid core, which agrees best with curves in *c*.

well defined and is in agreement with that of saturated solutions for *increasing* humidity only.

Figure 29 b shows that the growth curves for pure solutions do not vary much with the nature of the solution and become very similar for humidities above 90%. This is due to the validity of Raoult's law for dilute solutions. The growth curves for mixed particles (Fig. 29 c) show all transitions between a pure droplet of solution, in our example H_2SO_4, and a dry particle. The computed growth curves have by and large been confirmed by measurements (Junge, 1952 c). Figure 29 d gives average values for measured growth curves for giant and Aitken particles over Central Europe (Junge, 1952 a, c). They agree fairly well with curves for mixed particles which contain about 70 to 80% insoluble material and show that continental aerosols are mixed particles which behave more and more like droplets of a salt solution at higher relative humidities. Growth curves of *individual* natural giant particles show a great variety, which is to be expected for more complex chemical compositions.

The predominance of mixed particles over land, especially in the range of large and giant particles, is confirmed by the electron micrographs of various authors. Figure 30 shows an example for such particles collected with an impactor. Many of these particles apparently were drop-

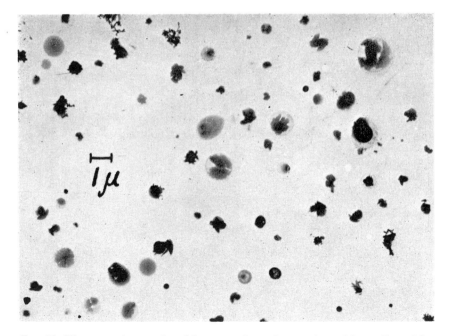

FIG. 30. Electron micrographs of large continental aerosol particles, collected by impactor at 800 meters above s.l. in Central Europe. Typical mixed particles; the areas of less contrast correspond to evaporated salt solutions.

lets before evaporation in the vacuum of the electron microscope (Jacobi *et al.*, 1952). Further information of the nature of aerosol particles in central Europe was obtained by collecting aerosols at various relative humidities simultaneously on clean, *dry* glass plates, which catch only droplets, and on plates covered with a *viscous film*, which catch both droplets *and* dry particles. The ratio of the collected particle numbers indicated that below 70% relative humidity a noticeable fraction of the particle behaved as though they were dry, but above 70% they soon assumed the properties of droplets (Junge, 1952 c).

Sea-salt particles in pure maritime air contain practically no insoluble components. The sharp phase transition at 73% r.h. can be used to identify them (Twomey, 1954). The equilibrium droplet size at a controlled high humidity was used by Woodcock to determine the amount of sea salt in these particles. More recently, Orr *et al.* (1958) confirmed by measurements the calculated growth curves for the Aitken size range as well. For these particle sizes, the increase of water vapor pressure due to the curvature of the droplets can no longer be neglected and the phase transition of crystals occurs at lower humidities, due to the higher solubility of smaller crystals.

Expression (2), for the equilibrium humidity of salt droplets, indicates that the influence of the dissolved salt decreases more rapidly with increasing size than does the influence of the curvature. Consequently, the growth curves cross the 100% line, reach a maximum, and approach the 100% line asymptotically with increasing particle size. True water vapor condensation occurs only along the unstable part of the curve after the peak in passed. To pass this peak, each condensation nucleus requires a certain critical supersaturation. For the giant and large particles, the critical supersaturation amounts to only a few tenths of a per cent, but increases rapidly to several per cent for the Aitken nuclei.

In Fig. 31 we plotted the critical supersaturation as a function of particle size, in our case the particle radius, at 100% relative humidity. The critical supersaturation depends on the amount of soluble material in the nucleus, and curves 5 a and 5 b represent the limiting cases of an insoluble particle with a wet surface and a pure salt droplet. Mixed particles will have values between these curves, except if the surface is not wettable. In the latter case the supersaturation will be higher than curve 5 a, up to 1% even for giant particles, depending on the contact angle of water at the particle surface.

The supersaturation spectrum is of great importance for cloud formation. If air is cooled and a fog or a cloud starts to form, only the largest condensation nuclei, or rather those with the lowest supersaturation, are activated for condensation, whereas the smaller ones do not reach the peak and remain on the stable branch of the growth curve. In

Fig. 31 we depicted schematically the growth of condensation nuclei by humidity (curve 2) and the formation of cloud droplets (curve 3), with curve 1 representing the original aerosol size distribution. It is clear that the number of nuclei activated, i.e., the number of droplets formed, depends on the size distribution of the nuclei, on the rate of cooling of the air, and on the chemical nature of the particles. More recently, Moordy (1959)

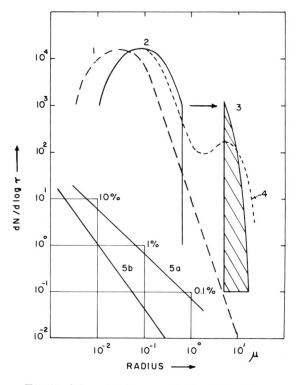

FIG. 31. Schematic diagram of activated and unactivated condensation nuclei for continental aerosols: Curve 1, continental aerosol distribution at 70% relative humidity. Curve 2, unactivated condensation nuclei at 100% relative humidity. Curve 3, cloud droplets formed around activated condensation nuclei, according to Moordy (1959). Curve 4, expected combined distribution of unactivated nuclei and cloud droplets for clouds with an inhomogeneous temperature field, coagulation, and mixed nuclei. Curve 5, critical supersaturation as a function of radius at 100% relative humidity; curve 5 a, insoluble but wettable particle (Thomson formula); curve 5 b, NaCl particle. The difference between curves 5 a and 5 b is enhanced due to particle growth below 100% relative humidity.

studied this process by extensive and careful calculation, assuming different spectra of hygroscopic nuclei and vertical velocities. His main results can be summarized as follows:

(1) For a given size distribution of atmospheric aerosols, the number of cloud droplets increases with an increasing rate of cooling. The calculated numbers are in agreement with observed droplet concentrations of about 10 in slowly forming fog, and of a few hundred in convective clouds, if particle distributions are assumed that are somewhere between the continental and the maritime distributions shown in Fig. 26.

(2) For a given cooling rate, higher numbers of cloud droplets are obtained for size distributions with higher concentrations of *large* nuclei, i.e., for continental distributions.

(3) The dividing line between activated and nonactivated nuclei (see Fig. 31) is located in the range 0.05-0.5 μ radius, depending on the size distribution and the cooling rate.

Moordy's nuclei spectra are generally closer to the maritime type and do not include a typical continental distribution with concentrations of large and Aitken nuclei as high as those shown in Fig. 23. For these distributions, the dividing line will be shifted to larger particle sizes and the droplet numbers will increase further. For pure maritime distributions such as indicated in Fig. 26, all particles, including the Aitken particles, may be activated.

The basic assumption in these calculations was that the temperature and humidity fields are completely uniform within the cloud. In reality there are always fluctuations and this results in local variations of the dividing line and subsequently of the droplet distributions within the clouds. Further, if the aerosol consists of mixed nulcei, the critical supersaturation is not a simple function of particle size, and there will be no sharp dividing line between activated and nonactivated particles, although the largest nuclei are still used preferentially. All these facts combine to modify the nuclei and droplet distribution in a way which is pictured schematically in Fig. 31, curve 4. The actual droplets now form only a more or less pronounced secondary maximum with a smooth transition to the inactivated nuclei, but there is no longer a sharp distinction between both types of droplets.

These conclusions are generally in good agreement with observations. Junge (1935) first showed experimentally that indeed the supersaturated spectrum for atmospheric nuclei is limited to just a few per cent and corresponds to the particle size spectrum, in approximate agreement with Koehler's theory. Recently, more refined experimental techniques were used by Twomey (1959). He produced very small steady state supersaturations in isothermal diffusion cloud chambers using HCl solutions and obtained a large variety of supersaturation spectra in southeastern Australia. They could be grouped into continental, maritime, and modified maritime spectra. The differences in concentration among these groups are striking, with continental aerosols being higher by one to two orders of magnitude than maritime aerosols. The modified maritime spectra show higher counts for the higher supersaturations (smaller particles) only. These supersaturation spectra can be explained satisfactorily by the known size distribution curves, as was pointed out by Junge (1960). Twomey's results clearly point to the continents as the major source of condensation nuclei, if the size distribution data had left any doubt. Twomey (1960) estimates that, besides pollution, a major nuclei source over land may be the drying and heating soil, where soluble material crystallizes in fine particles on the surface and is swept up by the wind.

Since clouds with large numbers of small droplets are colloidally more stable than those with fewer and larger ones, the differences in the aerosol size distribution can account for the observed differences in rain production between maritime and continental clouds (Squires and Twomey, 1960).

There is further direct evidence available to show that, preferentially, the large particles serve as condensation nuclei. Kuroiwa (1953) and Yamamoto and Ohtake (1953), for instance, took individual cloud and fog droplets (mountain and ocean fogs) and studied the size distribution and origin of the evaporation residues under the electron microscope. In Table 30, their results are summarized and compared with our nuclei size distribution. Both series of observations (lines 3 and 6) show fair agreement as to the very heterogeneous materials that can act as condensation nuclei. In lines 4 and 5, it is assumed that the largest particles are 100% active. A comparison with a continental size distribution then indicates that the percentage of activated nuclei drops considerably with decreasing size. Such a comparison is, of course, only approximately valid because of the widely separated locations of data sources. The basic result, however, is considered reliable and in good agreement with our earlier discussion. Over land apparently only a small fraction of the particles of 0.1 μ radius and less are used in condensation, unless there is a lack of large and giant nuclei as over the ocean or in other remote places.

The older impaction techniques that were used to measure the droplet distribution in fogs and clouds were able to collect only droplets larger than about 3 μ radius. It became apparent that these droplets represent most of the liquid water but cannot account for the low visibility or high opacity observed. More refined optical techniques in fogs (Stewart, 1957) and clouds (Eldridge, 1957) and electrical methods in clouds (Keily and Millen, 1960) were able to measure distributions down to 0.5

TABLE 30

COMPARISON OF THE SIZE DISTRIBUTION OF A CONTINENTAL AEROSOL AND THE OBSERVED SIZE DISTRIBUTION OF NUCLEI FOUND IN CLOUD AND FOG DROPLETS

	Size distribution of particles of radius (μ):						Ave. (%)
	0.1-0.2	0.2-0.4	0.4-0.6	0.6-1.0	1.0-2.0	2.0-4.0	
Particle concentration per cm³ for a continental aerosol	1200	150	16	5	1.2	0.15	
Percentage of observed nuclei in cloud and fog droplets according to Yamamoto and Ohtake (1955): 12% with $r \leq 0.1\ \mu$ are not included	28	18	16	17	7	<1	
Total numbers according to Yamamoto when percentage figures are normalized for the largest particles between 1 and 2 μ of line 1	4.8	3.0	2.8	3.0	1.2	—	
Origin of these nuclei: 26% sea salt, 57% combustion products, 13% soil, 4% unknown, total number 217							
Percentage of total nuclei which served as true condensation nuclei in various size ranges (line 3 compared with line 1)	0.4	2	17	60	100	—	
Percentage of total nuclei which served as true condensation nuclei in various size ranges according to Kuroiwa (1953), calculated in the same way as those of Yamamoto et al. in line 4	0.2	1.7	15	24	100	—	
Origin of nuclei of Kuroiwa							
Total number of:							
Sea salt	5	1	1	6	7		24
Combustion products	11	16	11	4	2		52
Soil matter	6	5	8	0	1		24

to 1.0 μ radius. All these data show the highest number of droplets at the lowest limit of detection, with concentrations from several to many thousands per cm³. If the particles smaller than 3 μ are subracted from these figures, the droplet concentrations are comparable to those obtained with the older methods which were of the order of a hundred to a thousand per cm³. However, calculations show that the numerous small droplets below 3 μ contribute most to the opacity and can in fact explain the observed visibilities.

Eldridge made his measurements in very freshly formed orographic clouds on Mt. Washington and found a *bimodal* distribution with a rather pronounced second peak at 5 to 8 μ radius and concentrations from 10^2 to 10^1/cm³. We think that these conditions are close to those assumed in Moordy's calculations which are represented in Fig. 31. It is suggested, but not proven, that the large number of small droplets are identical with the nonactivated but grown nuclei, and that the second peak represents the real droplets of condensed water. Keily and Millen's data were obtained in stratus and cumulus clouds by aircraft and there is only a very slight indication of a bimodal distribution. Coagulation and mixing of cloud air with a different condensation history has perhaps smoothed out any bimodal distribution and a clear distinction between droplets and inactivated nuclei is no longer possible.

Stewart's data on fogs in Kew, near London, clearly indicate a bimodal distribution with very high concentrations from 10^4 to 10^5/cm³ below 0.5 μ radius. He observed an interesting difference between "thin" fogs, with very few large droplets, and "thick" fogs. In the normal sequence of events, the "thick" fogs form first with a rather rapid drop in visibility to about 100 meters and less. Usually, after dawn, an irregular rise in visibility through a "thin" fog starts which can persist for many hours, particularly in winter, and which has a very low content of liquid water (dry fog). This asymmetry of events points to the conversion of gaseous substance to particulate matter (e.g., SO_4 formation by SO_2 oxidation) within the *nonactivated* nuclei, resulting in their substantial growth. Similar but less striking effects are to be expected in unpolluted air in each cycle of condensation and evaporation.

From the standpoint of air chemistry, another important conclusion can be drawn from Fig. 31 and our discussion. Since the giant and most of the large nuclei are used for condensation in continental air, it must be expected that cloud droplets will contain most of the aerosol mass present, either as dissolved or as undissolved material. This shows that rainout within the cloud should be fairly efficient for aerosols, except for the Aitken nuclei which, however, represent only a small fraction of the total aerosol mass. Over the oceans, the rainout in clouds must be 100%.

At subzero temperatures, most nuclei produce water drop-
lets and only very few ice crystals. The number of ice nuclei, as a function
of subzero temperature, is of great importance for the Findeisen-Bergeron
rain process, which involves the ice phase. Georgii (e.g., 1959) studied the
relation between ice nuclei and aerosol size spectra. He showed conclusively
that the giant particles provide the ice nuclei which become active at the
highest temperatures and that the activation temperature decreases with
decreasing particle size and is about — 30°C for Aitken nuclei. This result
is in agreement with the concept that the most active ice nuclei in the
atmosphere are mineral particles from the soil.

2.2.4 Optical Properties of Aerosols

Under normal conditions—as we will see in the course of this
discussion—the optical properties of atmospheric aerosols over land are
determined almost exclusively by the large particles (Fig. 21). The most
striking feature of these particles is the steep and straight slope of the
size distribution and it can be expected that a study of the optical properties of atmospheric haze will provide further insight into the subject. This
is particularly helpful since it is difficult to obtain *direct* determinations of
the size distribution between 0.08 nd 0.5 μ radius.

The various optical phenomena concerned with atmospheric
haze, as. e.g., extinction or scattering and their mutual relationships, were
not properly understood until the concept of a continuous size distribution
with a power law was introduced. Although considered valid only within
certain limits and as a simple approximation, application of the concept
to atmospheric optics has proved to be very successful, particularly in the
comprehensive work of Volz (1954, 1956).

Here, of course, we shall concentrate only on those phenomena which can provide further information on the atmospheric aerosols.
These are the total scattering or extinction by haze and its wavelength
dependence, on the one hand, and scattering as a function of the angle
between incident and scattered light, on the other. Both are sensitive to
size distribution and are well documented by numerous investigations.

We assume a spherical particle of radius r and refraction in-
dex m and introduce the quantity $x = 2\pi r/\lambda$, where λ is the wavelength
of visible light, $0.3 < \lambda < 0.7$ μ, with the center of gravity around 0.55 μ.
The *fraction* K of parallel light scattered by this particle into the directions
φ and ω, where φ is the angle between incident and scattered light and
ω is the angle around the incident light as axis, is given by the theory of
Mie and is a function of λ, x, and m:

$$K(\lambda,\ x,\ m,\ \varphi) = \frac{\lambda^2}{4\pi^2}\ i(\varphi,\ x,\ m)\ \sin\ \varphi\ d\varphi\ d\omega.$$

The total fraction of light scattered in all directions is thus

$$\bar{k}(\lambda,\ x,\ m) = \frac{\lambda^2}{4\pi^2} \int_{\omega=0}^{2\pi} \int_{\varphi=0}^{\pi} i(\varphi,\ x,\ m)\ \sin\ \varphi\ d\varphi\ d\omega$$

$$= \frac{2\pi r^2}{x^2} \int_{\varphi=0}^{\pi} i(\varphi,\ x,\ m)\ \sin\ \varphi\ d\varphi \equiv \pi r^2 \varkappa(x,\ m).$$

The scattering cross section $\varkappa(x,\ m)$ gives the fraction of totally scattered light falling on the cross section of the particle πv^2. It depends only on x and m, and numerical values are available for the important parameter ranges of x and m. Very little is known about the refraction index m, which is expected to vary somewhat with the relative humidity. At high relative humidities, it will approach the refraction index of water, 1.33. For calculations, $m = 1.5$ is often used.

For an aerosol distribution

$$dN/dr = (c/2.3)\ r^{-(1+\beta)}$$

with the limits r_1 and r_2, and $\beta > 2$, the total fraction of light scattered by all the particles in 1 cm³ within the wavelength band $d\lambda$ is

$$\sigma_A = \int_{r_1}^{r_2} \bar{k}\ \frac{dN}{dr}\ dr = \frac{\pi c}{2.3} \int_{r_1}^{r_2} \varkappa r^{1-\beta}\ dr$$

$$= \frac{\pi c}{2.3} \left(\frac{\lambda}{2\pi}\right)^{2-\beta} \int_{x_1}^{x_2} \varkappa x^{1-\beta}\ dx \equiv c\lambda^{2-\beta}\ I \quad \text{(cm}^{-1}). \tag{1}$$

The lowest limit for the "straight" section is $r_1 = 0.08\ \mu$, but at this value $x_1 < 1$ and k is practically zero, so that r_1 can be replaced by zero. The giant particles, on the other hand, contribute so little that we can put $x_2 \to \infty$. The integral I thus becomes independent of r and λ and we obtain

$$\sigma_A \sim \lambda^{2-\beta}.$$

This expression can be compared with Angström's well-known empirical formula for the wavelength dependence of the total haze scattering,

$$\sigma_A \sim \lambda^{-\alpha},$$

which results in

$$\alpha = \beta - 2. \tag{2}$$

Angström found an average value $\alpha = 1.3$, which corresponds to $\beta = 3.3$, in close agreement with our value of 3. The power law gives a simple and satisfactory explanation of Angström's law, which is of general importance with respect to atmospheric visibility. It indicates that the range of vision even in hazy atmospheres is larger for red than for blue light.

For $\beta = 2$, $\alpha = 0$ and haze scattering would be neutral. Exact calculations show that for this extreme case, the fixed upper limit of the giant particles cannot be ignored and that α is still about 0.2. Since α is the difference of β and 2, it is very sensitive to variations of β and thus a powerful tool for the investigation of aerosol distributions. However, it should be kept in mind that only a small section of the total "straight" part is covered, from about $r = 0.08 \ \mu$ to $r = 0.6 \ \mu$. The particle size for which I is maximum, i.e., the particle size which contributes most to total scattering, is given by $r/\lambda \approx 0.5$, or $r \approx 0.25 \ \mu$ for $\lambda = 0.5 \ \mu$. Variations of β outside this range have little effect on α, but within this range the optical properties of haze are very sensitive to small deviations and irregularities. Volz (1956) demonstrates that α varies between 1.5 and 0.5 if the concentration of particles with $r = 0,3 \ \mu$ are varied by a factor of 2 with respect to the adjacent size distribution.

Volz (1956) compiled and discussed all available data on α. Values for α can be deduced only from observations of the wavelength dependence of total scattering. The total atmospheric scattering or the extinction is measured either directly by using the sun or an artificial light source, or by determining the visibility V. The visibility V can be converted to total scattering σ by use of Koschmieder's formula. This relates the brightness of a black target area B_z at the distance z to the brightness of the horizon B_h and to σ:

$$B_z = B_h(1 - e^{-\sigma z}).$$

The limit of contrast detectable by eye is about 0.02,

$$(B_h - B_v)/B_h \approx 0.02,$$

which results in the relation $V = 3.9/\sigma$ (V in km, if σ in km^{-1}).

All these measurements give the *total* atmospheric scattering, which is the sum of σ_A, the molecular (Rayleigh) scattering σ_M, and perhaps some gas absorption σ_g at certain wavelengths,

$$\sigma = \sigma_A + \sigma_M + \sigma_g.$$

The molecular scattering σ_M and also σ_g can be calculated, so that σ_A is obtained by subtracting these values from σ. It is conceivable that the values of σ_A become increasingly inaccurate for clean atmospheres. For a visibility of 100 km, σ_A is about equal to σ_M. Since $\sigma_M \sim \lambda^{-4}$, the total scattering is proportional to $\lambda^{-\alpha'}$, where $\alpha \leq \alpha' \leq 4$, depending on the amount of haze.

Since the size distribution was established for continental aerosols near the ground, comparison should be made with direct meas-

urements of artificial light sources or of horizontal visibility. There are numerous sets of data for α, e.g., by Middleton (1935) and Schmolinsky (1944).
Almost all these α values scatter between 1.5 and 0.5, with an over-all
average of 1.3. They tend to be lower at visibilities above 40 km and below
1 km. Exceptional high values of 1.8 were found by Volz (1956) in Mainz
in the summer. There is a tendency for higher values in summer than in
winter, but otherwise no correlation with meteorological conditions is
apparent.

The result that α does not vary systematically over the wide
range of aerosol concentrations which corresponds to a visibility range of
1 to 100 km is of great importance. It confirms the power distribution with
a β value of about 2.5 to 3.5, or sometimes higher, as a world-wide phenomenon for a wide variety of continental conditions and gives the few direct measurements of β greater weight.

Measurements with solar radiation show similar α values,
but the variation is generally larger — between 0.5 and 2.0. Some extreme
values obtained in very clean air from mountain observatories are not
likely to be reliable. On the other hand, it may well be that atmospheric
condensation processes, or the possible prevalence of maritime aerosols
in higher layers, would perturb conditions. One has the impression that the
processes which try to establish a $\beta = 3$ distribution are most active in
aerosols of high concentration, i.e., near the ground and in populated areas,
and that the deviations become more pronounced in clean air. There is
no indication, however, of a systematic trend of α with altitude.

No data are available for maritime aerosols. The maritime size
distribution in Fig. 26 suggests small α values. There is only one observation of $\alpha = 0$ for the beach area of the Marshall Islands (see, Volz, 1956).

Relation (1) shows that the absolute value of σ_A can be determined for given values of c and I, but quantitative calculations are unsatisfactory because m remains uncertain. If m varies from 1.4 to 1.7, I
increases by a factor of 1.6 (Junge, 1952 b). For some aerosols, *absorption*
may also become important. For these reasons, a comparison of observed
and computed absolute values has not been attempted. In general the c
values obtained from size distributions are the right size to account for the
observed values of σ or visibility V.

There are many series of observations which show that the
visibility decreases with increasing relative humidity (e.g., Wright, 1940).
For $\beta = 3$, a change in particle size over the whole spectrum by a factor ε
is equivalent to a change in dN/d (log r) by a factor of ε^3 (Fig. 26). Measurements on natural aerosols over a wide range of sizes (Junge, 1952 a)
indicate a value $\varepsilon = 1.3$ for a humidity change from 60 to 95%. For pure
droplets of a salt solution, ε is equal to 1.8 for the same humidity interval.
This means an increase of σ_A by factors of 2.2 and 5.8, respectively. Most

visibility statistics are more in agreement with the latter value. However, this value may be influenced by a correlation between the origin of the aerosol and the humidity or other meteorological parameters.

The growth curves in Fig. 29 suggest that the phase transition for a sea-salt particle between 40 and 75% r.h. should change σ_A by a factor of 8, if we disregard the change in the refraction index. Wright's (1940) data obtained in westerly winds at the west coast of Ireland can be expected to represent maritime aerosols, but they show only small variations of visibility with humidity below 70%. The same is true for other statistics in more continental air, in agreement with the growth curves of mixed particles which contain considerable amounts of insoluble material. It must be concluded, therefore, in agreement with Simpson (1941), that even in maritime air masses, sea salt is not an important constitutent for particles in the size range of a few tenths of a micron, a conclusion which is supported by the earlier discussion on the sea-salt component in aerosols (Fig. 26).

Increasing humidity should also influence α when saturation is approached. At humidities below 95%, particles of all sizes grow fairly uniformly, so that β does not change. Above 95%, the larger particles grow faster, so that β drops to values of 2.0 to 2.5 at 100%. Just prior to the onset of fog formation, one should expect, therefore, that α also drops. This was indeed observed, e.g., by Foitzik (1938), but it does not seem to be a regular phenomenon (Volz, 1956).

Summarizing, we can say that the observed characteristics of σ_A are in agreement with the conclusions drawn from the measured size distributions. A similar result is obtained for the *scattering function*.

The scattering function for a continuous size distribution with a power law shows the following characteristics: The intensity of scattered light drops at a certain rate up to angles between incident and scattered light of 10 to 30° and drops at a higher rate between 30 and 90°. Large particles exhibit stronger forward scattering than smaller particles so that the drop in intensity within the first 20° decreases with increasing β. The theory shows further that the *intensity ratio* of the scattered light for different wavelengths is independent of the scattering angle. Therefore, simple power distributions should not exhibit color phenomena. Colors occur only for considerable deviations from the power law and these are indeed rare phenomena in the atmosphere. The "Bishop ring," a large reddish ring around the sun as a consequence fo the Krakatoa eruption, and the "blue sun," which was observed as a result of tundra fires in Canada in 1950 are well-known examples of extreme irregularities in the atmospheric aerosol size distribution.

The conclusion that power distributions do not exhibit color phenomena is, however, strictly correct only if the upper and lower limits of the size distribution are disregarded, i.e., only for an infinite distribution. Systematic calculations of the scattering function for various models of aerosol distributions with finite limits were recently made by de Bary and Bullrich (1962). Their main result is that a lack of smaller particles results primarily in a decrease of scattering intensity in the range of large scattering angles of about 130° (back scattering) and primarily for smaller wavelengths. Such a lack of smaller particles can be due either to a rather high lower limit of the size distribution (e.g., $r \geq 0.08 \ \mu$), or due to a smaller value of β or to a combination of both. A lack of relatively large particles, on the other hand, results in a decrease of scattering intensity at small scattering angles (forward scattering). Such a lack of larger particles can be due either to a rather low upper limit of the size distribution (e.g., $r \geq 3 \ \mu$) or due to high values of β or to a combination of both. Comparison between observations and calculations indicate that such variations do indeed occur in the atmosphere.

If we compare the theoretical conclusions with observations, it should be considered that scattering functions around the sun contain variable amounts of molecular scattering and are difficult to correct for quantitative considerations. Volz was able to separate qualitatively various types of scattering functions observed around the sun and he related them to deviations from the power law.

Searchlight measurements of the scattering function in ground air are more reliable for quantitative considerations. Bullrich (1960) found that down to scattering angles of 10°, i.e., to the limit of his observations, the scattering function is practically independent of visibility and other meteorological parameters and shows no color dispersion. The drop of intensity was in good agreement with $\beta = 3$. Simultaneous measurements of α gave 1.1 with a rapid decrease for visibilities below 500 meters.

The observations of the scattering function apparently lead to the same general conclusions as did those of σ_A. In aerosols of high concentrations near the ground, β is close to 3 and deviations are relatively small. Observations around the sun, which include those of higher layers, show larger deviations, but the data and their interpretation are less reliable.

2.2.5 Electrical Properties of Atmospheric Aerosols

The electrical properties of the natural aerosols are of great importance for the conductivity of the air, for the space charge and, subsequently, for the electrical field and the vertical current. Furthermore, they also provide useful information on aerosol behavior; the determination of ion spectra is still the most important method of obtaining informative on particle size distributions below radii of 0.1 μ. These reasons would seem to justify a more detailed discussion of the electrical properties of natural aerosols.

We denote:

n = concentration of small ions

q = rate of small ion pair production $(cm^{-3} sec^{-1})$

α = recombination coefficient of small ions (cm^3/sec)

$N = N(r)$ = concentration of all particles of radius r

$N_0 = N_0(r)$ = concentration of uncharged particles

$N_i = N_i(r)$ = concentration of positive or negative charged particles with $i = 1, 2, 3... -$ number of elementary charges

$\eta_0 = \eta_0(r)$ = recombination coefficient between small ions and uncharged particles (cm^3/sec)

$\eta_{ie} = \eta_{ie}(r)$ = recombination coefficient between small ions and charged particles of equal sign with $i = 1, 2, 3... =$ number of elementary charges

$\eta_{iu} = \eta_{iu}(r)$ = recombination coefficient between small ions and charged particles of unequal sign, with $i = 1, 2, 3... =$ number of elementary charges.

In the following considerations, we can assume that all the ion concentrations of opposite sign are equal and that $N = N_0 + 2N_1 + 2N_2 + ...$

On the average, the ratio n_+/n_- is 1.2 in air and differences of a similar magnitude are found for the large ions. However, this deviation from our assumption is not serious and will not affect the following considerations to any great extent.

The equations for the ionization balance can then be written as follows:

$dn/dt = q - \alpha n^2 - \eta n N_0 - \eta_{1e} n N_1 - \eta_{1u} n N_1 - \eta_{2e} n N_2 - \eta_{2u} n N_2,$

$dN_0/dt = 2\eta_{1u} n N_1 - 2\eta n N_0,$

$dN_1/dt = \eta n N_0 + \eta_{2u} n N_2 - \eta_{1u} n N_1 - \eta_{1e} n N_1,$

$dN_2/dt = \eta_{1e} n N_1 + \eta_{3u} n N_3 - \eta_{2u} n N_2 - \eta_{2e} n N_2,$

$dN_3/dt = \eta_{2e} n N_2 + \eta_{4u} n N_4 - \eta_{3u} n N_3 - \eta N_{3e} n_3.$

For ionization equilibrium, the left-hand sides are zero. Under natural conditions, equilibrium will prevail since the adjustment times are of the order of half an hour for particles of $r = 3 \times 10^{-2} \mu$ and a few minutes for $r = 10^{-1} \mu$ (Junge, 1955 a).

For equilibrium conditions we obtain

$$N_1/N_0 = \eta_0/\eta_{1u}$$
$$N_2/N_1 = \eta_{1e}/\eta_{2u}$$
$$N_3/N_2 = \eta_{2e}/\eta_{3u}.$$

Important for our considerations is the ratio of *total* particles to *charged* particles

$$P_1 = P_1(r) = N/(2N_1 + 2N_2 + 2N_3 + \ldots)$$

and sometimes the ratio of *total particles* to total number of *elementary charges*

$$P_2 = P_2(r) = N/(2N_1 + 4N_2 + 6N_3 + \ldots).$$

P_1 can be determined easily by measuring the number of Aitken particles before and after elimination of the charged particles in a cylindrical condenser and P_2 can be determined by measuring the number of charges precipitated in the same condenser. The quantity P_1 is important for the conversion of ion spectra into particle spectra below $r = 0.1\ \mu$ (Junge, 1955 a). Sometimes the quantity

$$\Pi = N/N_0 = P_1/(P_1 - 1)$$

is measured and used. P or Π and the various η's are interrelated. If the η_i are known by theory, P or Π can be calculated, e.g.,

$$P_1 = 1 + \left(\frac{2\eta}{\eta_{1u}} + \frac{2\eta_{1e}\eta}{\eta_{2u}\eta_{1u}} + \frac{2\eta_{2e}\eta_{1e}\eta}{\eta_{3u}\eta_{2u}\eta_{1u}} + \ldots \right)^{-1}.$$

If, on the other hand, P_1 is known from theory or measurements, the η_1 values have to be determined independently. It should be emphasized that all relations mentioned so far do not presume anything about the attachment process itself and are generally valid for ionization equilibrium.

The first expression for η_0 was given by Wright (1936), who assumed it to be proportional to the surface area of the particle. This is valid, however, only if $r \ll l$ where l is the mean free path length of the small ions, which is smaller than that for air. Bricard (1949) assumed a diffusion field for ions around the particle. An equilibrium diffusion field is established only after a certain time period, but the charging mechanism of large ions is a single event and is always concerned exclusively with the first ion in this process. In addition, the diffusion regime, and thus the validity of Bricard's formula, is restricted to $r > l$, i.e., it is not quite applicable to the range important for our considerations.

Junge (1955 a) applied statistical considerations used for bimolecular reactions, etc., and arrived at an expression for η_0 which is practically identical to that given by the Smoluchowsky theory of coagulation:

$$\eta_0 = 4\pi dr$$

where the diffusion coefficient d for small ions and is equal to 3.7×10^{-2} cm²/sec. Similar to Whipple (1933), he obtained

$$\eta_{iu} = \eta_0 + 4\pi iew \quad \text{and} \quad \eta_{ie} = \eta_0 - 4\pi iew$$

where e = elementary charge = 4.77×10^{-1} esu

w = small ion mobility = 1.34 cm²/sec volt.

Calculated values for P and Π are given in Fig. 32 as well as the *average* number of elementary charges $\bar{e}$ for any charged particles

$$\bar{e} = P_1/P_2.$$

Keefe *et al.* (1959) approach the problem in an entirely different way. They assert that the energy E of the aerosol particles, which is distributed according to Boltzmann's law, also includes the electrical energy due to its charge

$$E = E_0 + i^2 e^2/2r ,$$

where E_0 is the energy of the particle in the absence of e. This gives

$$N_i/N_0 = \exp(-i^2 e^2/2rkT)$$

where k = Boltzmann's constant

T = absolute temperature.

For large particles, these ratios N_i/N_0 agree with those obtained by Bricard.

Recently Lassen and associates (Lassen and Rau, 1960; Lassen and Weichsel, 1961) developed an improved theory for attachment of radon decay products to aerosol particles and confirmed it by careful experiments over the radius range 0.04 to 5 μ. They modified Smoluchowsky's expression of the coagulation rate for $r < l$ (l = mean free path length of the small ions) by postulating that the flux at the particle surface is limited to

$$4\pi r^2 \bar{v}/4$$

where $\bar{v}$ is the average gas kinetic velocity of the diffusing particle. They obtained in our notation

$$\eta_{0l} = 4\pi dhr^2/(1 + hr)$$

where $h = \bar{v}/4d$. For the two extreme and limiting cases we obtain

$$\eta_{0l} = 4\pi r^2 \bar{v}/4 \qquad \text{for } r \ll l$$

and

$$\eta_{0l} = 4\pi d r \qquad \text{for } r \gg l$$

as was to be expected. By applying the differences,

$$n_i - \eta_0 = \pm\, 4\pi i e w\,,$$

we calculated the corresponding P_1 and Π values in Fig. 32.

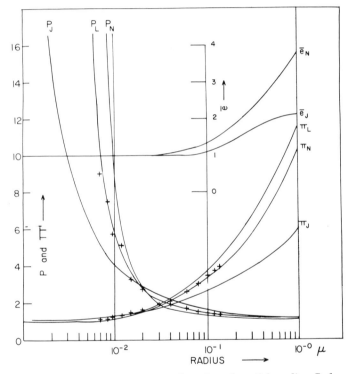

FIG. 32. P, Π, and $\bar{e}$ values as a function of particle radius. Index $N =$ calculation based on Boltzmann's law (Keefe *et al..*, 1959). Index $L =$ calculated by applying Lassen's η_0 values (Lassen and Rau, 1960; Lassen and Weichsel, 1961). Index $J =$ calculated by applying Junge's η_0 values (Junge, 1955 a). The crosses are observed values by Nolan and Kennan (1949).

The only data available to check these calculations are those by Nolan and Kennan (1949). They generated aerosols by heating a platinum wire, and measured their size and the Π values. These values were converted to P values and both are plotted in Fig. 32. It is likely that the platinum particles are not quite spherical and are not homogeneous in size. It is, therefore, hard to judge how representative these data are.

Figure 32 shows that the various theoretical expressions do not differ much within the important size range of the Aitken particles. The P_1 values are more sensitive to changes in r for $r < 2 \times 10^{-2}$ μ and the Π values are more sensitive for $r > 8 \times 10^{-2}$ μ. The calculation of Lassen's expression is based on an assumption for the mass of small ions which is not known and which, on the basis of their size, was estimated to be 30 times the mass of an air molecule (Przibram, 1933). With this in mind, it is difficult to say what curve is in best agreement with the observations. For the larger particles, Keefe's curve is better; but the rapidly rising P values below $r = 10^{-2}$ μ are difficult to reconcile with the observations because they imply that practically no large ions can exist for $r < 10^{-2}$ μ, although their presence down to $r = 4 \times 10^{-3}$ μ has been confirmed by many observers.

For most of the Aitken particles, e is unity; i.e. the charged particles carry only one single elementary charge. At $r = 0.1$ μ, the percentage of doubly charged particles begins to increase markedly.

Around $r = 3 - 5 \times 10^{-2}$ μ, where the peak of the size distribution is normally located, P is about 2. As a rule of thumb, therefore, one can expect one-third of the particles to be positively charged, one-third negatively charged, and one-third neutral. P values of about 2 are indeed very commonly observed. For smaller particles, the fraction of charged particles decreases very rapidly and becomes increasingly uncertain.

P_1, P_2, or Π can easily be measured and data are available from various parts of the world (e.g., Israël, 1941). These values can be converted into mean radius values $\bar{r}$. For fairly homogenous aerosols, the average $\bar{r}$ will be identical with the true mean value $\bar{\bar{r}}$. For broad size distributions, as in the atmosphere, $\bar{r}$ calculated from P_1 can be smaller than $\bar{\bar{r}}$ by a factor of 2. If the peak of the size distribution occurs closer to $r = 0.1$ μ, this factor decreases (Junge, 1955a).

The $\bar{r}$ data obtained from these observations show a pronounced correlation with the total number of Aitken particles N. The absolute values of r will, of course, vary somewhat with the specific curve in Fig. 32 chosen for conversion, but the character of the correlation will not be affected by these uncertainties. Figure 33 shows this relation for a number of stations. Except for Kew, where pollution from London may interfere, N decreases with increasing $\bar{r}$. We also included in Fig. 33 N and r values calculated for the coagulation curves in Fig. 28. The agreement with the observations is good and this provides strong evidence that coagulation is responsible for the observed relation and is a general and important factor in determining the concentration and size distribution of the

Aitken particles. Laboratory measurements of aerosols stored in large containers show the same effect, but more pronounced because of additional diffusion of the smaller particles towards the walls (e.g., Nolan and Galt, 1950). It should be mentioned that the determination of $\bar{r}$ from P values becomes increasingly incorrect for $r > 8 \times 10^{-2}\ \mu$. More recently, Rich *et al.* (1959) used the Π and $\bar{r}$ values to characterize the size distribution of aerosols. For somewhat aged aerosols, the $\bar{r}$ and $\bar{\bar{r}}$ values derived from measurements of Π are in satisfactory agreement.

If we consider the relationship $\eta_{ie} + \eta_{iu} = \eta_0$, the first equation for the ionization balance can be written

$$q = \alpha n^2 + \eta_0 nN = n(\alpha n + \eta_0 N).$$

The quantities α and q do not vary much in the atmosphere, so that parallel determinations of n and N allow the calculation of η_0 and thus, in

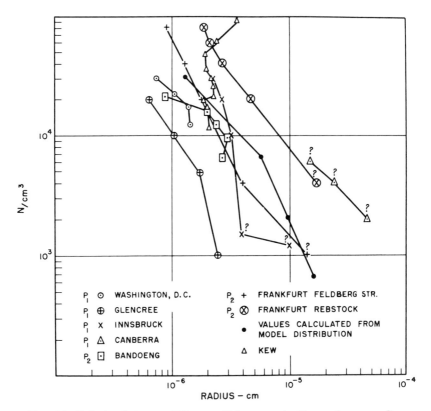

FIG. 33. Relation between Aitken particle concentration and mean radius computed from P_1 and P_2 values (Junge, 1955 a). (By courtesy of the *Journal of Meteorology*.)

turn, a value for $\bar{r}$, which again may not be quite identical with $\bar{\bar{r}}$. From the data available in the literature, we find the same correlation between N and $\bar{r}$ as we found for the P data in Fig. 33 (Junge, 1955 a).

The equation for q shows that when $\eta_0 N' \ll n\alpha$, the influence of aerosol particles on n, and therefore on the conductivity of air and the electrical field, becomes negligible. Usually $n = 300/cm^3$ and $\eta_0 = 1.4 \times 10^{-6}$ cm^3/sec with $\bar{\bar{r}} \approx 3 \times 10^{-2}$ μ. This gives a limiting value N' of

$$N' \leq \frac{n\alpha}{10\eta_0} = \frac{300 \times 1.6 \times 10^{-6}}{1.4 \times 10^{-5}} = 35/cm^3.$$

Since α and n increase with altitude, N^1 will also increase with altitude. If we apply this estimate to stratospheric aerosols (see Section 2.4), we must conclude that no influence on air electrical parameters should be detectable up to 30 km, except for the first 5 km above the tropopause.

Summarizing, we may say that data on large ions indicate that coagulation is an important factor in the dynamics of atmospheric aerosols. Up to the present time, most of the information on the size distribution of the Aitken particles has come from ion spectra. For $r > 0.1$ μ, the electrical mobility is so small that ion measurements become impossible. The charging mechanism of aerosol particles, even under equilibrium conditions, is still not understood properly and the relevant experimental data are inadequate.

2.3 Chemical Composition of Tropospheric Aerosols

2.3.1 Nature and Origin of Aitken Particles

For a long time the study of atmospheric condensation nuclei was almost synonymous with the study of Aitken particles. These particles attracted special attention because of their high concentrations and their pronounced fluctuations with geographical location and weather. Aitken developed the handy condensation nucleus counter to determine their concentration, and numerous observations were made all over the world. The preoccupation with Aitken nuclei was further enhanced by their role in air electricity, which was an active field of research in the first half of this century.

All these studies favored the erroneous concept that natural aerosols are identical with Aitken particles. The importance of the less numerous large and giant particles for atmospheric optics, cloud physics, and finally for air chemistry was almost completely overlooked or at least underestimated. This delayed the proper understanding of the nature and role of atmospheric aerosols.

The numerous observations and investigations of Aitken nuclei concentrations were primarily concerned with the origin and the meteorological and geographical variations of the concentration rather than the chemical composition. Cauer (1949, 1951) attempted to determine the composition by analyzing water condensed on cold surfaces. This method was based on the concept that condensation occurs on Aitken nuclei and that their composition controls that of cloud, fog, or artificially condensed water. Later it became apparent that the composition of atmospheric water is largely determined by the larger particles and the trace gases. The Aitken nuclei are normally not involved in condensation processes, at least over land, and they represent only a small fraction of the total aerosol mass. This fraction is so small and difficult to separate from the larger particles, that no direct analyses of the composition of Aitken nuclei have yet been made.

Several attempts were made to infer the composition of Aitken nuclei by indirect observations. It was, for instance, suggested that the Aitken counter responds only to hygroscopic or water soluble substances, but not to dry dust. However, it could be demonstrated that *all* substances can act as condensation nuclei provided the supersaturation is high enough (as in the counter), the particles are in the proper size range, and the particle concentration is sufficient (e.g., Junge, 1936).

Another approach to the question of their composition was the investigation of possible sources of natural Aitken nuclei. Considerable effort was devoted to these studies which were started by Aitken (e.g., 1923) and continued by others (Forster, 1940). It was found that these particles can be generated by numerous processes which fall into three major categories.

(1) Condensation and sublimation of materials with very low or no vapor pressures, as in all smokes produced by heating and combustion. There are only a few natural sources of this type, e.g., volcanoes and forest fires, but the variety of particles produced by human activities in enormous. The importance of anthropogenic sources is strongly reflected in the geographical distribution of Aitken particles (see Section 2.2.1).

(2) Reactions between trace gases through the action of heat, radiation, or humidity. Examples are the formation of NH_4Cl by reaction of NH_3 and HCl, the oxidation of SO_2 to H_2SO_4, and the formation of particles by short-wave radiation. All these processes are efficient sources of Aitken particles even with gas concentrations as low as a few $\mu g/m^3$. This is best illustrated by the photooxidation process of SO_2. According to Gerhard and Johnstone (1955), SO_2 is oxidized in bright sunlight at a rate of 0.1 to 0.2% per hour, forming H_2SO_4 droplets when traces of water are present. A concentration of 10 $\mu g/m^3$ of SO_2 would yield about 0.03 $\mu g/m^3$

of H_2SO_4 per hour, which corresponds to the following rates of particle production for various assumed particle sizes:

Radius $5 \times 10^{-3} \mu$:	$1 \times 10^5/cm^3$ hour
Radius $1 \times 10^{-2} \mu$:	$1 \times 10^4/cm^3$ hour
Radius $3 \times 10^{-2} \mu$:	$3 \times 10^2/cm^3$ hour.

However, these possible production rates can hardly be observed directly because the formation of aerosols by gas reactions is a rather complex phenomenon. Initially, molecules are formed, but these molecules are likely to grow very rapidly into small clusters by adsorption of other polar molecules, such as water. A similar process is observed in the case of small ions. These clusters or "primary particles" are of the order of 5 to $8 \times 10^{-4} \mu$ and are highly mobile. If no, or not enough, other aerosol particles are present, the concentration of these clusters will increase linearly with time until coagulation among themselves or with other particles becomes important. When this occurs, the rate of increase will diminish and eventually the concentration will reach saturation or go through a maximum, because the rate of attachment of the primary particles to the older and larger ones will increase rapidly as they grow. After this initial period a quasi-steady state is reached with a constant concentration of primary particles controlled by the rate of formation and coagulation and a slow, steady growth of the older particles.

If foreign aerosols are present in sufficient concentrations, steady state is readily established. In this case the original aerosol particles grow and new ones form only if the steady state concentration of primary particles becomes so large that coagulation among themselves starts. These considerations are in qualitative agreement with observations made by Verzár and Evans (1959). If properly exploited, measurements of Aitken particle concentration can be used to determine very small reaction rates of gases (Dunham, 1960).

The process of accretion of these primary particles to natural aerosols is the same as for the attachment of radon decay products (see Section 3.2). The accretion rate as a function of particle size is given by Fig. 54 on the basis of Smoluchowsky's and Lassen's theories of coagulation. For a continental size distribution, the accretion rate has a maximum at or slightly below 0.1 μ radius. Most of the material produced by gas reactions, e.g., by photooxidation of SO_2 should, therefore, be found on particles in this size range.

It is apparent from this discussion that the rate at which *new* aerosol particles are formed by gas reactions is a rather complex function of the concentration of aerosols already present, of the reaction rate, and perhaps of the chemistry of the compounds involved. However, no quantitative information on this subject is available.

(3) Dispersion of material at the earth's surface, either as
sea spray over the oceans or as mineral dust over the continents. In contrast to categories (1) and (2), which preferentially yield particles below
1 μ radius, the mechanical processes in this group usually produce much
coarser particles. Knelman *et al.* (1954) suggested that a large number of
minute droplets were produced by the rupture of the liquid film which forms
the upper surface of bubbles in sea water. Mason (1954) provides evidence
that about 200 particles in the 0.1 μ range are formed per bubble. Twomey
(1960) confirmed this production rate; he thinks that the particles formed
in this way can be as small as 10^{-2} μ and can account for most of the sea-
spray particles found over the ocean.

The production of sea-salt particles produced by the jet
formed in bursting bubbles is probably restricted to the large or even the
giant particles. Blanchard and Woodcock (1957) studied the size spectrum
of bubbles in sea water produced by breaking waves and by falling rain
and snow; they showed that small air bubbles enter into solution easily
because the bubbles rise to the surface very slowly and require a supersaturation of sea water with respect to the atmospheric gases to prevent dissolution. Therefore, one can expect a lower limit of sea-spray particles produced by the jet mechanism, probably somewhere below 1 μ radius, corresponding to bubble sizes of less than 50 μ, but the complexity of the
limiting factors makes it difficult to draw definite conclusions. It is likely
that most sea-spray particles smaller than 1 μ are produced by the rupture
of bubble films.

Nothing is known about the quantity of soil particles smaller
than 0.1 μ released into the air. Under the climatic conditions of the rainy
middle latitudes, this source may be unimportant; but this is not the case
for arid regions since dust particles of this size will have a strong tendency
to form aggregates with larger soil particles unless the relative humidity
is low and disintegration by the mechanical action of wind becomes effective. Another possibility in dry areas is the crystallization at the surface
of salt dissolved in the ground water, either by low humidity or by heating.
Twomey (1960) finds that 10^4-10^5 particles/cm^2 can be produced and that
these particles can be rather small. Particles formed in this way will be water soluble, but the production rate does not seem large enough to explain
high concentrations over land. The fact that excess of K and Ca (with
respect to sea salt) is found even in the ice of central Greenland suggests
the presence in air of a certain number of very small particles which originated somewhere over land and traveled long distances.

This brief discussion makes it obvious that the variety of
processes of Aitken particle formation is considerable and does not allow
us to draw any conclusions as to their average composition. The same is
true for the careful compilation of individual observations of Aitken nuclei

concentrations and their correlation with location, time of day, wind direction, and other geographical or meteorological factors by Landsberg (1938) and by Burckhards and Flohn (1939). All these data definitely point to the ground and to continental area with dense populations and much industry as the major sources of Aitken nuclei.

To a certain extent the Aitken particle concentration can even be used as an index for pollution, although Aitken particles represent only a very small portion of the pollutants. Hower, again all these studies failed to provide information on the average chemical composition of the Aitken nuclei or to specify one or several of the major sources involved.

Despite the development of the electron microscope and of advanced microchemical techniques, this situation has not changed in recent yars. Identification ot particles smaller than 0.1 μ on electron micrographs is even more difficult than identification of larger nes, because of the very low contrast of evaporated solution droples of this size and thickness. Suitable microanalytical techniques are now available, but have not been applied. Therefore, the chemical composition of the Aitken particles and their main sources remain an open question.

Two facts are of some help in this situation. In Central Europe the average growth curves of the Aitken particles are very similar to those of the giant particles, as indicated in Fig. 29. From this we can infer that the ratio of soluble to insoluble material is similar over the whole size range. Further, according to Fig. 28, there is a mass exchange between Aitken and large particles due to coagulation. This suggests that both size ranges will have some constituents in common. These considerations are supported by the observation that a large number of anthropogenic sources of Aitken particles also produce large or even giant particles. For these reasons it can be expected that the Aitken particles are somewhat similar in composition to the large particles, for which there is some information available. This will be discussed in the next sections.

2.3.2 Sea-Salt Aerosols

The oceans are the largest world-wide source of aerosols. Woodcock and his co-workers (Kientzler et al., 1954; Blanchard and Woodcock, 1957) demonstrated convincingly that the vast majority of the sea-salt particles larger than 1 μ are produced by the bursting of the numerous small air bubbles produced by breaking waves. Figure 34 shows schematically how the bursting of a bubble creates a small jet which breaks up into approximately 2-10 droplets of nearly the same size and ejects them into the air to altitudes up to 15 cm, depending on the bubble size. The droplet size is about one-tenth the size of the bubble, so that the particle size distributions is largely determined by the production rate and the size distribution of the bubbles.

A few large droplets are also produced by the foam of the „white caps" when it is carried away by the wind, but they are too large to remain airborne for long. These large particles may be partly responsible for the high sea-salt concentrations of 50 to 1000 $\mu g/m^3$ observed in the immediate vicinity of the coast (Neumann, 1940). This coastal concentration drops rapidly within a few kilometers farther inland.

Seawater droplets will evaporate in air because of the low salt concentration in sea water. Depending on the relative humidity of the air, the droplets will shrink by a factor of 2 to 3 before they are in equilibrium with air. Blanchard and Woodcock (1957) suggest that the lower size

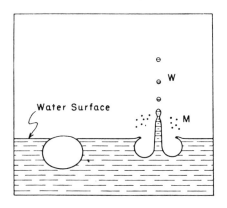

FIG. 34. The formation of sea-salt particles from the bursting of bubbles. The large droplets W originate upon disintegration of the jet and have been studied by Woodcock and his associates (Kientzler *et al.* 1954). More numerous and smaller particles M can form from the bursting of the bubble film (Mason, 1954).

limit of the bursting bubbles is determined by the dissolution of bubbles in sea water. The air in sea water must be slightly supersaturated for small bubbles to exist, otherwise they will dissolve in a breaking wave when they rise slowly to the surface after formation. The smallest bubbles observed to reach the ocean surface in "white caps" were about 100 μ in diameter, corresponding to dry salt particles of about 2 μ radius. Much smaller bubbles with a mean diameter of 40 μ were observed only when snow flakes melted in sea water. Under normal conditions the lower size limit of bubbles is thus not small enough to explain the observed lower size limit of sea-salt particles of about 0.1 μ radius (Metnieks, 1958).

Very likely these smaller particles are formed by another process. Mason (1954) observed that each bursting bubble produces 100-

200 small particles, which he counted in an expansion chamber. The largest particles had a dry radius of 0.15 μ. He suggested that these particles are formed by the rupture of the bubble film, as indicated in Fig. 34, and found that this mechanism is limited to the larger bubbles. Twomey (1960) confirmed this process.

The bubble concentration in "white caps" decreases rapidly with increasing bubble size. The largest bubbles observed by Blanchard and Woodcock were about 1500 μ in diameter, which would form dry salt particles of about 25 μ radius. It is likely that larger bubbles occur, but have escaped observation, so that under normal wind conditions the upper production limit is slightly larger than the sedimentation limit of 10 to 20 μ.

It is very difficult to obtain values for the large-scale production rate of sea-salt particles from these studies. Eriksson (1959) calculates the average deposition rate of sea-salt over the ocean from Woodcock's observations of the size distribution and concentration of particles in air; he concludes that under steady state conditions, 0.3% of the sea surface must be covered with "white-caps." This would correspond to an average production rate of about 1 particle/cm² sec, a figure which gives only the order of magnitude. The information available on production, sedimentation, and washout is not yet sufficient to estimate the average residence time of sea-spray aerosols over the ocean, but 1 to 3 days seems to be a reasonable value.

The size distribution of sea-salt particles over the ocean has already been discussed in Section 2.2.1 on the basis of Figs. 25 and 26. Data for different wind forces and various heights above the ocean have been obtained by Woodcock (e.g., 1953), Moore and Mason (1954), Fournier d'Albe (1955), and Lodge (1955). All these researchers were interested primarily in the giant particles which are considered to be important for the initiation of rain. Particles smaller than 1 μ radius were either not collected or not counted. In a more recent study on the west coast of Ireland, Metnieks (1958) evaluated particles down to 0.1 μ.

Except for the studies of Lodge and Metnieks, who employed microchemical techniques for chloride determination, all the hygroscopic particles were counted under the assumption that they consisted of sea salt. The circumstances of the collection of the particles as well as the physical behavior, justify this assumption. The particles were collected by impactors on glass slides exposed against the wind or from an aircraft. For microchemical determination of chloride, the particles are collected on a gelatine substrate treated by a sensitive reagent; the resulting reaction spots can be calibrated. It can be seen from Fig. 24 that the agreement between data from trade-wind areas (Woodcock) and from the North Atlantic (Moore and Mason) is fairly good. The same is true of a comparison of Woodcock's observations in Florida, the Gulf of Mexico, Hawaii, and Australia. Figure 25 shows examples of distributions which he obtained at a height of about 600 meters. It can be seen that the concentration increases with the wind force and that this increase is most pronounced for the larger particles. This shifts the peak in the log radius-mass distribution from about 2 to 10 μ radius, without changing the character of the distribution. The concentrations found by Metnieks seem to be somewhat smaller (Fig. 25). He also made measurements in Dublin, where he found generally higher concentrations (Table 31) and a steeper slope of the distribution curves ($\beta = 2.9$) than on the west coast of Ireland. This is an interesting observation since Rau (1955) in Germany also found rather high concentrations for the smallest chloride particles. This increase of small chloride particles can be due either to production over land or to disintegration of the larger sea-spray particles.

It was reported that microscopic salt droplets shatter when they crystallize in air of low humidity (e.g., Dessens, 1946). However, a quantitative check on this process did not reveal any measurable effect of the number concentration of sea salt particles (Lodge and Baer, 1954). Twomey and McMaster (1955) claim that sea-salt droplets, instead of breaking up into a few larger pieces when dried, produce numerous very small particles, which they detected with a nucleus counter. In their experiments, they attached the salt particles to spider webs within the expansion chamber. Unpublished investigations by the author did not substantiate any formation of Aitken particles when sea-salt droplets were freely suspended in air and subjected to large humidity changes. From these observations, it seems unlikely that sea-salt particles can disintegrate in any form and it is thus probable that the increase of small chloride particles over land is due to other sources.

Podzimek (1959) and Podzimek and Cernoch (1961) measured vertical profiles of chloride particles larger than 1 μ over Czechoslovakia and found higher concentrations below 2 km, particularly during winter and anticyclonic conditions. This seems to point to continental and most likely industrial sources of giant particles. It is supported by data on rain water composition (see Section 4.3.2) and indicates that chloride particles, at least over Central Europe cannot be used as a sure indication of the maritime origin of air masses.

The long-debated question of the role of sea-salt particles as atmospheric condensation nuclei has now been settled. The total number of sea-salt particles is far too small to be of any importance for the formation of cloud droplets. This is clearly shown by Table 31, which gives the total concentrations determined by various observers. Particles larger than 1 μ radius rarely go beyond 1/cm³ and the concentration of all chloride particles larger than 0.1 μ is of the order of 1 to 10/cm³. On the other hand, the lowest concentration of Aitken nuclei observed, e.g., by Moore (1952)

TABLE 31

DATA ON THE TOTAL CONCENTRATION OF SEA-SALT PARTICLES

Observer	Remarks		Total number (concentration/cm³)
Woodcock	All particles larger than 1.5 μ radius at 80% humidity for various wind speeds over subtropical oceans	Beaufort: 1	0.05
		3	0.15
		5	0.30
		7	0.36
		12	20
Moore	All particles larger than 2 μ radius at 80% humidity over the Atlantic Ocean	Wind: 10 meters/sec	0.3
		15 meters/sec	0.8
Metnieks	All particles larger than ~0.1 μ radius; range of concentration on the west coast of Ireland (C) and in Dublin (D)	C	0.017–4.5
		D	0.13–23
Rau	All particles larger than 0.25 radius at 80% humidity; 9-month observation in Central Europe	Maximum concentration	18
		96% of all observations	<1
Moore	Lowest Aitken particle concentration during 3 weeks over the Atlantic Ocean		77

during his investigations, was 77/cm³. He also found no relationship between the Aitken nuclei and the wind velocity or wave height over the
Atlantic Ocean, quite in contrast to the case of the giant particles. Despite
their low numbers, the sea-salt particles may be important for the formation
of a few large droplets in clouds and thus for the initiation of rain.

These conclusions about the total number of sea-salt particles are also supported by the relation of visibility to relative humidity
in maritime air, as reported by Wright (1940). As we pointed out in Section
2.2.4, the observation that the visibility does not change very much below
70% relative humidity is quite incompatible with the fact that sea-salt
nuclei comprise a considerable portion of the large nuclei. The majority of
these particles must either be rapidly modified (e.g., SO_2 oxidation) or
be of other origin. Most likely they represent aged and modified continental
aerosols.

Figures 24 and 25 suggest a close relationship between the
total content of sea salt in air and the wind velocity. Woodcock (1953)
showed that all his values fall between the two dashed lines in Fig. 35.
His observations were usually made slightly below the base of the clouds,
at about 600 meters, in the trade-wind regions of Florida and Hawaii.
We have supplemented his data with values of Fournier d'Albe, Moore,

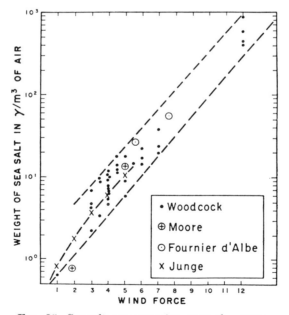

FIG. 35. Sea-salt concentration over the ocean
(Woodcock, 1953; Moore, 1952) or at the coast
(Fournier d'Albe, cited in Moore, 1952; Junge,
1954) as a function of the wind force ($\gamma = \mu$g).

and Junge (1954) obtained at sea level. The agreement is good, considering the different conditions under which these observations were made. This relationship seems to be generally valid and is of some importance for estimates of the sea-salt budget. It shlould be mentioned, however, that deviations occur, but they seem to be the exceptions to the rule.

The relation in Fig. 35 suggests steady state conditions for the concentration of sea salt for a given wind velocity. Production at the sea surface must be balanced by sedimentation and washout. In the trade-wind areas the production and sedimentation rate are rather uniform over wide areas, but washout occurs only in isolated cloud systems and irregularly. The vertical sea-salt profiles over the ocean generally show a decrease of concentration with altitude that is rather independent of particle size. This indicates a flux of particles upward, as is to be expected, and also a removal process which is independent of size. It must be concluded, therefore, that removal by precipitation rather than sedimentation is the dominant process even over subtropical oceans. However, any estimates of the sea-salt budget remain highly speculative as long as two of the three processes which determine this budget, namely, production and removal by precipitation, are not known.

Normally, the observations show a decrease in particle concentration with altitude, which becomes more pronounced for higher wind speeds. However, there is a tendency for a maximum at the cloud base, at about 500 meters, in Woodcock's (1957) data from Hawaii and also from other areas, whenever the total sea-salt concentration is rather high for a given wind velocity. High concentrations for a given wind speed point to advection of sea salt from areas with higher winds, viz., higher production rates. Since the wind speed increases with altitude up to the cloud layer, these maxima can be explained by a preferential advection.

Woodcock found a rapid decrease of particle concentration within and above the cloud layer, as indicated in Fig. 36. This is to be expected under the meteorological conditions of the semi-steady trade-wind inversion at about 1 km altitude with slow subsidence aloft. The particle distribution must represent a steady state between vertical transport and subsidence, and perhaps some removal by clouds.

Observations show that sea-salt particles can penetrate far into the interior of the continents. On a flight over the U.S.A. at a height of 3000 meters, Crozier et $al.$ (1952) collected chloride particles larger than 10^{-13} g, which is equivalent to 0.5 μ radius at 80% relative humidity. They identified the particles by a microchemical technique. The highest concentration of 0.46/cm^3 was encountered in an air mass of marine origin. Twomey (1955) counted hygroscopic salt particles (probably sea salt) larger than 10^{-10} g (4 μ at 80% relative humidity) at altitudes of 700 to 2700 meters, on a 600-mile flight over the southeastern corner of Australia. He found little correlation between the particle concentration and the water vapor mixing ratio, considering this as an indicator of the maritime origin of the air, or with the length of the air mass trajectory over land. However, his data show that convection over land rapidly transforms the vertical profile into a rather uniform vertical distribution of salt particles.

This is demonstrated even better by the study of Byers *et al.* (1955) in the Central U.S.A. The particles were identified and measured by a microchemical method. Samples were collected on several flights from Illinois southward to the Gulf of Mexico. Figure 36 presents a summary

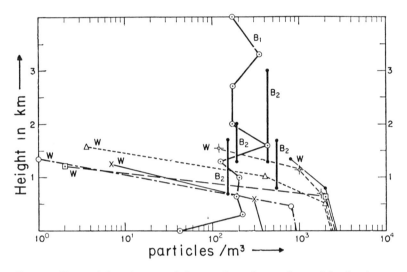

Fig. 36. Vertical distribution of the number of sea-salt particles having a dry radius $\geq 3\ \mu$ (equivalent to a radius of $7\ \mu$ at 80% relative humidity and a mass of 5×10^{-10} g). The curves marked W are measured by Woodcock (1953) in regions of the trade winds; the portion of the curve between the ocean surface and the measured values around 0.5 km is assumed. The values show the rapid decrease at the level of the trade-wind inversion. The curves marked B are given by Byers *et al.* (1955). Curve B_1 is an average of three soundings made in Illinois. Curves B_2 are average concentrations for four overland flights southward from Chicago. The length of the bar indicates the altitude range during each flight.

of the results for particles larger than $3\ \mu$. It can be seen that the profiles over land and those over the subtropical ocean are basically different, due to convection over the continent and perhaps also to some removal by washout in the lower layers. The particle concentration over land is fairly constant with altitude. The sharp drop in the lowest 200 meters is perhaps caused by fallout and impaction of particles on obstacles at the earth's surface. It shows that the earth's surface acts as a sink for aerosols, at least for giant particles, and that surface measurements must be interpreted with caution.

It is interesting to compare the total number of sea-salt particles above 1 m² over land and ocean on the basis of Fig. 36. If we assume a uniform mixing over land throughout three-fourths of the troposphere, Byers' data give 2.3×10^6 particles/m² and Woodwock's data 1.8×10^6/m². The approximate agreement of the two figures indicates that the loss of sea salt due to washout is small, even in air masses which have traveled at least 1000 miles over land. Eriksson (1959) calculated the vertical mass distribution of sea salt for Woodcock's and Byers' data and obtained the following values for the total sea-salt content in a vertical column of air: Woodcock: Hawaii, 11.2 mg/m²; Caribbean, 7.2 mg/m²; Florida, 6.8 mg/m³; Byers: Central U.S.A., $\sim 5^*$ mg/m³. This comparison of total chloride over sea and land may be influenced by industrial contamination as mentioned previously. However, this influence cannot be very large in view of the general tendency toward increasing Cl concentration with altitude in Byers' data.

When speaking of sea salt, thus far we have assumed that the sea-spray particles have the same composition as sea water (Table 32).

TABLE 32

AVERAGE COMPOSITION OF SEA WATER FOR THE MAIN CONSTITUENTS

Constituent	Concentration (mg/kg)	Constituent	Concentration (mg/kg)
Cl	18.980	K	380
Na	10.561	C [a]	28
S	0.890	CO_3	140
SO_4	2.650	Br	65
Mg	1.272	Sr	13
Ca	400	B	4

[a] Inorganic carbon.

A first change in composition may occur during the process of formation. We do not know of any data on the composition of particles freshly generated by bubbles. It is conceivable, though not very likely, that the bubble film or the top of the jet in the bursting bubble shows some fractionation. For the time being, however, we have to assume that newly formed sea-spray particles have the same composition as sea water.

---

* Assuming uniform mixing to 7 km.

Sugawara *et al.* (1949) suggested that the change in the composition of rain water as opposed to sea water, e.g., the increase of the ratios SO_4/Cl and Ca/Cl with the distance from the coast, is due to disintegration of particles in dry air as a consequence of crystallization. We have already mentioned that it is very doubtful whether this process is of any importance. The small quantities of very hygroscopic salts (e.g., $Mg\,SO_2$) in sea water tend to form a thin film of concentrated solution around the particle after most of the salts, e.g., NaCl, have crystallized. This film makes disintegration practically impossible and observations of the phase transition of salt droplets under the microscope confirm this conclusion. However, rain water analyses in coastal areas or on islands always show a tendency toward a lower Cl/Na ratio than that of sea water which is 1.80. Oddie (1959) found monthly averages of 1.17 to 1.69 in Lerwick on the Shetland Islands. The Mg/Na and K/Na ratios, on the other hand, were close to that of sea water. As we shall see later in Chapter 4, the Cl/Na ratio decreases still more in coastal areas or farther inland over continents, but at the same time the ratios Mg/Na, K/Na, and Ca/Na increase rapidly. These observations clearly point to two different processes. The decrease of the Cl/Na ratio in Lerwick or similar sites must be due to a release of Cl, without changing the cation composition. The change in the cation ratios farther inland, on the other hand, must be due to additional aerosols, that contain proportionally higher amounts of Mg, K, and Ca than Na. This latter process may not affect the individual sea-salt particles, but the process of Cl release will do so.

Recently, Eriksson (1959) discussed the possible reactions with gases. The reaction with O_3, first suggested by Cauer, results in the release of Cl_2, but under atmospheric conditions its rate is much too small. A more promising reaction is the release of HCl when SO_3 or H_2SO_4 is added to the particles. Eriksson assumes a pH of the salt particle of 1 which corresponds to a pH of rainwater of 4,5, a common value. For a pH of about 1, the partial pressure of HCl over this droplet is comparable to observed concentrations of gaseous chlorine of 1 $\mu g/m^3$. It should be mentioned, though, that we do not know the composition or this gaseous Cl component. The SO_3 added to the aerosol particles can be supplied in sufficient quantity by the photooxidation of SO_2 (Gerhard and Johnstone, 1955). The accretion of primary SO_3 or H_2SO_4 particles as a function of particle size would proceed according to Fig. 54 and it becomes clear that the smaller particles receive a higher proportion of H_2SO_4 than the larger ones receive. This is in agreement with observations of the aerosol composition in coastal areas (Junge, 1956) where the S/Cl ratio was higher than it was in sea water and where this ratio decreased with increasing particle size. The excess of sulfur is a well-established fact also in rain water, even in very remote places. However, there are two difficulties involved in this explanation. The assumption of a particle pH of 1 is most unlikely in the presence, even over the ocean, of NH_3 (Tables 23 and 24), which would be readily absorbed. It is more likely that the pH of the rainwater is assumed during the condensation process of water and does not reflect the original pH value of the nucleus. The second difficulty is the concentration of the gaseous Cl component. This concentration is of the same order as the concentration of aerosols over sea (Table 25), which would imply considerable losses of HCl (if it is HCl) unless it is assumed that the residence time of HCl is much longer than that of the aerosol. The geographical distribution of the gaseous Cl component also suggests more efficient sources over land than over sea (Fig. 18). If the suggested mechanism of Cl release is valid, one would expect that chloride is replaced on an equivalent basis by sulfur. Eriksson checked this for rains in coastal areas in Northern Europe where interference by pollution is excluded. He found some correlation, but the deviations from the expected relation were considerable.

If sea-spray droplets are exposed to SO_2, oxidation will also occur *in* the solution as long as the pH value of the droplet does not decrease too much (Junge and Ryan, 1958). Thus, oxidation can proceed in the presence of sufficient NH_3 and will be enhanced at high relative humidities or in cloud droplets. However, again, this process does not provide a pH value sufficiently low to account for the observed gaseous chlorine component.

An interesting reaction is the formation of nitrate in sea-salt particles when they are exposed to NO_2. Junge (1956) found the highest nitrate content in coastal areas of the northeastern part of the U.S. in the size range of the giant particles, which also contain most of the chloride (see also the next section). The nitrate content in air masses of continental origin drops by a factor of 10 and a similar large decrease is observed in such purely maritime places as Hawaii (see Figs. 41 and 42). It became apparent from these field studies that the production of aerosol nitrate depended on the presence of both sea-spray particles *and* NO_2, the latter having higher concentrations in certain coastal areas due to pollution. In coastal areas near Boston, the ratio of NO_3/Cl in giant particles was about 0.5, i.e., quite considerable. No nitrite was found.

On the basis of these results, Robbins *et al.* (1959) studied this reaction in the laboratory. In the presence of H_2O, NaCl reacts with NO_2 at room temperature, forming nitrosyl chloride, which is very easily hydrolyzed or photolyzed:

$$NaCl + 2NO_2 \rightarrow NaNO_3 + NOCl$$

$$NOCl + H_2O \rightarrow HCl + HNO_2$$

$$NOCl + h\nu \rightarrow NO + Cl.$$

This reaction is slow but rather complete. In contrast to this bulk reaction, the reaction of NaCl aerosols in NO_2 concentrations of the order of several thousand $\mu g/m^3$ is rather fast but incomplete. In less than 10 minutes, a fixed fraction of chloride is converted, and this fraction increases with relative humidity. This chloride fraction is approximately independent of the actual concentrations, as long as the ratio of NaCl to NO_2 concentration remains the same. No nitrite was found.

Robbins et al. (1959) suggest that NO_2 forms HNO_3 by hydrolysis, which in turn is adsorbed by the dry NaCl particles or dissolved in the solution droplets. This results in the release of HCl with the process being more efficient in more dilute droplets.

These laboratory studies explain the field data very well. They show that in populated and industrialized coastal areas, considerable quantities of Cl can be relased from sea-salt particles. However, the amounts of nitrate formed in this way are negligible in coastal areas with unpolluted atmospheres. Thus, the formation of nitrate can scarcely explain the discrepancies in the chloride deficiencies and the sulfur excess mentioned above in connection with the release of HCl from sea-salt particles.

Summarizing, we can say that the observations show a release of Cl from sea-salt particles, but that the mechanism of this process is not quite clear. There is no indication of changes in the ionic composition of individual sea-salt particles other than the release of Cl. It should be kept in mind, however, that combination of sea-salt particles with other aerosol particles in rain drops may lead to a variety of reactions, depending on the chemical composition of these other particles.

2.3.3 Continental Aerosols

We have already noted that the Aitken nuclei are predominantly of continental origin. This section will deal with the continental aerosol component with radius larger than 0.1 μ.

In Section 2.2.3 we showed that for continental air, under normal conditions, the giant and most of the large particles are used as active condensation nuclei. However, this does not imply that the chemical composition of cloud and rain water over land is identical or almost identical with the average composition of the particles larger than 0.1 μ. Unfortunately, other processes interfere and the numerous rain water samples cannot serve as a convenient source of information with respect to our subject. During the water condensation process, trace gases such as SO_2, NH_3, and NO_2 will react and increase the amount of soluble components in cloud water to an unknown degree. On the other hand, giant particles will be intercepted by falling raindrops and this will further modify the composition of rain water in a rather uncontrolled way, although this latter process does not modify the *relative* composition with respect to aerosols unless the giant particles below the cloud are different from the large and giant particles within the cloud. These and other, perhaps less efficient, processes, to be discussed in more detail in Chapter 4, will tend to increase primarily the relative concentration of the soluble rain water components derived from gases, such ar $SO_4^=$, NH_4^+, NO_3^-, and perhaps Cl^-. The relative composition of ions such as Na^+, K^+, Ca^{++}, Mg^{++}, etc., or the amount of insoluble materials is expected to be approximately representative for aerosols. Unfortunately, the data on the concentration of insoluble material in rain water are not reliable since particulate matter has a tendency to separate from the rain samples and since microanalytical techniques for insoluble materials are less suited to routine work. Therefore, in the present discussion of the composition of continental aerosols, we will limit our use of rain water analyses to the nonvolatile cations only.

In Section 2.2.3 we pointed out that most particles over the continent consist of a mixture of soluble and insoluble substances. Undoubtedly the mixing ratio varies considerably. The growth curves with humidity indicated about 70 to 80% insoluble materials for Central Europe. This high percentage of insoluble material in continental aerosols becomes evident if impactor samples are treated with a droplet of water to dissolve the soluble material. Unfortunately, in our aerosol studies no micromethods were available to determine the total amount of these insoluble residues or their composition, so that the above estimates seem to be the only data available on this subject.

Several researchers, primarily in Japan, applied the electron microscope to studies of the origin and composition of aerosols and condensation nuclei. To obtain information on their composition, Kuroiwa (1953, 1956) observed the residue of cloud droplets and their structural changes resulting from repeated exposures to high and low humidities. He was able to classify the particles into three broad groups: sea salt, combustion products, and soil material. In sea fog and in clouds in northern Japan, combustion products were most abundant, followed by sea-salt and soil particles. In fog, most combustion and soil particles were smaller than 1 μ, but most sea-salt particles were between 1 and 2 μ radius. He concludes that the composition of the population of actual condensation nuclei is controlled by the abundance of the various particles in the aerosol rather than by selective activation due to solubility ("hygroscopicity") or chemical composition. This is certainly true until one deals with particles of unwettable substances.

The inferences drawn from the appearance of particles in the electron microscope are always ambiguous, unless supplemented by other techniques. Yamamoto and Ohtake (1955) observed the behavior of particle evaporation with increasing electron beam intensity. Isono (1955) made electron diffraction diagrams of individual aerosol particles. Their results are similar to those of Kuroiwa. All these investigations were made for particles found in cloud or fog droplets, i.e., true condensation nuclei. Jacobi and Lippert (1953) collected the particles directly with an impactor in Central Europe at 800 meters above sea level. They determined the presence of ammonium sulfate by electron diffraction. Most of the particles had the appearance of droplets with more or less insoluble material imbedded in them (Fig. 30).

These methods and results are useful for identifying the *approximate* character of the particle. Electron diffraction can only indicate the presence of such components which are crystallized, and can provide no information on their relative amounts. Junge (1953, 1954, 1956) tried more direct microanalytical techniques. Using a cascade impactor, he separated two particle size ranges with radii of 0.08 to 0.8 μ and 0.8 to 8 μ, which represent approximately the large and giant particles, respectively. According to Fig. 24, the total mass for both size ranges should be about equal. The aerosol samples were precipitated on plexiglass plates, dissolved with a drop of distilled water, and then analyzed for NH_4^+, Na^+, Mg^{++}, SO_4^{--}, Cl^-, NO_3^-, and NO_2^- by microtechniques, primarily color reactions. The selection of these ions was partly determined by the sensitivity of available methods for handling absolute amounts as low as a few tenths of a microgram with a reasonable accuracy of $\pm 20\%$.

The first measurements were carried out in densely populated areas of West Germany (Frankfurt and vicinity). They confirmed the presence of ammonium and sulfate. For the large particles, NH_4^+ and $SO_4^=$ apparently were essential constituents of the soluble material. The concentration ratio was approximately that of $(NH_4)_2SO_4$. The giant particles, on the other hand, showed only small amounts of NH_4^+, and it must be assumed that a considerable fraction of the $SO_4^=$ was bound by other cations. No NO_2^- was found, and analyses for NO_3^- were not made at this site.

Chloride was found to be present in both size ranges. With advection of fresh maritime air in Central Europe, the Cl^- concentration *increased* for the giant particles and *decreased* for the large particles. This suggests that giant sea-spray particles can penetrate far inland and that Cl^- particles smaller than 0.8 μ are formed over land and accumulate in stagnant continental air masses.

These findings have been confirmed by measurements on the east coast of the U.S.A., some 50 miles south of Boston (Round Hill). This coastal area is rural, in contrast to the site in Central Europe, although the air in this area is still influenced to some degree by the concentration of big cities and industrial activities in that part of the country.

Figures 37 and 38 give the daily values of the analyses. It is seen that NH_4^+ and $SO_4^=$ again predominate in the large nuclei and show about the same mass ratio as in Frankfurt. In Fig. 39 the NH_4^+ values are plotted against the $SO_4^=$ values. The correlation is fairly good and the average ratio corresponds to a mixture of $(NH_4)_2SO_4$ and $(NH_4)HSO_4$. The Cl^- and Na^+ ions were found almost exclusively in the giant nuclei even

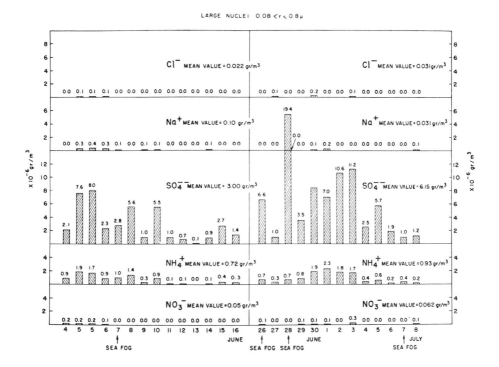

FIG. 37. The daily variation in the chemical composition of large particles at Round Hill. The "mean values" are erroneously given in "gr/m^3" instead of $\mu g/m^3$. (By courtesy of the *Journal of Meteorology*.)

when the wind came directly from the ocean, which was not more than 100 meters away. Only in a few cases did the large nuclei contain Cl^- and Na^+ in amounts above the detection limit. Again, no NO_2^- was found, but the results of the NO_3^- analyses were surprising. As in the case of Cl^-, NO_3^- was found only in the giant particles, and a relationship between Cl^- and NO_3^- was indicated.

Basically all these findings were confirmed in the southeastern trade winds, south of Miami, Florida, and also on the east coast of the Island of Hawaii in onshore trade winds. The data obtained in Florida, together with the concentrations of trace gases, were plotted in Fig. 40. With the exception of sea salt, all aerosol concentrations are lower than at the previous places. The Cl⁻ and Na⁺ analyses agree with Woodcock's data.

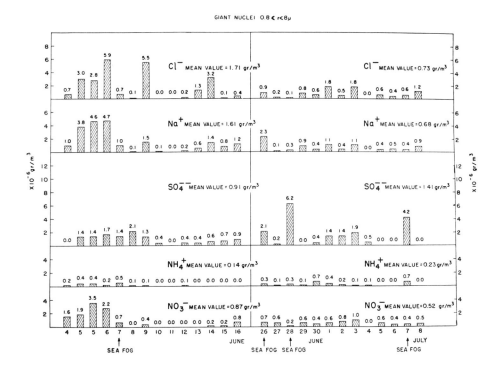

FIG. 38. The same as Fig. 37, but for giant particles. (By courtesy of the *Journal of Meteorology.*)

All results for large and giant particles are summarized in Figs. 41 and 42. The sampling sites are arranged in the order of increasing maritime influence and the mean values are plotted for each site. For the maritime areas, the average detection limit is added and the difference is indicated by hatching. For large nuclei, an NH_4^+ value is included which was obtained above the trade-wind inversion at Mauna Kea, Hawaii, at an altitude of 3200 meters.

Figure 41 shows a decrease of all values with increasing maritime influence. The correlation between $SO_4^=$ and NH_4^+ is very pronounced as far as Florida. Beyond Florida, the method employed for $SO_4^=$ was not

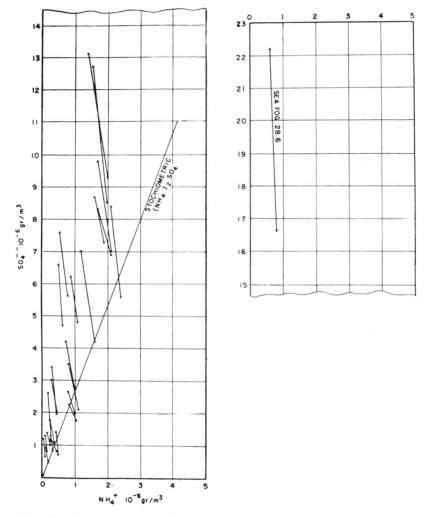

FIG. 39. Relation between $SO_4^=$ and NH_4^+ content for large particles at Round Hill. Each set of values is represented by a line indicating the limits of accuracy. The line corresponds to $(NH_4)_2SO_4$. (By courtesy of the *Journal of Meteorology.*)

sensitive enough. The line "*b-b*" represents the SO_4 content calculated for the observed NH_4^+ concentrations, assuming the stoichiometric ratio for $(NH_4)_2SO_4$. As we see, the actual $SO_4^=$ values are a little higher, indi-

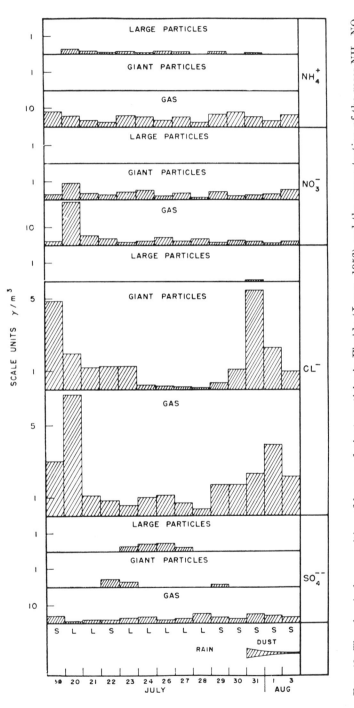

Fig. 40. The chemical composition of large and giant particles in Florida (Junge, 1956) and the concentration of the gases NH₃, NO₂, Cl₂, (?) and SO₂, measured simultaneously and plotted as NH₄, NO₃, Cl, and SO₄ for better comparison. *S* and *L* indicate sea and land breeze, respectively. Note the different scales for gases and aerosols. (By courtesy of *Tellus*.)

cating perhaps some $(NH_4)HSO_4$. Very likely a corresponding amount of $SO_4^=$ can be expected for the Mauna Kea NH_4^+ value.

Chloride decreases as far as Florida and then starts to rise. The line "a-a" corresponds to 1.5% of the Cl^- content of the giant nuclei of Fig. 42 and suggests the presence of the maritime component in this

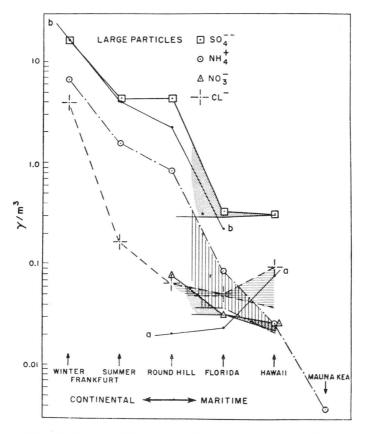

FIG. 41. Survey of the average chemical composition of large particles. The various sites are arranged with respect to their continental and maritime character. The shaded areas indicate the difference between the actual values and the corresponding limits of detection. Lines "a-a" and "b-b" are explained in the text. (By courtesy of *Tellus*.)

size range. This value of 1.5% was used in Fig. 24 to extrapolate the mass distribution. The difference between the actual Cl^- values and the line "a-a" indicates the continental Cl^- component in the large-particle size range. This continental Cl^- component of the large particles is quite substantial and is no doubt identical with the higher Cl^- particle concentrations observed by Metnieks and Rau in Dublin and in Central Europe, as discussed in the previous section. The nitrate content of the large particles is small and there are no data available for Frankfurt.

The giant particles in Fig. 42 present a similar picture with respect to NH_4^+ and $SO_4^=$, except that the SO_4 excess compared to $(NH_4)_2SO_4$ is large. The SO_4 content in Hawaii is due to sea salt. This is shown by the line "a-a", which is computed for sea-water composition on the basis of

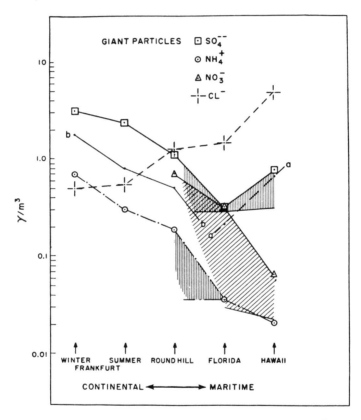

FIG. 42. The same as Fig. 41, but for giant particles. (By courtesy of *Tellus*.)

the observed Cl^- values. The maritime origin of Cl^- is clearly indicated by its considerable increase with maritime influence. Nitrate decreases and is apparently not of maritime origin.

Summarizing, we can state that the sea-spray component can clearly be distinguished from that of continental origin, and that the influence of the latter can be traced to the center of large oceans. This corresponds to the penetration of sea salt into the interior of the continents and is in agreement with aerosol lifetimes of one to several weeks. It should be mentioned that on Mauna Kea, above the trade-wind inversion, NH_4^+ was detected in the aerosols, but no Cl^- was found for similar limits of detection. This shows that both the geographical origin and the meteorological history of air masses are important for the chemistry of aerosols.

In Section 2.3.2 we briefly discussed the main features of the occurrence of nitrate in the giant particles and explained it by a reaction of sea-spray particles with NO_2. Figure 42 indicates a decrease of the NO_3^- concentration in maritime air. However, additional measurements in the vicinity of Boston, U.S.A., showed that the NO_3 content also decreased to the level of that of Hawaii for air masses from the interior of the continent. With the influx of marine air, on the other hand, the NO_3^- concentrations become comparable to the values from Round Hill. Parallel measurements of the NO_3^- content in the center of Boston and in the suburban area, on the other hand, indicated that the urban atmosphere was not an important NO_3^- source *per se*. These findings agree with the results of the U.S. Public Health network (Chambers *et al.*, 1955) which showed the highest values on the west coast in San Francisco (3.4 $\mu g/m^3$) and Los Angeles (14.4 $\mu g/m^3$). All these observations suggest that NO_3^- occurs whenever maritime air comes in contact with higher NO_2 concentrations in continental or polluted air and that it is formed by a reaction of NO_2 in sea-salt particles.

The U.S. Public Health Service (Chambers *et al.*, 1955) made a comprehensive study of the composition of aerosols in nonurban and polluted atmospheres. In 30 cities and nonurban areas, aerosol particles larger than 0.3 μ were collected on glass filters for a period of over 1 year and were analyzed for a considerable number of substances, mostly metals. The components were selected with regard to their importance for air hygiene.

Tables 33 and 34 give the average values for medium-sized cities and nonurban areas. These nonurban areas are mostly suburbs and may not be quite representative of the background in unpolluted air.

The only water-soluble substances analyzed in this study, and the only ones in common with the previous investigation, are $SO_4^=$ and NO_3^-. The data show that these watersoluble components represent less than 1% or, at the most, a few per cent of the total aerosol mass. This is less than our previous estimate of 20 to 30%; but the data do not include Cl^-, and it may be that other water-soluble components are included in the fraction not further analyzed.

The tables show that cities are efficient sources of $SO_4^=$ and to some extent also of NO_3^-. The high NO_3^- concentration of 3.4 $\mu g/m^3$ in San Francisco was explained earlier. The $SO_4^=$ figures are a little lower than

TABLE 33

PARTICULATE ANALYSES IN $\mu g/m^3$ FROM CITIES HAVING POPULATIONS BETWEEN 500,000 AND 2,000,000 [a]

	Cincinnati	Kansas City	Portland (Oregon)	Atlanta	Houston	San Francisco	Minneapolis
Total load	176	146	143	137	129	104	120
Acetone soluble	31.4	18.4	32.1	24.2	18.5	19.4	15.8
Fe	4.5	4.1	5.1	3.3	4.0	2.4	4.4
Pb	1.6	1.0	1.2	1.8	1.0	2.4	0.5
F$^-$	0.21	0.01	Nil	0.05	Nil	0.37	0.06
Mn	0.24	0.08	0.23	0.12	0.23	0.11	0.08
Cu	0.18	0.04	0.05	0.01	0.02	0.07	0.60
V	0.09	0.002	0.009	0.024	0.001	0.002	0.002
Ti	0.06	0.21	0.24	0.12	0.29	0.04	0.11
Sn	0.03	0.03	0.01	0.03	0.02	0.02	0.01
As	0.02	0.02	0.02	<0.01	0.01	0.01	0.01
Be	0.0002	0.0003	0.0003	0.0002	0.0002	0.0001	0.0002
$So_4^=$	5.6	1.5	0.8	1.0	2.4	1.8	0.8
NO_3^-	1.0	0.6	0.2	0.8	1.0	3.4	1.3

[a] Chambers et al. (1955).

TABLE 34

PARTICULATE ANALYSES IN $\mu g/m^3$ FROM NONURBAN AREAS [a]

	Boonsboro	Salt Lake City	Atlanta	Cincinnati	Portland (Oregon)
Total load	68	55	71	45	86
Acetone soluble	8.7	6.2	9.3	9.0	12.6
Fe	3.7	4.1	2.7	2.4	3.6
Pb	0.1	0.1	0.9	0.4	0.3
F^-	—	—	Nil	0.26	—
Mn	0.00	0.04	0.11	0.07	0.04
Cu	Nil	0.28	0.01	0.19	<0.01
V	0.003	Nil	0.004	<0.001	0.002
Ti	0.26	Nil	0.13	0.01	Nil
Sn	<0.01	<0.01	<0.01	0.01	<0.01
As	0.01	0.03	0.01	<0.01	0.04
Be	0.0001	<0.0001	0.0002	0.0001	0.0001
$SO_4^=$	0.3	<0.01	0.5	1.9	0.4
NO_3^-	—	—	—	0.7	—

[a] Chambers *et al* (1955).

those for Frankfurt, shown in Figs. 41 and 42; only the highest one in Cincinnati is comparable.

The concentrations of acetone-soluble material, that is, of organic material, are remarkably high. Apparently, most of it is produced in cities, but we are inclined to assume that there is a natural background of about 3 to 6 $\mu g/m^3$. Here again we refer to the estimates of Went, that 10^8 tons/year of terpene-like hydrocarbons or slightly oxygenated hydrocarbons are released by the biosphere into the atmosphere.

The highly aromatic sagebush of the dry southwestern U.S.A., for instance, can account for the release of 10^6 tons/year of volatile organic matter. Table 35 gives Went's estimates. Coniferous forests and the decomposition of organic material seem to be the main sources. It should be emphasized that these figures are considered to be only very tentative. If we compare this with the total release of sulfur over land, viz., 11×10^7 tons/year (Fig. 20), it becomes obvious that considerable quantities of organic matter are involved. Concentrations of natural organic material in aerosols of the order of a few micrograms per cubic meter thus appear reasonable compared with an average of about 1 $\mu g/m^3$ SO_4 over land.

TABLE 35

ESTIMATED RELEASE OF TERPENE-LIKE AND OTHER HYDROCARBONS [a]

Type of vegetation	% of earth's surface	Estimated release tons/year
Coniferous forest	14	5×10^7
Hardwood forest	6	
Cultivated land	6	5×10^7
Steppes	6	
Carotene-decomposition of organic material		7×10^7
Total		17×10^7

[a] According to Went (1960).

Goetz and Preining (1960) collected natural aerosols in forests and mountains, and in the desert in the western part of the U.S.A., with the aerosol spectrometer over the range 0.09-0.5 μ radius. A repeated evaluation of these samples after time intervals of days showed that the smallest particles apparently decreased in size and/or in number. This seems to indicate slow evaporation of volatile organic material, directly or after chemical reaction. A similar effect, but more pronounced, was observed in smog aerosols collected in Los Angeles (Goetz, 1960). These findings are of interest and seem to support the concept that organic compounds are important in natural aerosols.

Tables 33 and 34 show that the presence of certain elements, for instance F of Pb, is due entirely to artificial production, whereas the relatively small Fe differences between the two tables indicate a considerable natural component.

The average concentration of the total particulate material given in Tables 33 and 34 is 136 and 65 $\mu g/m^3$, respectively. It is interesting to compare these values with those in Fig. 24. The *volume* concentrations for Frankfurt and a nonurban place like the Taunus Observatory are 80 and 50 μ cm^3/cm^3, respectively, which correspond to mass concentrations of 120 and 75 $\mu g/m^3$, if we assume an average particle density of 1.5 g/cm^3. This is in fair agreement with the U.S. Public Health network data and at the same time confirms the experience of the author that the total particulate material fluctuates much less with time and space than does the number of Aitken nuclei.

Most of the water-insoluble materials in polluted areas are organic substances and ashes. In unpolluted continental atmospheres, the ashes are replaced by mineral dust. The role of soluble and insoluble soil material in atmospheric aerosols is certainly considerably underestimated and its role as condensation nuclei in continental cloud formation has still to be assessed. Very little quantitative information is available on this subject, but all the scattered data point in the same direction.

Reliable rain water analyses on a continental scale over the U.S.A. (see Chapter 4) show that the ratio of $Ca^{++} : K^+ : Na^+$ is of the order of $10 : 1 : 1$. Even if we assume that all the Na found in rain water over the interior of the U.S.A. is of maritime origin, considerable quantities of Ca^{++} and K^+ must have been added from the soil. Mg^{++} analyses show similar concentrations. However, the chemical similarity between K^+ and Na^+ makes it very likely that the soil will also contribute to the continental Na budget. The addition of SO_4 to aerosol particles will convert carbonates and perhaps other minerals into soluble sulfates.

There is considerable geological evidence that aerial transport and deposition of mineral dust is significant. Unfortunately, the geological investigations are primarily concerned with particles larger than 1μ since they carry most of the material, and very little is known about the size distribution of smaller particles, which are of great interest to us. It can be expected that the particle size range of airborne soil particles is quite large. The upper size limit of these particles is determined by sedimentation and not by the source, so that the airborne soil particles represent only the lower end of the size distribution. One can expect this upper limit to decrease with the distance from the source.

Chepil (1957) studied the characteristics of suspended dust at different altitudes during dust storms. He distinguishes between the particle size distribution of the airborne particles, which very often consist of aggregates, and the size distribution of soil particles, which is found after dissolution of the airborne particles in water. He finds that the *mass distribution* has a maximum at 25μ radius near the ground and that the radius at which the maximum occurs drops to 11μ in higher altitudes. This is in agreement with particle size determinations in loess deposits. Loess deposits in Illinois, e.g., show an average radius of 15μ near the source area of these deposits. At first this radius decreases rapidly and later more slowly to 8μ over a 100-km increase in distance from the source (Krumbein and Sloss, 1951). It is obvious that the loess particles represent the lower end of a very broad particle size distribution of soil material and that the maximum of the log radius-mass distribution is at the upper end of the particle size range, similar to sea spray.

The average particle size decreases further for soil material which is carried over even larger distances. Rex and Goldberg (1958) investigated the mineral composition of pelagic clays from the eastern Pacific Ocean, particularly the quartz content. The concentration of quartz particles shows a marked latitudinal dependence with a maximum around 30°N and the evidence indicates that quartz and perhaps other minerals are transported by the atmosphere from the exposed arid land areas far into and across the Pacific Ocean. The size distribution of the quartz particles has a maximum between 2 and 5 μ settling radius, with most of the particles between 0.5 and 15 μ settling radius. It can be expected that quartz serves as an indicator of other soil minerals which will show a similar size distribution but which cannot be separated as easily from marine deposits. The deposits do not show a decrease from the U.S. west coast to the western border of the investigated area at 180°W. The clays also show a pronounced decrease in the quartz content with depth, due to climatic changes during the Late Tertiary.

Considerable dust deposits are also found in the Atlantic Ocean west of North Africa as a result of frequent dust storms in the Sahara. The author collected Sahara dust in Florida, which was apparently transported by the steady trade winds during summer. Sahara dust was observed several times in Central Europe, and Glawion (1938) gives the following data:

Particle size: 68% $\leq$ 0.5, 24% = 0.5-1.0 μ, and 4% $\geq$ 1 μ radius.

Chemical composition (%): SiO_2, 37-75; Al_2O_3, 0-20; $CaCO_3$, 1-16; Fe_2O_3, 6-22; Mn_3O_4, 2-4; MgO, 0.4-3.

Small amounts of K, Na, Cu, H_2SO_4, and HCl.

The oxides of iron and of manganese appear to be strongly enriched, compared to the source of the dust. It is likely that processes of physical and chemical disintegration act selectively in producing fine dust so that its composition differs from the average composition of the soil from which it originates, but nothing is known about this fractionation.

Twomey (1960) provides evidence that desiccation and heating of soil generates 10^4-10^5 particles/cm^2 of surface. This is not a very efficient source, unless the process is repeated due to micrometeorological conditions. He thinks that these particles are formed by crystallization of salts dissolved in the soil water or by thermally induced rupture of salt layers on the soil surface. This would imply that these particles are entirely water soluble. The particles which he observed seem to be as small as 0.01 μ.

Summarizing, we may say that our knowledge of the production of natural aerosols over land is still very unsatisfactory. Undoubtedly, giant particles are formed easily in dust storms. However, almost no data are available on the production of large and Aitken particles at the soil surface and on their chemical composition. Possibly a considerable fraction of these soil particles consists of soluble salts.

2.4 Distribution of Aerosols in the Troposphere and Stratospheric Aerosols

2.4.1 Distribution of Aerosols within the Troposphere

In our discussion of sea-salt particles in Section 2.3.2, we have already touched briefly on the question of vertical distributions. Over the ocean in the trade-wind areas (data from other areas are not available), the concentration of sea-salt particles normally decreases with altitude *independently* of particle size, except for the larger giant particles for which sedimentation becomes important. Vertical profiles over land are similar to those shown by Figs. 43 and 44. A number of independent average profiles are compiled for comparison in Fig. 43. Two profiles deal with Aitken nuclei, the others with large particles. All measurements were made in Central Europe but at different times and seasons, and, therefore, it is somewhat difficult to compare them. The decrease with altitude in the lowest layers is more pronounced in winter than in summer, in agreement with known trends of thermal stability and eddy diffusion. The profiles show an exponential decrease with altitude, at least within certain altitude intervals. Above about 4 km there is a pronounced tendency for the concentration to become constant with altitude. The profiles do not show any systematic difference for Aitken and large particles, indicating that sedimentation plays no role and that the other processes involved are rather independent of particle size.

Individual profiles show certain characteristics which are lost when average values, such as indicated in Fig. 43, are taken. Sagalyn and Faucher (1954) obtained profiles of the positive large ion concentration over the eastern U.S.A., which exhibit little variation of concentration within a rather well defined turbulent exchange layer, somewhat like Woodcock's data in Fig. 36. These profiles are normalized in Fig. 44 with respect to the height of the exchange layer, the top of which is characterized mostly by a discontinuity in the temperature distribution and a sharp drop in particle concentration. It is well known how sensitive particle distributions reflect the vertical temperature distribution, and dust or haze horizons beneath temperature inversions are frequent, and quite striking, phenomena throughout the troposphere.

A frequent value for the actual height of the exchange layer is 2 km, but it varies considerably from day to day and with season and location. In more northerly latitudes, as in Central Europe, or during winter time when convection is weak, individual profiles are more like the average curves shown in Fig. 43. The fact that *average* profiles tend to show an *exponential* decrease is probably due to a certain correlation between the height of the exchange layer and the concentration of the particles within it. It should also be kept in mind that aircraft soundings, as in the case of Sagalyn and Faucher, tend to prefer fine weather conditions with some subsidence aloft and a well-developed temperature inversion above the convective zone.

Figure 45 gives an example of a vertical profile of Aitken nuclei in the upper troposphere and stratosphere in Central U.S. The recording nuclei counter used in these balloon flights did not allow an ac-

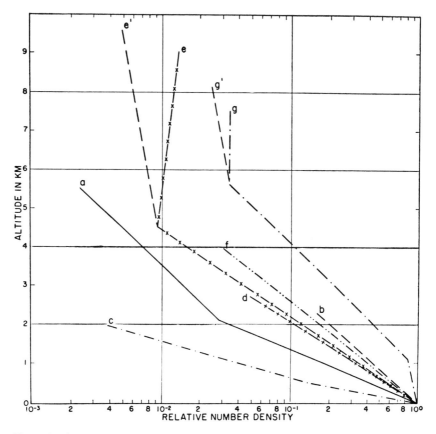

FIG. 43. Average vertical distribution of natural aerosol particles in relative number concentrations, according to various investigators (Penndorf, 1954). All data refer to Central Europe. Curves a and f represent *Aitken* particles; all other curves, *large* particles. Curve a, 28 balloon flights, condensation nuclei (Wigand). Curve b, 12 summer flights. Curve c, 8 winter flights, impactor (Siedentopf). Curve d, 18 flights, impactor (Rossmann). Curve e, calculated curves from observations on the attenuation of solar radiation (Krug, Penndorf). Curve f calculated curve from 22 flights based on potential-gradient measurements (Rossmann). Curve g calculated curve from zenith sky luminance measurements obtained on 18 flights (Siedentopf). Curves e' and g' represent a constant mixing ratio for comparison.

curate determination of concentrations larger than about 500/cm³ and thus the measurements were not evaluated below 5 km. Figure 46 gives the average of 7 such flights made during a period of 1 year. Similar to most aircraft data, these flights also pertain to fine weather conditions. The averaging was done with the tropopause as the datum level. All the individual flights show the same characteristics as the average curve, namely, a fairly constant concentration in the upper troposphere and a decrease above the tropopause. The concentrations in the upper troposphere vary between about 60/cm³ and 600/cm³, with frequent values of about 300/cm³. A few flights in India at 17°N show the same feature with an average of about 180/cm³. If the mixing ratio is used instead of the concentration, the independence with altitude in the upper troposphere is almost perfect (curve 2, Fig. 46).

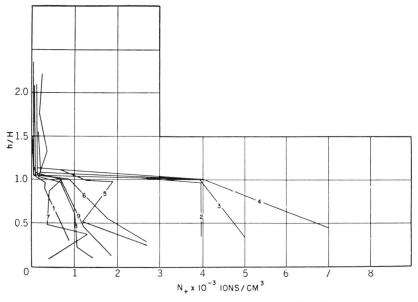

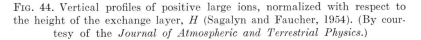

NORMALIZED PROFILE OF LARGE ION DISTRIBUTION

Fig. 44. Vertical profiles of positive large ions, normalized with respect to the height of the exchange layer, H (Sagalyn and Faucher, 1954). (By courtesy of the *Journal of Atmospheric and Terrestrial Physics*.)

Figure 46 also contains data by Wigand and Weickmann, which show a rapid decrease in the lower troposphere. These measurements were made with simple Aitken counters by observers in balloons and aircraft. They are likely to be somewhat too low at higher altitudes for two reasons. According to thermodynamics, the size of water droplets formed in an expansion chamber decreases with decreasing pressure, even if the expansion ratio and the operating temperature remain the same. Since

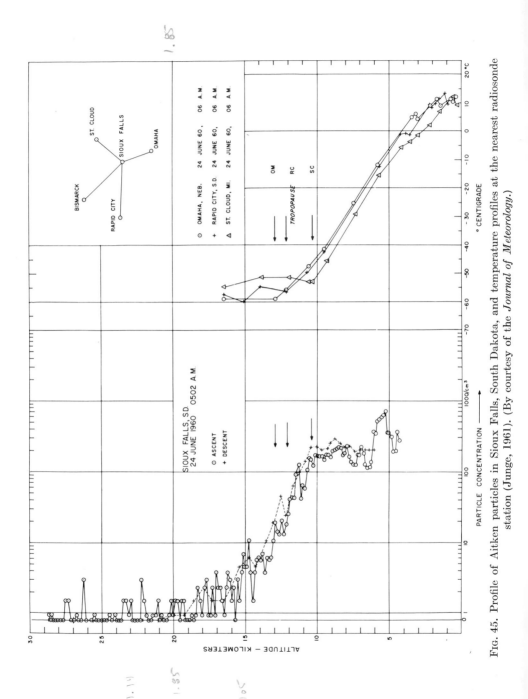

Fig. 45. Profile of Aitken particles in Sioux Falls, South Dakota, and temperature profiles at the nearest radiosonde station (Junge, 1961). (By courtesy of the *Journal of Meteorology*.)

visual or recording Aitken counters depend on optical detection, a decrease
in droplet size tends to give erroneous low counts when the pressure approaches 0.5 atm. In addition to this thermodynamic effect, there is apparently a tendency for the particles not to respond as well to condensation at
lower pressures. Schlarb (1940) observed a decrease of nuclei concentra-

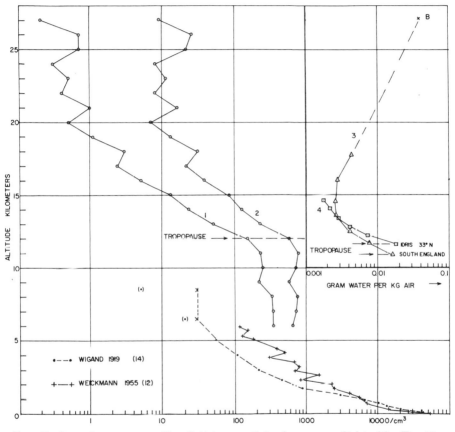

FIG. 46. Curve 1, average profile of Aitken particles from seven flights, like Fig. 45.
Curve 2, curve 1 in terms of concentration per cm³ STP, i.e., mixing ratio. Curves 3
and 4, water vapor mixing ratios for comparison (see Fig. 1). In the lower troposphere
average profiles of Wigand (1919), 14 balloon flights, and Weickmann (1955), 12 aircraft flights. At 6 and 8 km, Wigand could measure only the upper limit but estimated
lower values (Junge, 1961). (By courtesy of the *Journal of Meteorology*.)

tion in a big pressure chamber by a factor of about 5 when the pressure was
lowered to about 0.5 atm. This effect was recently confirmed by Pollack
and Metnieks (1960), but a satisfactory explanation has not yet been given.

The stratospheric Aitken nuclei measurements were made
with a recording counter in which the chamber was pressurized prior to

expansion so that pressure effects were positively eliminated. We think
that this may account for the difference with respect to Wigand's data and
perhaps to a smaller degree with respect to Weickmann's values. Our data
in India (4 flights) showed values of 180/cm³, close to those of Weickmann.

Day (1955) counted Aitken nuclei over England and the
adjacent parts of the East Atlantic, in aircraft up to 2 km. He found concentrations of about 200/cm³ in clean maritime air, a figure which agrees
favorably with the upper troposphere counts taken in India and those
shown in Fig. 46. At the sea surface, Day found concentrations of 3000/cm³,
which decrease rapidly with altitude when winds are light and do not decrease much with stronger winds. It should be emphasized, however, that
all these measurements over sea were still taken close to the British Isles,
to that the likelihood of contamination from land is rather large. His data
for England give counts of the order of several thousands per cm³.

The behavior of the large particles is similar to that of the
Aitken particles, as indicated by Fig. 47. Unfortunately, the data in the
upper troposphere are still very unsatisfactory and the only distribution
curve available for this part of the atmosphere was calculated by Penndorf
from optical data in Central Europe and does not give absolute numbers.

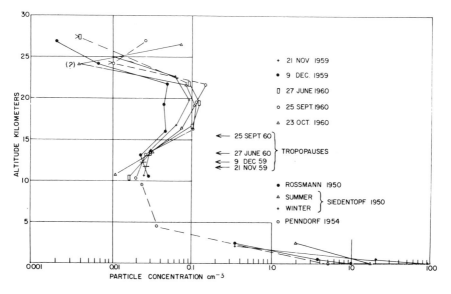

FIG. 47. Five stratospheric profiles of large particles with an average radius
of 0.15 μ, obtained in Sioux Falls, South Dakota. Data in the troposphere from
Central Europe represent average profiles from 18 (Rossmann), 12, and 8
(Siedentopf, summer and winter) flights. The profile of Penndorf (1954) was
calculated from radiation measurements and is normalized to match the other
data at 10-km altitude (Chagnon and Junge, 1961). (By courtesy of the *Journal
of Meteorology*.)

We fitted this curve in Fig. 47 in such a way that it agrees with the concentrations measured at the tropopause by Chagnon and Junge (1961). If we accept this curve as representative, we again see a rapid decrease in the lowest kilometers and a rather constant concentration above 5 km.

If all these data are combined, a large-scale picture of the global distribution of tropospheric aerosols in the Aitknen and large particle size range begins to emerge, which is of great interest and importance for all phenomena related to aerosols. Over the continents, the ground layers are highly polluted, naturally and artificially. These contaminated layers extend to about 5 km, or perhaps more if conditions are more cyclonic than they were for most of the measurements, but above this continental exchange layer and over the oceans, the troposphere seems to have a more constant and uniform particle distribution with average concentrations around 200 to 300/cm^3. Table 27 gives an average concentration of 940/cm^3 over the oceans, but this value includes many places near continents. In remote oceanic areas, the tropospheric particle "background" of about 200/cm^3 reaches down to the ocean surface.

This picture implies that the world-wide background of about 200 to 300/cm^3 represents an aged and perhaps modified continental aerosol and that the troposphere can be considered relatively well mixed with respect to Aitken particles, vertically and horizontally, except for the first 5 km over the continents and the adjacent parts of the oceans, which act as the source areas.

This concept of the world-wide distribution of tropospheric Aitken nuclei raises two questions: What processes determine the decrease of concentration in the continental exchange layer, and what is the significance of the average background concentration of 200 to 300/cm^3?

Considering the data from Central Europe in Fig. 43, it is tempting to explain the decrease in the following way (Junge, 1952 d): If maritime air masses move in over Europe from the Atlantic with the zonal circulation, their lower layers receive the aerosols produced over land. These aerosols build up higher concentrations and penetrate to higher layers as the air moves further inland. This process can be treated in a two-dimensional model by assuming constant wind velocity and eddy diffusion with altitude, and a uniform particle production at the ground over land. The resulting vertical profiles are approximately exponential with vertical concentration gradients which become smaller further inland or with increasing eddy diffusion. The length of the land trajectory for Central Europe is about 1000 km and the average wind speed in the lower part of the troposphere is about 8 meters/sec. Under these conditions, the observed profiles in Fig. 43 would correspond to eddy diffusion values ranging from $D = 5 \times 10^3$ cm^2/sec for stable layers near the surface to $D = 2 \times 10^5$ cm^2/sec for convection and 1-2 km altitudes. These figures are in agreement with generally accepted values. The smaller gradients in higher layers are transitions from the continental boundary layer to the vertically uniform background population of the maritime air masses. This model represents nonsteady state conditions and implies that all continental particles are finally distributed throughout the tropopause. One would expect that on the east side of large continents, the continental exchange layer would approach the tropopause. However, Fig. 46 seems to indicate that in central and eastern parts of North America, the upper boundary of the continental exchange layer is at about the same altitude as in Central Europe, viz., at 5 km. This suggests that other processes become effective in reducing the particle concentration with altitude. These processes can best be treated under the assumption of steady state conditions.

If we disregard horizontal gradients and transports and consider only vertical transports, a steady state is determined by the following equation (Junge, 1961):

$$D(\partial^2 n/\partial z^2) - an - bn^2 - v(\partial n/\partial z) = 0$$

where $D =$ eddy diffusion coefficient, assumed constant with altitude

$n =$ Aitken nuclei concentration

$a =$ removal rate by rainout, with $\tau = 1/a =$ avarage residence time

$b =$ coagulation coefficient

$v =$ gravitational sedimentation velocity

$z =$ altitude.

The first term represents the local increase in particle concentration by eddy diffusion. The second term gives the rate of removal by rainout, assuming that this process is proportional to the concentration and constant with time and altitude. These assumptions can be considered only as crude approximations. The third and fourth terms give the decrease by coagulation and sedimentation, assuming the aerosol to be homogeneous in size.

Numerical estimates of the various terms show that sedimentation is negligible and that near the ground coagulation is more important than rainout, but that this relationship is reserved above 3 km. If the coagulation term is neglected and an eddy diffusion-washout steady state is assumed, the observed profiles can be explained by D values ranging from 10^5 cm²/sec to 5×10^5 cm²/sec and aerosol residence times τ ranging from 2 to 10 days. These figures are again acceptable. However, coagulation is also an important factor, at least for the lower layers. Earlier we pointed out (Section 2.2.5) that on a world-wide basis coagulation seems to be responsible for the relation between concentration and mean size of Aitken particles. Sagalyn and Faucher (1956) measured the vertical distribution of the charged component of the Aitken nuclei at altitudes from 0.2 to 5 km over various parts of the U.S. and at different times of day. These flights were made during fair weather. The change of the vertical profiles during the day is characterized by the increase in particle concentration within the exchange layer and an increase in its height from 1 to 3 km. During the night, the height of the exchange layer decreases again. However, the particle concentration within the exchange layer also decreases and in the absence of advection and cloud formation this can only be due to coagulation. Their calculations show that the rate of decrease is compatible with Smoluchowsky's theory.

These conditions apply primarily to fair weather situations with slow subsidence. In cyclonic situations or during periods of strong convection aerosols will be carried to higher tropospheric layers, but at the same time part of them will be removed by processes of water condensation and rainout. We think that large scale upward transport on the one hand and water vapor condensation, rainout, or subsidence on the other hand are the controlling factors for the main features of the vertical distributions observed in the troposphere, particularly of the decrease in concentration up to 5 km. In lower layers and especially during periods of fine weather these processes will be supported by coagulation. As a result there is a constant flux of particles leaving the continental exchange layers, but part of the particles will be removed already within the exchange layers, before they reach the 5 km level or the continental boundaries.

To consider the troposphere outside the continental exchange layers to be a relatively well-mixed reservoir of Aitken particles is certainly an oversimplification, but it allows an approximate estimate of the global budget for Aitken nuclei in maritime areas. We assume an average lifetime of tropospheric aerosols of 30 days (see Chapter 3), an average background concentration of $250/cm^3$, and an average height of the troposphere of 12 km. The total particle content in a vertical column is then $3 \times 10^8/cm^2$. With a lifetime of 30 days, the removal rate must be $10^7/cm^2$ day. The average amount of precipitation is about 60 cm or about 0.2 cm/day. This corresponds to 2×10^{-8} g water per condensation nuclei, or to an average radius of cloud droplets in a raining cloud of 17 μ, a value which seems to be of the right order of magnitude.

Our discussion seems to imply that an average Aitken particle concentration of about $250/cm^3$ in undisturbed areas is an equilibrium value between supply and removal. It is interesting to note, though, that this is also about the average concentration of cloud droplets if convective and stratiform clouds are taken together. We feel that this agreement is more than a coincidence. The discussions in this chapter have shown that there are various processes by which the concentration of Aitken particle decreases; mainly, coagulation in dry air, capture by droplets in clouds, and removal by precipitation. The first two processes are very important

for high Aitken particle concentrations, but if the concentration approaches
that of the average cloud droplet concentration, only the third process
remains active and the relative rate of decrease of Aitken particles will
slow down considerably. Therefore, it is conceivable that outside the continental supply areas the Aitken nuclei concentration asymptotically approaches the average cloud droplet concentration. This, in turn, supports
the thesis by Squires and Twomey (1960) that the lack of condensation
nuclei and the subsequently more rapid growth of cloud droplets are of
great importance for rain formation within large portions of the troposphere
outside of continental boundaries.

Our discussion has primarily been centered around Aitken
nuclei, but it is also valid for large particles, except that coagulation becomes negligible. Unfortunately, the data are rather scanty for this size
range for most parts of the troposphere. At present, our information about
the stratosphere, which we shall discuss next, is much more complete.

2.4.2 Stratospheric Aerosols

Our information about stratospheric aerosols is based primarily on recent studies by aircraft and high-altitude balloons (Junge
et al., 1961; Chagnon and Junge, 1961; Junge and Manson, 1961; Junge,
1961). Figure 45 shows an individual vertical profile of Aitken nuclei and
Fig. 46 gives the average profile of 7 such profiles over the period of about
1 year. The decrease of the concentration above the tropopause implies that
at least the *majority* of the stratospheric Aitken particles are of tropospheric origin and enter the stratosphere by mixing. The concentration drops
continuously, though somewhat slower, with increasing altitude and finally
reaches values of the order of 1/cm³. This is the lower limit for the recording
Aitken nuclei counter used in these balloon flights and the data above
17 km cannot be considered reliable. Since all the individual profiles were
rather similar, the average profile in Fig. 46 can be regarded as fairly representative.

The low relative humidities in the stratosphere exclude
the possibility that particles are removed by water vapor condensation.
The coefficient a in the equation on page 000, is, therefore, equal to zero and
the upward flux of particles must be balanced by sedimentation and coagulation. For particle concentrations of 200/cm³ at the tropopause, coagulation turns out to be the more important process for the first few kilometers above the tropopause. This eddy diffusion-coagulation equilibrium
changes to an eddy diffusion-sedimentation equilibrium when the particle
concentration decreases with altitude, which may account for the increasing
slope of the profiles.

The rapid decrease of the particle concentration above the
tropopause is similar to that of the water vapor mixing ratio (Brewer, 1949),

as indicated in Fig. 46. If we assume that the particle radius varies between 0.01 and 0.04 μ, equilibrium conditions require an eddy diffusion coefficient of $D = 500\text{-}1000$ cm²/sec above the tropopause. Considering the high wind shear normally encountered in this part of the atmosphere, these values appear to be somewhat low and D values of 10^3 to 10^4 would seem more likely. The decrease in water vapor mixing ratio in the lower stratosphere of the temperate latitudes and the assumption that D is of the order of 4000 cm²/sec forced Brewer (1949) to conclude that subsiding air motions of the order of 30 meters/day must be involved. Consistent and widespread air motions of this kind in the stratosphere are not very likely for various reasons, but unless one is willing to accept smaller D values it is difficult to explain the observed profiles in both cases.

It should be mentioned that observations of mother-of-pearl clouds between 25 and 30 km indicate droplet concentrations of a few per cm³ (Hesstvedt, 1959) in approximate agreement with the concentration of Aitken nuclei.

The vertical distribution of *large particles* in Fig. 47 shows the surprising feature of a stratospheric maximum between about 16 and 23-km altitude. A similar profile was obtained at 17°N in India, except that the maximum was shifted about 4 km upward, corresponding to the higher tropopause level. These profiles were obtained by a set of balloon impactors designed in such a way that the lower limit of the collection efficiency was independent of altitude. The mean radius of the particles collected was 0.15 μ. The five profiles cover a period of approximately one year and show little variation with time. In most cases the particle concentration increases with altitude at the tropopause level, indicating a downward flux as to be expected if the particle source is in the stratosphere. Unfortunately, these profiles are composed of only a few points and it would be desirable to have more information on their fine structure. Some of the profiles seem to indicate another aerosol layer at peak altitude, but these values are not very reliable.

Collection of these particles with direct-flow impactors on U-2 aircraft at 20 km confirmed the presence of this aerosol layer from 60°S to 70°N. Figure 48 shows the distribution of sulfur, the main constituent of these particles, in a latitudinal cross section. By a happy coincidence the 20-km level is right in the center of the layer (Fig. 47) and remains within the main layer in the tropical regions as well. As a result, Fig. 48 does not show any systematic variation of the sulfur concentration with latitude. The agreement between balloon and aircraft data in Fig. 48 indicates that both sets of data are fairly representative.

The size distribution of the stratospheric aerosol particles is given by Fig. 49. Curves 7 and 8 are the limits of the size distributions obtained for balloon samples, which were evaluated by electron and light microscopes. Between 0.1 and 1 μ radius, the log radius number distribution is apparently inversely proportional to the square of the radius. The samples collected by aircraft were much larger and permitted a better evaluation of the upper end of the size distribution. The five size distributions in Fig. 49 show a sharp drop in concentration between 1 and 2 μ and thus indicate an upper limit of the particle population. Curves 5 and 6 are distributions of the particle background on the collection substrates and it seems as if no or only few particles were collected beyond 3 μ radius. However, the data beyond 3 μ cannot be reliable until the collection techniques are improved and the background suppressed.

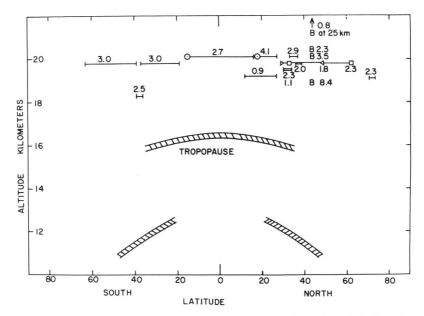

FIG. 48. Latitudinal cross section of aerosol sulfur collected by U-2 aircraft with direct-flow impactors. The unit is 10^{-15} g sulfur/cm³ (Junge and Manson, 1961). (By courtesy of the *Journal of Geophysical Research*.)

$(SO_4^=) \simeq 72 \times 10^{-14}$

$[S] = 2.4/scc$

In Table 28 we included figures of a model size distribution of stratospheric aerosols at 1 and 4 km above the tropopause. Below 0.1 μ these figures are estimated on the basis of the total number of Aitken particles and the assumption that their average radius is 0.03 μ, similar to that found in the lower troposphere.

Numerous samples from balloon and aircraft impactors were analyzed by electron microprobe and x-ray flourescence techniques. The advantage of these methods is a rather uniform sensitivity for a large range of atomic numbers from 12 (magnesium) to 30 (zinc), which contains most of the important and interesting elements. Table 36 contains the results.

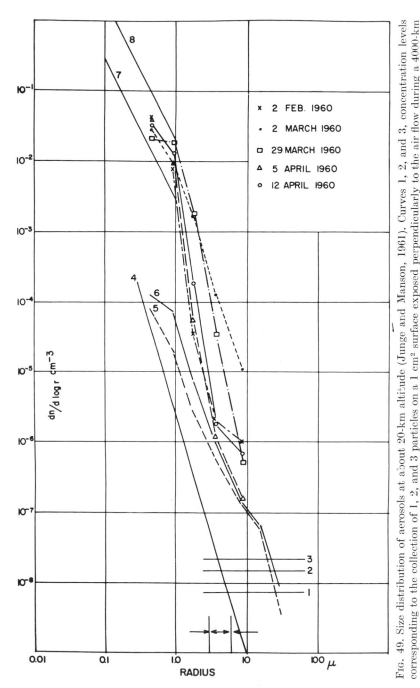

FIG. 49. Size distribution of aerosols at about 20-km altitude (Junge and Manson, 1961). Curves 1, 2, and 3, concentration levels corresponding to the collection of 1, 2, and 3 particles on a 1 cm² surface exposed perpendicularly to the air flow during a 4000-km flight at 20 km. Curve 4, size distribution of zodiacal dust at 20 km, calculated from Öpik's (1957) data and on the assumption of a sedimentation equilibrium in the atmosphere. Curves 5 and 6, size distributions of background particles on the collection substratd used. Curves 7 and 8, limits of the size distribution data from balloon collections. The size range between 3 and 7 μ is apparently best suited for stratospheric collection of extraterrestrial dust in the presence of the sulfate aerosol layer. (By courtesy of the *Journal of Geophysical Research*.)

One can see that sulfur (given as sulfate) is the dominant element, but traces of Al, Cl, Ca, and perhaps Fe also, seem to be present. For sulfur, the concentrations are higher than the limit of detectability by more than two orders of magnitude. The concentrations were high enough to permit direct spot tests for $SO_4^=$, which proved that sulfur is predominantly present in this form. Electron microscope and light microscope investigations show that the particles have the appearance of evaporated droplets of a salt solution, similar to those of $(NH_4)_2SO_4$. They are rather hygroscopic and water soluble and the phase transition seems to occur between 72 and 80% relative humidity.

Spot tests for NH_4^+ indicate that this cation can account for only about 30% of the $SO_4^=$. It is possible that Na is another cation or that the particles consist partly of sulfuric acid. No nitrate was detected.

In a parallel study of U-2 samples, Friend and Sherwood (1961) found particles of the same type and concentration. They found an indication for $(NH_4)_2S_2O_8$ by electron diffraction, though spot tests did not confirm the presence of persulfate.

Figures 47-49 and Table 36 demonstrate the presence of a world-wide aerosol layer about 3 to 9 km above the tropopause. The size of the particles ranges from 0.1 to 2 μ radius and their concentration at the 20-km level is rather uniform between 60°S and 70°N. The layer does not vary much with the season and must represent a steady state. The shape of the vertical profile excludes the possibility that the particles enter the stratosphere from the troposphere by direct mixing unless they are injected in a narrow band along the equator and spread northward and southward by a Brewer-Dobson type circulation, a process which is not very likely. The chemical composition, on the other hand, excludes the possibility of an extraterrestrial origin, unless future investigations show that sulfur is a predominant constituent of cosmic dust.

We think that the particles are formed *in situ* by the oxidation of SO_2 or H_2S. These gases are known to be present in the troposphere in sufficient quantities and can penetrate into the stratosphere by mixing. A sulfur concentration of 3×10^{-15} g/cm³ at 20 km (Fig. 48) corresponds to a SO_2 concentration of 8×10^{-2} μg/m³ STP, a figure which is quite reasonable to assume for the upper troposphere according to Section 1.5. The contact with ozone and the exposure to more intense short-wave radiation would favor more complete oxidation than in the troposphere. It is suggested that these sulfate particles grow around some of the Aitken particles as "condensation nuclei" until they reach a radius of 1 to 2 μ and drop out by sedimentation. The downward flux of sedimentation can be calculated from the data available, and the concept of a steady state phenomenon then leads to an estimated lifetime of the aerosol layer of 1/2 year, somewhat shorter than the average residence time of stratospheric air. This results in a strat-

TABLE 36

ABSOLUTE AND RELATIVE COMPOSITION OF STRATOSPHERIC AEROSOLS FOR ELEMENTS OF ATOMIC NUMER 12 TO 30 [a,b]

Component	A	B	C	D
Mg	4	0.000	0.000	0.006
Al+	4	0.43	0.056	0.006
Si	12	0.11	0.014	0.003
P	4	0.000	0.000	0.01
SO₄	11	→ 6.82	0.890	0.001
Cl	4	0.01	0.0013	0.0013
K	7	0.13	0.017	0.01
Ca	8	0.10	0.013	0.0005
Ti	3	0.000	0.000	0.05
V	4	0.000	0.000	0.01
Cr	4	0.000	0.000	0.01
Mn	4	0.000	0.000	0.005
Fe	12	0.071	0.0093	0.004
Co	4	0.000	0.000	0.006
Ni	7	0.000	0.000	0.01
Cu	4	0.000	0.000	0.01
Zn	4	0.000	0.000	0.02
Total	12	7.68	—	—

[a] Junge and Manson (1961).

[b] A, number of samples; B, absolute concentration (10^{-15} g/cmC^6); , relative composition; D, limit of dectability relative to C.

ospheric sulfur budget of 3×10^4 tons/year. Figure 20 shows that this is less than one-thousandth of the estimated total tropospheric sulfur cycle and that budgetwise the assumption of a tropospheric origin poses no problem.

The presence of a stratospheric aerosol ("dust") layer was indicated by earlier optical observations. The study of the purple light in the twilight sky led Gruner (1958) to the conclusion that it is most likely caused by scattering from particles above the tropopause. Bigg (1956) measured the intensity of the twilight as a function of time after sunset and found irregularities which he interpreted as a dust layer between 15 and 20 km. Similar observations by Volz (1961) confirm this and seem to indicate a seasonal variation of the upper limit of the stratospheric dust layer between 15 km (spring) and 25 km (fall). These twilight data give lower altitudes of the stratospheric aerosol layer, but the quantitative interpretation is complex and not yet final.

A few visual observations from manned balloons report dust horizons or "clouds" in the stratosphere (briefly surveyed in Junge *et al.*, 1961) up to 25 km. Some of these observations imply much higher particle concentrations than are obtained by direct sampling, but it is hard to draw quantitative conclusions from these data.

The phenomenon of stratospheric aerosols is closely connected with the question of extraterrestrial dust in the atmosphere. A constant influx of particles will result in a sedimentation equilibrium. If the mean free path length of air molecules is long compared to the particle size, this equilibrium shows an almost constant mixing ratio of particles to air. Because of rapid removal of the particles in the troposphere by washout, their concentration below the tropopause will drop considerably, unless they are larger than about 5 μ. Under these conditions one should expect the highest particle concentrations in the lower stratosphere.

The most important source of extraterrestrial material in the atmosphere is the zodiacal dust cloud. The mass influx from this source is about a thousand times larger than the total influx from meteorites of all sizes. The particles in the zodiacal dust cloud range from a few tenths of a micron to about 300 μ radius and their density and size distribution can be expressed by

$$dn/dr = c \cdot r^{-p}$$

with $p \approx .2.8$ and $c \approx 10^{-20}$ cm$^{-1.2}$ (Öpik, 1957). There is some evidence from recent satellite measurements that c is larger in the vicinity of the earth, due to a certain hold-up by orbiting around the earth, but this should not have much of an effect on the steady influx.

Curve 4 in Fig. 49 is based on Öpik's estimates of the particle influx into the atmosphere under the assumption of sedimentation equilibrium. These estimates cannot be considered more accurate than one order of magnitude. Recent measurements of particle concentrations with rockets and satellites, though still very tentative, seem to confirm these figures. Figure 49 shows that the sulfate aerosol layer has much higher concentrations and thus makes it difficult to collect extraterrestrial particles smaller than 3 μ radius. Conditions become more favorable for particles larger than 3 μ, but for these sizes the concentrations are already extremely small. This is demonstrated by curves 1, 2, and 3, which represent the particle concentrations when 1, 2, or 3 particles are collected on an area of 1 cm^2 during a flight of 4000 km, assuming a collection efficiency of 1. Thus, the successful collection of extraterrestrial material requires an extremely low background of the sampling substrate and great care in avoiding any contamination prior to during, and after collection. For these reasons, the few attempts to collect ane analyze extraterrestrial particles in the upper atmosphere cannot be considered satisfactory (e.g., Hodge and Rinehart, 1958).

The only particles now generally assumed to be of extraterrestrial origin are small spheres composed mostly of magnetite, Fe_2O_3, with some FeO, (e.g., Buddhue, 1950; Laevastu and Mellis, 1955; Crozier, 1960). These spherules are found in deep-sea deposits, and in rain and snow, and can easily be separated by a magnet. Since similar particles can be produced by certain industries, collection of spherules is reliable only in areas remote from human activities.

These spherules range in radius from about 3 to 100 μ. Their size distribution seems to be such that their mass is the same for equal size intervals. The influx rate is estimated to be 0.3 g per km² and per hour (Laevastu and Mellis, 1961). The spherules are likely to be residues of melted meteoritic material or of that fraction of the zodiacal dust which enters the atmosphere under conditions whereby the melting temperature is reached. Although these particles certainly constitute only a fraction of the total material which enters the atmosphere, they are the only ones which can be positively distinguished from terrestrial matter.

We have no direct knowledge of aerosols beyond 28 km. The mother-of-pearl clouds observed in winter time over Scandinavia and the North Atlantic consist of supercooled water droplets or, more likely, of ice spheres and appear during weather situations leading to exceptionally low stratospheric temperatures (e.g., Hesstvedt, 1959).

The second type of high altitude clouds, the noctilucent clouds, which are observed during summer over the polar regions at 80-km altitude, are much more of a mystery (Ludlam, 1957). It is speculated that these clouds are composed of dust particles associated with the temperature inversion at 80 km, similar to dust horizons in the troposphere, or that they represent temporary injections of extraterrestrial dust. In either case, it is very difficult to explain the main characteristics of these clouds: The positive appearance of a thin discrete layer, their occurrence only at high latitudes during summer, and no apparent correlation with meteor showers.

The apparent increase in the water vapor mixing ratio (Fig. 1), together with more recent rocket observations of the temperature at these altitudes in polar latitudes during summer, offers the more likely explanation that they consist of ice particles. The temperature at 80 km during summer and in polar regions is the lowest temperature observed in the whole upper atmosphere. If the mixing ratios in Fig. 1 are assumed constant beyond 30 km, these temperatures are close to the frost point calculated on this basis for 80 km. Optical observations, e.g., polarization, indicate a particle size of 0.3 μ, and estimates show that particles of this size can grow in a few hours at the H_2O vapor pressures to be assumed at 80 km. Thus, it appears that all the major features of this phenomenon are consistent with this concept.

List of Symbols

a = removal rate by wet removal

A = Austausch coefficient

b = roughness parameter; coagulation coefficient

B = brightness; mobility of particle

c = various constants

d = diffusion coefficient of particles or molecules

D = eddy diffusion coefficient

e = elementary electrical charge

$\bar{e}$ = average number of elementary charges of aerosol particles

E = energy of aerosol particle

g = gravity acceleration

h = parameter

i = number of elementary charges; intensity of light

$I_{1,2}$ = integral values

k = Boltzmann's constant; Karman's constant; general constant or fraction of light scattered

l = mean free path length of particles or air molecules

m = mass of air molecule or aerosol particle; refraction index of particle; log radius-mass distribution of aerosol particles

n = concentration of particles and molecules; log radius-number distribution of aerosol particles

N = number of particles smaller than a given radius; total number of particles of radius r

N' = concentration limit of aerosol particles which influences electrical conductivity in air

p = exponent; water vapor pressure over solution

P = ratio of particle concentration

q = rate of small ion production

r = particle radius

R = gas constant

s = log radius-surface distribution of aerosol particles

S = surface of aerosol particles smaller than a given radius

t = time

T = absolute temperature

u_5 = wind velocity in 5 meters above ground

v = fall velocity of particles; mol volume of water; log radius-volume distribution of aerosol particles

$\bar{v}$ = average gas kinetic velocity of particles

V = volume of aerosol particles smaller than a given radius; visibility

w = small ion mobility

x = parameter in Mie theory

z = altitude above ground; distance

α = recombination coefficient of small ions; exponent; parameter

β = exponent; parameter

γ = fraction of light scattered

ε = ratio of particle concentration; parameter and factor

η = viscosity of air; recombination coefficient between small ions and aerosol particles

$\varkappa$ = parameter of Mie theory

λ = wavelength

σ = light scattered by particles or molecules; free surface energy

ϱ = density of air or aerosol particle

Π = ratio of particle concentration

φ = scattering angle of light

ω = scattering angle of light

Subscripts:

A = aerosol particles

c = refers to Stokes-Cunningham formula

e = equal electrical charge

G = spectral absorption of gases

h = horizon

i = number of elementary charges

k = refers to formula of kinetic theory of gases

M = refers to molecules

s = refers to particle

u = unequal electrical charge

V = refers to limit of visibility

z = refers to distance

0 = uncharged particles

REFERENCES

AITKEN, J. (1923). "Collection of Scientific Papers." Cambridge Univ. Press, London and New York.

BIGG, E. G. (1956). The detection of atmospheric dust and temperature inversions by twilight scattering. *J. Meteorol.* **13**, 262-268.

BLANCHARD, D. C., and WOODCOCK, A. H. (1957). Bubble formation and modification in the sea and its meteorological significance. *Tellus* **9**, 145-158.

BREWER, A. W. (1949). Evidence for a world circulation provided by the measurements of helium and water vapor distribution in the stratosphere. *Quart. J. Roy. Meteorol. Soc.* **75**, 351-363.

BRICARD, J. (1949). L'equilibre ionique du basse atmosphère. *J. Geophys. Research* **54**, 39-52.

BUDDHUE, T. D. (1950). "Meteoritic Dust." New Mexico Press, Albuquerque, New Mexico.

BULLRICH, K. (1960). Streulichtmessungen in Dunst und Nebel. *Meteorol. Rundschau* **13**, 21-29.

BURCKHARDT, H., and FLOHN, H. (1939). "Die atmosphärischen Kondensations-kerne," pp. 1-101. Abhandlungen aus dem Gebiet der Bäder und Klimaheilkunde. Springer, Berlin.

BYERS, H. R., SIEVERS, J. R., and TUFTS, B. J. (1955). Distribution in the atmosphere of certain particles capable of serving as condensation nuclei. *In* "Artificial Stimulation of Rain," Proc. Ist Conf. Physics Cloud and Precipitation Particles (H. Weickmann and W. Smith, eds.), pp. 47-70. Pergamon, New York (published 1957).

CAUER, H. (1949). Ergebnisse chemisch-meteorologischer Forschung. *Arch. Meteorol. Geophys. u. Bioklimatol.* **B1**, 221-256.

CAUER, H. (1951). Some problems of atmospheric chemistry. *Compendium Meteorol.* pp. 1126-1136.

CHAGNON, C. W., and JUNGE, C. E. (1961). The vertical distribution of sub-micron particles in the stratosphere. *J. Meteorol.* **18**, 746-752.

CHAMBERS, L. A., MILTON, J. F., and CHOLAK, C. E. (1955). A comparison of particulate loadings in the atmospheres of certain American cities. Presented at Third National Air Pollution Symposium, Pasadena, California.

CHEPIL, W. S. (1957). Sedimentary characteristics of dust storms: III. Composition of suspended dust. *Am. J. Sci.* **255**, 206-213.

CROZIER, W. D. (1960). Black, magnetic spherules in sediments. *J. Geophys. Research* **65**, 2971-2974.

CROZIER, W. D., SEELY, B. K., and WHEELER, L. B. (1952). Correlation of chloride particle abundance with the synoptic situation on a cross-country flight. *Bull. Am. Meteorol. Soc.* **33**, 95-100.

DAVIS, C. N. (1945). Definitive equations for fluid resistance of spheres. *Proc. Phys. Soc. (London)* **57**, 259-270.

DAY, G. J. (1955). Some airborne observations of condensation nucleus concentration. Proceedings First International Symposium Condensation Nuclei. *Geofis. pura e appl.* **31**, 169-181.

DE BARY, E., and BULLRICH, K. (1962). Über den Anteil der Rayleighstreuung und den Einfluss der Aerosolgrössenverteilung auf die Extinktion und spektrale Intensität der Streustrahlung eines Luftvolumens. *Arch. Meteorol. Geophys. u. Bioklimatol.* B (in press).

DESSENS, H. (1946). Les noyeaux de condensation de l'atmosphère. *Compt. rend. acad. sci.* **223**, 915.

DESSENS, H. (1949). The use of spiders' threads in the study of condensation nuclei. *Quart. J. Roy. Meteorol. Soc.* **75**, 23-27.

DUNHAM, S. B. (1960). Detection of photochemical oxidation of sulphur dioxide by condensation nuclei techniques. *Nature* **188**, 51-52.

EFFENBERGER, E. (1940). Kern-und Staubuntersuchungen am Collmberg. *Veröffentl. Geophys. Inst. Univ. Leipzig* **12**, 305-359.

ELDRIDGE, R. G. (1957). Measurement of cloud drop-size distributions. *J. Meteorol.* **14**, 55-59.

ERIKSSON E. (1959). The yearly circulation of chloride and sulfur in nature; meteorological, geochemical and pedological implications. Part I: *Tellus* **11**, 375-403; Part. II: *Tellus* **12**, 63-109.

FENN, R. W. (1960). Measurement of the concentration and size distribution of particulates in the arctic air of Greenland, U. S. Army Signal Research and Development Laboratory, USASRDL Technical Report 2097, pp. 1-14.

FOITZIK, L. (1938), Über die Lichtdurchlässigkeit der stark getrübten Atmosphäre im sichtbaren Spektralbereich. *Wiss. Abhandl. Reichsamt Wetterdienst No.* **5**, 21 pp.

FORSTER, H. (1940). "Studie über Kondensationskerne," Promotionsarbeit, pp. 1-163. Eidenössische Technische Hochschule, Zürich.

FOURNIER D'ALBE, E. M. (1955). Giant hygroscopic nuclei in the atmosphere and their role in the formation of rain and hail. *Arch. Meteorol. Geophys. u. Bioklimatol.* **A8**, 216-228.

FRIEDLANDER, S. K. (1960). Similarity considerations for the particle size spectrum of a coagulating, sedimenting aerosol. *J. Meteorol* **17**, 479-483.

FRIEND, J. P., and SHERWOOD, R. D. (1961). Size distribution and composition of stratospheric particles. Report February 20, 1961, Isotopes Incorp., Westwood, New Jersey.

GEORGII, H. W. (1958). Ein Beitrag zum Grössenverteilungsgesetz des atmosphärischen Aerosols über dem Kontinent. *Meteorol. Rundschau* **11**, 33-34.

GEORGII, H. W. (1959). Neue Untersuchungen über den Zusammenhang zwischen atmosphärischen Gefrierkernen und Kondensationskernen. *Geofis. pura e appl.* **42**, 62-72.

GERHARD, E. R., and JOHNSTONE, H. F. (1955). Photochemical oxidation of sulfur dioxide in air. *Ind. Eng. Chem.* **47**, 972-976.

GLAWION, H. (1938). Staub und Staubfaelle in Arosa. *Beitr. Phys. freien Atmosphäre*, **25**, 1-43.

GOETZ, A. (1960). Ursprung, Verhalten und Bestimmung der Submikronen-Aerosole des Smogs. *Staub*. **20**, 303-308.

GOETZ, A., and PREINING, O. (1960). The aerosol spectrometer and its application to nuclear condensation studies. *In* "Physics of Precipitation," Monograph 5, NAS-NRC No. 746, pp. 164-182. Am. Geophys. Union, Washington, D. C.

GREEN, H. L., and LANE, W. R. (1957). *In* "Particulate clouds: Dusts, smokes and mists." Spon, London, pp. 225-227.

GRUNER, P. (1958). Dämmerungserscheinungen. *In* "Handbuch der Geophysik" (F. Linke and F. Möller, eds.), Vol. 8, Bornträger, Berlin, pp. 432-526.

HESSTVEDT, E. Mother of pearl clouds in Norway. *Geofys. Publikasjoner Norske Videnskaps-Akad.* Oslo **20**, 1-29.

HODGE, P. W., and RINEHART, T. S. (1958). High altitude collection of extra-terrestrial particulate material. *Astron. J.* **63**, 306.

ISONO, K. (1955). On ice-crystal nuclei and other substances found in snow crystals. *J. Meteorol.* **12**, 456-462.

ISRAËL, H. (1941). Ionen und Kerne, eine kritische Studie. *Gerlands Beitr. Geophys.* **57**, 261-282.

ISRAËL, H., and SCHULZ, L. (1932). Über die Grössenverteilung der atmosphärischen Ionen. *Meteorol. Z.* **49**, 226-233.

JACOBI, W., and LIPPERT, W. (1953). Quoted in Junge (1953).

JACOBI, W., JUNGE, C., and LIPPERT, W. (1952). Reihenuntersuchungen des natürlichen Aerosols mittels Elektronenmikroshops. *Arch. Meteorol. Geophys. u. Bioklimatol.* A **5**, 166-178.

JUNGE, C. E. (1935). Übersättigungsmessungen an atmosphärischen Kondensationskernen. *Gerlands Beitr. Geophys.* **46**, 108-129.

JUNGE, C. E. (1936). Zur Frage der Kernwirksamkeit des Staubes. *Meteorol. Z.* **53**, 186-188.

JUNGE, C. (1952 a). Das Grössenwachstum der Aitkenkerne. *Ber. deut. Wetterdienstes US-Zone* **38**, 264-267.

JUNGE, C. (1952 b). Gesetzmässigkeiten in der Grössenverteilung atmosphärischer Aerosole über dem Kontinent. *Beri. deut. Wetterdienstes US-Zone* **35**, 261-277.

JUNGE, C. (1952 c). Die Konstitution des atmosphärischen Aerosols. *Ann. Meteorol.* **1952**, 1-55.

JUNGE, C. (1952 d). Austausch und grossräumige Vertikalverteilung von Luftbeimengungen. *Ann. Meteorol.* **1952**, 380-392.

JUNGE, C. (1953). Die Rolle der Aerosole und der gasförmigen Beimengungen der Luft im Spurenstoffhaushalt der Troposphäre. *Tellus* **5**, 1-26.

JUNGE, C. E. (1954). The chemical composition of atmospheric aerosols. I. Measurements at Round Hill Field Station, June-July 1953, *J. Meteorol.* **11**, 323-333.

JUNGE, C. E. (1955 a). The size distribution and aging of natural aerosols as determined from electrical and optical data on the atmosphere. *J. Meteorol.* **12**, 13-25.

JUNGE, C. E. (1955 b). Remarks about the size distribution of natural aerosols. *In* "Artificial Stimulation of Rain," Proc. 1st Conf. Physics Cloud and Precipitation Particles (H. Weickmann and W. Smith, eds.), pp. 3-17. Pergamon, New York (published 1957).

JUNGE, C. E. (1956). Recent investigations in air chemistry. *Tellus* **8**, 127-139.

JUNGE, C. E. (1960). Discussion remark. *In* "Physics of Precipitation," Monograph No. 5 NAS-NRC No. 746. pp. 216-218. Am. Geophys. Union, Washington, D. C.

JUNGE, C. E. (1961). Vertical profiles of condensation nuclei in the stratosphere. *J. Meteorol.* **18**, 501-509.

JUNGE, C. E., and MANSON, J. E. (1961). Stratospheric aerosol studies. *J. Geophys. Research* **66**, 2163-2182.

JUNGE, C. E., and RYAN, T. G. (1958). Study of the SO_2 oxidation in solution and its role in atmospheric chemistry. *Quart. J. Roy. Meteorol. Soc.* **84**, 46-55.

JUNGE, C. E., CHAGNON, C. W., and MANSON, J. E. (1961). Stratospheric aerosols. *J. Meteorol.* **18**, 81-108.

KEEFE, D., NOLAN, P. J., and RICH, T. A. (1959). Charge equilibrium in aerosols according to the Boltzmann Law. *Proc. Roy. Irish Acad.* **A60** (4), 27-45.

KEILY, D. P., and MILLEN, S. G. (1960). An airborne cloud-drop-size distribution meter. *J. Meteorol.* **17**, 349-356.

KIENTZLER, C. F., ARONS, A. B., BLANCHARD, D. C., and WOODCOCK, A. H. (1954). Photographic investigation of the projection of droplets by bubbles bursting at a water surface. *Tellus* **6**, 1-7.

KNELMAN, F., DOMBROWSKI, N., and NEWITT, D. M. (1954). Mechanism of the bursting of bubbles. *Nature* **173**, 261.

KOEHLER, H. (1936). The nucleus in and the growth of hygroscopic droplets. *Trans. Faraday Soc.* **32**, 1152-1162.

KRUMBEIN, W. C., and SLOSS, L. L. (1951). "Stratigraphy and Sedimentation" p. 169. Freeman, San Francisco, California.

KUP, J. (1942). Vergleichende Untersuchungen mit dem Konimeter und dem Owen' schen Dust-Counter. *Bioklim. Beibl.* **9**, 34-52.

KUROIWA, D. (1953). Electromicroscope study of atmospheric condensation nuclei. *In* "Studies on Fogs" (T. Hori, ed.), pp. 35-382. Tenne Trading Co., Sapporo, Hokkaido, Japan.

KUROIWA, D. (1956). The composition of sea-fog nuclei as identified by electron microscope, *J. Meteorol.* **13**, 408-410.

LAEVASTU, T., and MELLIS, O. (1955). Extra-terrestrial material in deep-sea deposits. *Trans. Am. Geophys. Union* **36**, 385-389.

LAEVASTU, T., and MELLIS, O. (1961). Size and mass distribution of cosmic dust. *J. Geophys. Research* **66**, 2507-2508.

LANDSBERG, H. (1938). Atmospheric condensation nuclei. *Ergeb. kosmischen Phys.* **3**, 155-252.

LASSEN, L., and RAU, G. (1960). Die Anlagerung radioaktiver Atome an Aerosole (Schwebestoffe). *Z. Physik* **160**, 504-519.

LASSEN, L., and WEICKSEL, H. (1961). Die Anlagerung radioaktiver Atome an Aerosole (Schwebestoffe) im Grössenbereich 0.7-5 μ (Radius). *Z. Physik* **161**, 339-345.

LETTAU, H. (1951). Diffusion in the upper atmopshere. *Compendium Meteorol.* pp. 320-333.

LODGE, J. P. (1955). A study of sea-salt particles over Puerto Rico. *J. Meteorol.* **12**, 493-499.

LODGE, J. P., and BAER, F. (1954). An experimental investigation of the shatter of salt partilces on crystallization. *J. Meteorol.* **11**, 420-421.

LUDLAM, F. H. (1957). Noctilucent clouds. *Tellus* **9**, 341-364.

MASON, B. J. (1954). Bursting of air bubbles at the surface of sea water. *Nature* **174**, 470-471.

MAY, K. R. (1945). The cascade impactor: an instrument for sampling aerosols. *J. Sci. Instr.* **22**, 187-195.

METNIEKS, A. L. (1958). The size spectrum of large and giant sea-salt nuclei under maritime conditions. *Geophys. Bull. School of Cosmic Phys. Dublin* **15**, 1-50.

MIDDLETON, W. E. K. (1935). Experiments with a telephotometer. The dependence of extinction coefficient upon wave length. *Gerlands Beitr. Geophys.* **44**, 358-375.

MOORDY, W. A. (1959). Computations of the growth by condensation of a population of cloud droplets. *Tellus* **11**, 16-44.

MOORE, D. J. (1952). Measurements of condensation nuclei over the North Atlantic. *Quart. J. Roy. Meteorol. Soc.* **78**, 596-602.

MOORE, D. J., and MASON, B. J. (1954). The concentration, size distribution and production rate of large nuclei over the oceans. *Quart. J. Roy. Meteorol. Soc.* **80**, 583-590.

MÜLLER, H. (1928). Zur allgemeinen Theorie der raschen Koagulation. *Kolloid-Beih.* **27**, 223-250.

NEUMANN, H. R. (1940). Messungen des Aerosols an der Nordsee. *Gerlands Beitr. Geophys.* **56**, 49-91.

NOLAN, P. J., and DOHERTY, D. J. (1950). Size and charge distribution of atmospheric condensation nuclei. *Proc. Roy. Irish Acad.* **A53**, 163-179.

NOLAN, P. J., and GALT, R. I. (1950). The equilibrium of small ions and nuclei. *Proc. Roy. Irish Acad.* **A53**, 179-189.

NOLAN, P. J., and KENNAN, E. L. (1949). Condensation nuclei from hot platinum wire, coagulation and charge distribution. *Proc. Roy. Irish Acad.* **A52**, 171-190.

ODDIE, B. C. V. (1959). The composition of precipitation at Lerwick, Shetland. *Quart. J. Roy. Meteorol. Soc.* **85**, 163-165.

ÖPIK. E. J. (1957). Interplanetary dust and terrestrial accretion of meteoritic matter. *Irish Astron. J.* **4**, 84-135.

ORR, C., HURD, F. K., HENDRIX, W. P., and JUNGE, C. E. (1958). The behavior of condensation nuclei under changing humidities. *J. Meteorol.* **15**, 240-242.

PENNDORF, R. (1954). The vertical distribution of Mil particles in the troposphere. *Geophys. Research Papers USAF* **25**, 1-12.

PODZIMEK, J. (1959). Measurement of the concentration of large and giant chloride condensation nuclei during flight. *Studia Geophys. et Geodaet. (Ceskoslov. akad. ved.)* **3**, 256-280.

PODZIMEK, J., and CERNOCH, I. (1961). Höhenverteilung der Konzentrationen von Riesenkernen aus Chloriden und Sulphaten. *Geofis. pura e appl.* **50**, 96-101.

POLLAK, L. W., and METNIEKS, A. L. (1960). The influence of pressure and temperature on the counting of condensation nuclei. *Geofis. pura e appl.* **47**, 123-141.

PRZIBRAM, K. (1933). Die Ionen in Gasen. *In* "Handbuch der Physik" (S. Flügge, ed.), 2nd ed., Vol. 22, Springer, Berlin.

RAU, W. (1955). Groesse und Haeufigkeit der Chloridteilchen im kontinentalen Aerosol und ihre Beziehungen zum Gefrierkerngehalt. *Meteorol. Rundschau* **8**, 109-175.

REX, R. W., and GOLDBERG, E. D. (1958). Quartz content of pelogic sediments of the Pacific Ocean. *Tellus* **10**, 153-159.

RICH, T. A., POLLAK, L. W., and METNIEKS, A. L. (1959). Estimation of average size of sub-micron particles from the number of all and uncharged particles. *Geofis. pura e appl.* **44**, 233-241.

ROBBINS, R. C., CADLE, R. D., and ECKHARDT, D. L. (1959). The conversion of sodium chloride to hydrogen chloride in the atmosphere. *J. Meteorol.* **16**, 53-56.

SAGALYN, R. C., and FAUCHER, G. A. (1954). Aircraft investigation of the large ion content and conductivity of the atmosphere and their relation to meteorological factors. *J. Atmospheric and Terrest. Phys.* **5**, 253-272.

SAGALYN, R. C., and FAUCHER, G. A. (1956). Space and time variations of charged nuclei and electrical conductivity of the atmosphere. *Quart. J. Roy. Meteorol. Soc.* **82**, 428-445.

SCHLARB, G. (1940). Untersuchungen über Kondensationskerne und Leichtionen in künstlich klimatisierten Räumen. *Bioklim. Beibl.* **7**, 86-105.

SCHMOLINSKY, F. (1944). Die Wellenlängenabhängigkeit der Sichtweite und des Koeffizienten der Dunstextinktion. *Meteorol. Z.* **61**, 199-203.

SIMPSON, G. C. (1941). Sea-salt and condensation nuclei. *Quart. J. Roy. Meteorol. Soc.* **67**, 163-169.

SQUIRES, P., and. TWOMEY, S. (1960). The relation between cloud droplet spectra and the spectrum of cloud nuclei. *In* "Physics of Precipitation," Monograph No. 5, NAS/NRC No. 746, pp. 211-219. Am. Geophys. Union, Washington, D. C.

STEWART, K. H. (1957). Some observations on the composition of fogs. *Meteorol. Research Paper No.* **1074**, S. C. 111/246 Air Ministry, London.

SUGAWARA, K., OANA, S., and KAYANA, T. (1949). Separation of the components of atmospheric salts and their distribution. *Bull. Chem. Soc. Japan.* **22**, 47-52.

TWOMEY, S. (1954). The composition of hygroscopic particles in the atmopshere. *J. Meteorol.* **11**, 334-338.

TWOMEY, S. (1955). The distribution of sea-salt nuclei in air over land. *J. Meteorol.* **12**, 81-86.

TWOMEY, S. (1959). The nuclei of natural cloud formation - Part I: The chemical diffusion method and its application to atmospheric nuclei. *Geofis. pura e appl.* **43**, 227-242.

TWOMEY, S. (1960). On the nature and origin of natural cloud nuclei. *Bull. observatoire Du Puy De Dome* **1**, 1-19.

TWOMEY, S., and McMASTER, K. N. (1955). The production of condensation nuclei by crystallizing salt particles. *Tellus* **7**, 458-461.

VERZAR, F. (1959). The discovery of atmospheric condensation nuclei by Paul-Jean Coulier in 1875; a historical note. *Experientia* **1519**, 362-363.

VERZAR, F., and EVANS, H. D. (1959). Production of atmospheric condensation nuclei by sunrays. *Geofis. pura e appl.* **43**, 259-268.

VOLZ, F. (1954). Die Optik und Meteorologie der atmosphärischen Trübung. *Ber. deut. Wetterdienstes No.* **13**, Teil 2.

VOLZ, F. (1956). Optik des Dunstes. *In* "Handbuch der Geophysik" (F. Linke and F. Möller, eds.), Vol. VIII, pp. 823-897. Bornträger, Berlin.

VOLZ, F. (1961). Scattering in the atmosphere during twilight and ozone absorption. Paper presented at the Symposium on Radiation, Wien, 1961.

WEICKMANN, H. (1955). Recent measurements of the vertical distribution of Aitken nuclei. *In* "Artificial Stimulation of Rain," Proc. 1 st Conf. Physics Cloud and Precipitation Particles (H. Weickmann and W. Smith, eds.), pp. 81-88, Pergamon, New York (published 1957).

WENT, F. W. (1960). Organic matter in the atmosphere, and its possible relation to petroleum formation. *Proc. Natl. Acad. Sci. U. S.* **46** (2), 212-221.

WHIPPLE, F. J. W. (1933). Relations between the combination coefficients of atmospheric ions. *Proc. Phys. Soc. (London)* **45**, 367-380.

WHYTLAW-GRAY, R., and PATTERSON, H. S. (1932). "Smoke: A Study of Aerial Disperse Systems," p. 27. E. Arnold, London.

WIGAND, A. (1919). Die vertikale Verteilung der Kondensationskerne in der freien Atmosphäre. *Ann. Physik* **59**, 689-742.

WOODCOCK, A. H. (1952). Atmospheric salt particles and rain drops. *J. Meteorol.* **9**, 200-212.

WOODCOCK, A. H. (1953). Salt nuclei in marine air as a function of altitude and wind force. *J. Meteorol.* **10**, 362-371.

WOODCOCK, A. H. (1957). Atmospheric sea salt nuclei data for Project Shower. *Tellus* **9**, 521-524.

WRIGHT, H. L. (1936). The size of atmospheric nuclei: Some discussions from measurements of the number of charged and uncharged nuclei at Kew Observatory. *Proc. Phys. Soc. (London)* **48**, 675-689.

WRIGHT, H. L. (1940). Atmospheric opacity at Valentia. *Quart. J. Roy. Meteorol. Soc.* **66**, 66-77.

YAMAMOTO, G., and OHTAKE, T. (1953). Electron microscope study of cloud and fog nuclei. *Sci. Repts. Tôhoku Univ. Fifth Ser.* **5**, 141-159.

YAMAMOTO, G., and OHTAKE, T. (1955). Electron microscope study of cloud and fog nuclei. II. *Sci. Repts. Tôhoku Univ. Fifth Ser.* **7**, 10-16.

ZEBEL, G. (1958). Zur Theorie der Koagulation elektrisch ungeladener Aerosole. *Kolloid-Z.* **156**, 102-107.

3. *Atmospheric radioactivity*

3.1 Introduction

Atmospheric radioactivity can be divided into three separate fields. The oldest deals with the emanations radon and thoron, their escape into the air from the ground, and the formation of their decay products in the atmosphere. Investigations of this type started soon after the discovery of the radioactive elements, and a considerable amount of data from various parts of the world has been accumulated and the results summarized. Almost all of this research was concerned with measurements near the ground or in soil air. Only recently has it been realized that the long-lived decay products like RaD to RaF are useful tracers for world-wide and stratospheric circulation, and new interest has been stimulated in measurements of high-reaching vertical profiles and global distribution.

The second field concerns those radioactive isotopes generated by cosmic rays primarily within the upper troposphere and lower stratosphere. These isotopes were discovered and determined fairly recently, after the true nature of cosmic radiation and its interaction with air became clear and after very refined low-level counting techniques became available for the extremely small quantities and concentrations involved. They became famous and important far beyond meteorology through the carbon-14 dating method developed by Libby and his associates in the late 1940's. Tritium is another interesting isotope, but the possibilities which it had to offer atmospheric and hydrological research were soon spoiled or modified by the large-scale contamination of the atmosphere by atomic tests.

This leads us to the third field, namely, that dealing with bomb-produced isotopes, which has gained wide public interest because of the potential radiation hazard of large-scale radioactive fallout to mankind.

All these fields have stimulated atmospheric research considerably. Except perhaps for the cosmic-ray produced isotopes, the lit-

209

erature in these fields is so extensive that it is impossible to cover all the aspects in detail within the framework of the present book. Emphasis has been placed on the large-scale atmospheric distribution of the isotopes and its implications for circulation and removal processes. Most of our information on residence times for tropospheric and stratospheric constituents became available through these studies. The bomb test moratorium since November 1958 has created a breathing spell for research in the third area and has shifted the emphasis back to the natural atmospheric tracers, active or nonactive. The global problems are now clearly recognized and meteorology can expect more basic results from future work in this field.

The radioisotopes C^{14} and T, which form gases, were also discussed to some extent in Chapter 1.

A few remarks about the units used in atmospheric radioactivity may be useful.

(1) The radioactive life time τ given in seconds, minutes, days, or years is related to the decay rate λ (sec^{-1}, min^{-1}, etc.) by $\tau \cdot \lambda = 1$. The radioactive half-life is 0.690 τ.

(2) The activity a is defined as the number of radioactive disintegrations (d) per unit time and unit volume or unit mass, e.g.,

disintegrations per minute and $m^3 = dpm/m^3$ or d/min m^3
disintegrations per sec and $cm^3 = dps/cm^3$ or d/sec cm^3.

One curie (c) is defined as 3.700×10^{10} dps.
The activity is obtained by $a = n \cdot \lambda$, where n is the number of radioactive atoms.

(3) The volume concentration of radioactive material is usually given by number of atoms (n) per unit volume, e.g.,

$$n/cm^3, \qquad n/cu\ ft, \qquad etc.,$$

or it is expressed by *activity* per unit volume, see under (2).

(4) The mixing ratio of radioactive material in air is usually expressed as number of atoms (n) per unit mass, e.g.,

$$n/kg, \qquad n/m^3\ STP, \qquad etc.,$$

or it is expressed by activity per unit mass, e.g.,

$$dpm/kg, \qquad c/cm^3\ STP, \qquad etc.$$

The mixing ratio in air remains constant for vertical movements.

(5) The specific activity is defined as the number of disintegrations per unit mass, e.g.,

$$dpm/g, \qquad dpm/liter.$$

This is used for pure elements, rain water, or soil, and is for air, equivalent to the mixing ratio.

(6) The following conversion factors may be useful:

$$1 \text{ c} = 2.22 \times 10^{12} \text{ dpm}$$
$$1 \text{ } \mu\mu\text{c} = 2.22 \text{ dpm}$$
$$1 \text{ } \mu\text{c}/10^6 \text{ cu ft} = 78.5 \text{ dpm/m}^3$$
$$1 \text{ T.U. (tritium unit)} = 1 \text{ T atom per } 10^{18} \text{ H atoms}$$
$$= 6.6 \text{ dpm T per liter } H_2O.$$

3.2 Radon and Thoron and Their Decay Products

3.2.1 Exhalation of Emanations from the Ground

The sources of natural radioactivity in the atmosphere are radioactive materials in the earth's surface and spallation products of atmospheric gases produced by cosmic radiation. Most of the natural activity in the troposphere is generated by the first source. The earth's crust contains the radioactive nuclides, uranium-238, uranium-235, and thorium-232, which, by decay, produce isotopes of the *same* noble gas, radon. These radioactive isotopes are: radon, $Rn = Rn_{86}^{222}$; thoron, $Tn = Rn_{86}^{220}$; and actinon, $An = Rn_{86}^{219}$. The activity of actinon and its decay products is of minor importance (e.g., Israël, 1951) and will not be discussed here.

After formation in the ground, radon and thoron diffuse into the atmosphere. Without exception their decay products are heavy metals which soon become attached to natural aerosol particles. Eventually these particles and the longer-lived decay products will return to the ground by rain or other processes. The net result is a horizontal redistribution of the decay products with respect to the original source material in the earth's crust by the atmosphere and the ocean. For convenience, the important parts of the uranium-238 and thorium-232 decay series are listed in Tables 37 and 38.

Uranium-238 and thorium-232 are fairly common throughout the earth's crust. Table 39 gives the range of their average concentrations (Israël, 1958), but locally the values can be as high as 100×10^{-6} g/g for both elements ("Handbuch der Physik," 1956). By and large the concentrations by weight of both elements are equal and, since their decay rates are not too different, the same applies to their activities.

The mechanism of radon exhalation is strongly influenced by the varying local conditions of the soil and the atmosphere. Therefore, it is difficult to establish quantitative relations in individual cases, but

TABLE 37

URANIUM-238 (RADIUM) DECAY SERIES

Element		Symbol	Radiation	Half-lifetime
Uranium	U^{238}	U	α	4.5×10^9 years
.				
.				
.				
Radium	Ra^{226}	Ra	α	1.580×10^3 years
Radon	Rn^{222}	Rn	α, β	3.83 days
Radium A	Po^{218}	RaA	99.97% α	3.05 min
Radium B	Pb^{214}	RaB	β	26.8 min
Radium C	Bi^{214}	RaC	99.96% β	19.7 min
Radium C'	Po^{214}	RaC'	99.96% α	1.5×10^{-4} sec
Radium D	Pb^{210}	RaD	β	22 years
Radium E	Bi^{210}	RaE	β	5 days
Polonium	Po^{210}	RaF	α	140 days
Radium G	Pb^{206}	RaG	Stable	—

TABLE 38

THORIUM-232 DECAY SERIES

Element		Symbol	Radiation	Half-lifetime
Thorium	Th^{232}	Th	α	1.65×10^{10} years
.				
.				
.				
Thorium X	Th^{224}	Th	α	3.64 days
Thoron	Rn^{220}	Tn	α	54.5 sec
Thorium A	Po^{216}	ThA	α	0.158 sec
Thorium B	Pb^{212}	ThB	β	10.6 sec
Thorium C	Bi^{212}	ThC	33.7% α	60.5 min
			66.3% β	
Thorium C''	Tl^{208}	ThC''	β	3.1 min
Thorium D	Pb^{208}	ThD	Stable	—
Thorium C'	Po^{212}	ThC'	α	3×10^{-7} sec
Thorium D	Pb^{208}	ThD	Stable	—

TABLE 39

ESTIMATED VALUES FOR RADON AND THORON EXHALATION FROM SOIL

	Unit	Uranium-238–Thorium-232 (radium)	
Decay rate of mother substance	sec^{-1}	4.8×10^{-18}	1.6×10^{-18}
Range of average content of mother substance in igneous and sedimentary rocks	g/g	$1\text{-}4 \times 10^{-6}$	$4\text{-}15 \times 10^{-6}$
Accepted value of average content for model calculations, soil density $= 2$ g/cm^3	gr/cm^3	4×10^{-6}	20×10^{-6}
	atoms/cm^3	1×10^{16}	5×10^{16}
	curies/cm^3 ^{a}	1.3×10^{-12}	2.2×10^{-12}

		Radon	Thoron
Decay rate λ of emanations	sec^{-1}	2.1×10^{-6}	1.27×10^{-2}
Concentration $c_{so} = a/\lambda$ of emanation in undisturbed soil air ($= 0.1 \times$ equilibrium concentration)	atoms/cm^3	2.3×10^3	6.5×10^{-1}
	curies/cm^3	1.3×10^{-13}	2.2×10^{-13}
Production rate a of emanation in soil	atoms/cm^3 sec	4.9×10^{-3}	8.3×10^{-3}
	curies/cm^3 sec	2.7×10^{-19}	2.8×10^{-15}
Exhalation rate $E = a\sqrt{d/\lambda}$ ^{a}	atoms/cm^2 sec	7.4×10^{-1}	1.7×10^{-2}
	curies/cm^2 sec	4.0×10^{-17}	5.6×10^{-15}
Concentration of emanation in air near ground, $c_{ao} = c_{so}\sqrt{d/D}$ ^{a}	atoms/cm^3	2.3×10^0	6.5×10^{-4}
	curies/cm^3	1.3×10^{-16}	2.2×10^{-16}
Depth where $c_s = c_{so}/2$, $z = \ln 2 \sqrt{d/\lambda}$ ^{a} below ground	cm	100	1.5
Height where $c_a = c_{ao}/2$, $h = \ln 2 \sqrt{D/\lambda}$ ^{a} above ground	meters	1000	14

^{a} Constants used for calculation: $d = 0.05$ cm^2/sec; $D = 5 \times 10^4$ cm^2/sec. 1 curie $= 3.7 \cdot 10^{10}$ d/sec.

the basic processes involved are fairly well understood. Israël (1958) gave a simple but useful model for these processes, which demonstrates all the essential features and parameters involved and which will be discussed here in more detail.

Led c_s be the concentration of emanation in the soil air (atoms/cm^3), d its diffusion constant (cm^2/sec), and a its rate of production within the soil (atoms/cm^3 sec), which we assume to be independent of depth. If the soil is sufficiently porous, diffusion proceeds as if the soil were absent. Equilibrium conditions within the soil for the diffusion transport of emanation toward the earth's surface can then be expressed by the following equation:

$$\partial c_s/\partial t = 0 = d\ \partial^2 c_s/\partial z^2 + a - \lambda\,c_s \tag{1}$$

where z is the depth, t the time, and λ the radon decay rate. The solution of (1) is

$$c_s = (a/\lambda)\,[1 - \exp\,(-\sqrt{\lambda/d}\ z)]$$

where $c_{s0} = a/\lambda$ is the concentration of emanation in undisturbed soil air in deeper layers. This gives an exhalation rate

$$E = (d\ \partial c_s/\partial z)_{z=0} = a\sqrt{d/\lambda}\,.$$

The constants d and λ are fixed. Israël assumed $d = 0.05$ cm²/sec, which seems a little low compared with the corresponding value for ThB measured by Chamberlain and Dyson (1956) and discussed later in this section. Values for a can be calculated from the uranium or thorium content of the soil, if one considers that only a fraction of the equilibrium production of emanation escapes into the soil air prior to decay *within* the soil particles. If this fraction is assumed to be 10%, we obtain the calculated values given in Table 39. The values are also given in terms of activity.

The corresponding equation for the vertical transport of emanation above the earth's surface can be obtained from (1), if we put $a = 0$ and replace d by the eddy diffusion coefficient D. D is highly variable and dependent upon altitude above ground, but for simplicity we will assume it to be constant in this consideration. The concentration of emanation in air is then given by

$$c_a = c_{a0} \cdot \exp\,(-\sqrt{\lambda/D}\ h)$$

where h denotes the altitude above ground and c_{a0} the concentration at the ground. Steady state conditions require that the total decay in a vertical column of air must be equal to the rate of exhalation

$$E = \int_0^\infty c_a\,\lambda\,dh\,,$$

which yields

$$c_{a0} = c_{s0}\sqrt{d/D}$$

for our assumption of a constant D. However, besides our simplifying assumptions this relation between the local values of the exhalation rate and the air concentrations in a vertical column is only valid if there are no horizontal variations of these quantities. Since this is not so, it is difficult to apply these considerations to actual cases.

But these considerations are useful to obtain an idea of the magnitude of the various parameters involved. For this reason we assumed an average value for D near the ground of 5×10^4 cm²/sec and listed in Table 39 the resulting figures for E, for c_{a0}, and for the depth and altitude where $c_s = c_{s0}/2$ and $c_a = c_{sa}/2$.

Figure 50 shows a schematic picture of a combined soil and air profile for Israël's model. It may be mentioned that in a vigorous treatment z in (1) should be replaced by $z + z_0$, where z_0 can be adjusted so that $c_{a0} = c_s$ ($z = 0$).

The numerical values of our model given in Table 39 indicate that the exhalation rate for radon in terms of atoms is about 100 times larger than that for thoron, but that the escape of activity is higher for thoron. The concentration of activity at the soil surface is about equal for both, but decreases faster with altitude for thoron due to its shorter half-life. Naturally this model can indicate only the magnitude of the various quantities involved due to the simplifying assumptions, but the results agree satisfactorily with the numerous observations of the various parameters available in the literature. These were compiled by, e.g., Israël (1951, 1958), and are summarized in Table 40 for comparison with Table 39. The large variation of radium concentrations in soil and in soil conditions are reflected in the wide range of radon concentration in soil, line 1.

TABLE 40

OBSERVED VALUES FOR VARIOUS QUANTITIES CALCULATED IN TABLE 39

Radon-222 concentration c_{so} in soil (curies/cm³)	$\begin{cases} 0.5\text{-}10{,}000 \times 10^{-13} \ ^a \\ \text{average} \sim 3 \times 10^{-13} \ ^a \end{cases}$
Radon-222 exhalation rate E (curies/cm² sec)	$\begin{cases} 0.1\text{-}25 \times 10^{-17} \ ^b \\ 2\text{-}8 \times 10^{-17} \\ \text{average} \sim 4 \times 10^{-17} \end{cases}$
Radon-222 concentration in air near ground (curies/cm³)	Normal continental areas $70\text{-}330 \times 10^{-18} \ ^{b,c}$ Disturbed continental areas Innsbruck; Nauheim $400\text{-}600 \times 10^{-18} \ ^c$ Ocean $0.5\text{-}3 \times 10^{-18} \ ^c$ South America $20\text{-}70 \times 10^{-18} \ ^d$ Antarctica $0.2\text{-}2 \times 10^{-18} \ ^d$
Ratio of thoron to radon activity near ground	$\begin{cases} 0.04 \ ^e \\ 0.05\text{-}0.1 \ ^f \\ 0.01\text{-}0.05 \ ^d \end{cases}$

[a] Israël, 1958;   [b] Kosmath, 1935;   [c] Israël, 1951;   [d] Lockhart, 1960, South America;   [e] Wilkening, 1952; Schumann, 1956;   [f] Blifford et al. 1956, data primarily from the West Coast of the U.S.A.

In certain geologically disturbed areas, the concentration of Rn in soil can be extremely high as, for example, in Bad Nauheim (Israël-Köhler and Becker, 1936). The variation around the average value is much less if only

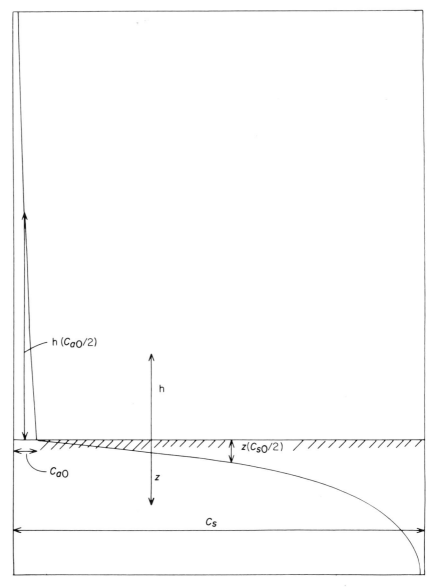

FIG. 50. Schematic diagram of soil and air concentrations for the exhalation of emanations from soil. c_s, undisturbed concentration in soil air; c_{a0}, concentration at the soil surface; $h(c_{a0}/2)$ and $z(c_{s0}/2)$, height and depth where concentration drops to one-half of c_{a0} and c_s.

normal conditions are considered. The exhalation rate E and the radon concentration near the ground vary over a range expected from the variation of soil and meteorological conditions. The average values are in satisfactory agreement with the calculated data in Table 39. The few data on thoron concentrations in air indicate a ratio of thoron to radon activity of 0.04 to 0.1 (Table 40), which is somewhat lower than the estimates in Table 39. However, this ratio will be strongly dependent on the altitude above ground, due to the short half-life of thoron and the fact that local conditions of the soil composition can be involved. The lowest ratios are found in Antarctica due to the considerable distance from any source area.

It can be expected that the *exhalation rate* depends on the soil conditions. Decreases by 70% are observed during rainfalls. The effect of soil temperature and soil moisture is not consistent. Generally, variations of the soil moisture result in larger fluctuations of E, but do not affect much the average values (e.g., Kosmath, 1935). In the eastern Alps there is an indication of a yearly variation with a maximum in late spring, and it is suggested that this is caused by the accumulation of radon during the winter when the soil is frozen and by its escape when the soil thaws.

The yearly variation at other places is quite different and the underlying causes are apparently rather complex. Blifford *et al.* (1956) present data from various locations in the U.S.A. and the Pacific Islands, which generally show a minimum during the summer and a maximum during the winter time. However, there are exceptions to this rule.

The *radon content of the surface air* depends in a complex way on the exhalation rate and the turbulent transport into upper layers, but the latter seems to be the dominant factor. During quiet days it shows a maximum around sunrise when turbulent mixing is at a minimum and exhibits a minimum during the afternoon when mixing is at a maximum. Figure 51 gives an example (Jacobi *et al.*, 1959). The lower part of the figure shows that the decay equilibrium with respect to the short-lived decay products is almost reached during the night. The formation of ground fog in this particular case demonstrates that turbulence was very slight throughout the night. Wilkening (1959) confirms this daily variation for New Mexico on the basis of a long series of observations and finds good correlation to the gustiness of the air. He observes a minimum in spring, which he relates to higher average wind speeds.

Kosmath (1930) observed the radon concentration in 10 cm and 11.5 meters above ground. The ratio of concentration 11.5 meters/10 cm was 0.82 on the average, with a maximum of 1.27 and a minimum of 0.51. This gradient reflects the average upward flux of radon due to the exhalation from the ground and the decay in higher tropospheric layers.

Table 40 shows that the radon concentrations over land are higher than over the ocean by about two orders of magnitude. This is an important fact. It indicates that radon is produced almost exclusively over land and that considerable fluctuations of the radon content in tropospheric air masses can be expected, particularly in coastal areas.

It is interesting to compare the radon distribution with that of sea salt in the air. Radon has a half-life of 3.8 days, which is of the same

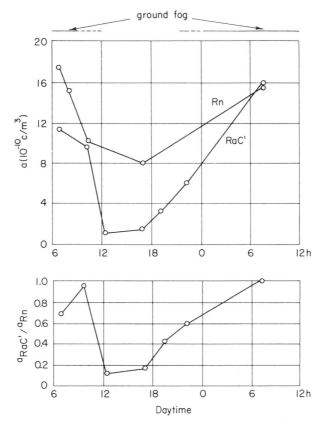

FIG. 51. *Upper;* the activity concentration of radon and RaC′ during a day in September, 1 meter above ground level (Jacobi *et al.*, 1959). *Lower;* the ratio of the activity indicates that decay equilibrium is almost reached during the night. (By courtesy of *Physik der Atmosphäre.*)

magnitude as that of the sea-spray aerosol. For both substances, the continents and oceans are large-scale source and sink areas, but for radon the continents are the sources and for sea spray, the oceans. The ratio of sea salt in *rain water* over seas and over continents, which closely reflects the ratio of *air* concentrations, is around 100, much like the radon ratio when land and sea are reversed. This indicates that the low concentration of radon over the sea and of sea salt over land near ground level are consistent with a removal rate of a few days.

Table 40 shows that the level of Rn in South America is lower than in corresponding sites of the northern hemisphere. This may reflect a generally lower level south of the equator due to a much smaller land area. The radon concentrations over Antarctica are very low, as expected. The values at the South Pole station in turn were lower by a factor of 3 to 4 than those of the Little America station at the coast of the Antarctic continent. This implies that the average exchange time between these two areas is about 1 week.

The continental origin of radon is supported by vertical profiles (Fig. 52) obtained by Wexler *et al.* (1956). In the interior of the United

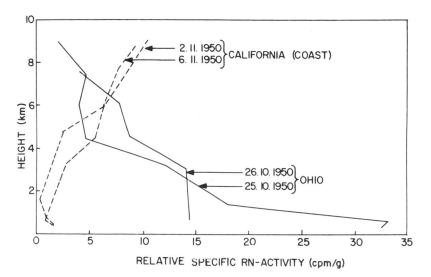

FIG. 52. Vertical profiles of radon in continental (Ohio) and maritime (California) air masses according to Wexler *et al.* (1956). Values in counts per minute per gram air represent a mixing ratio which is independent of vertical air movement.

States (Ohio) we see a pronounced decrease with altitude, and the radon flux is upward. On the West Coast (California) within air of maritime origin, the radon flux is downward toward the ocean surface as a sink. Israël (1958) points out that the radon content of ocean water is considerably higher than is to·be expected from its radium content. It is unlikely that this excess radon is released from deep sea sediments and diffuses upward, because we know from the CO_2 cycle that the exchange rate of deep ocean water is slow compared to the lifetime of radon. Therefore, it is more likely that this radon enrichment is due to absorption from the air and is thus of continental origin.

3.2.2 Attachment of Decay Products on the Natural Aerosols

After radon leaves the soil, its decay products start to accumulate in the air. Decay equilibrium for short-lived daughters is approached as altitude increases. Jacobi *et al.* (1959) calculated the activity ratio of RaA and RaC to radon as a function of altitude under the simplifying assumption that eddy diffusion is constant with altitude (Fig. 53). If mixing is weak, decay equilibrium will be reached at lower altitudes than with stronger mixing. The observations in Fig. 51 confirm these calculations qualitatively and show that during a day with light winds the RaC′ activity compared to decay equilibrium can vary between 0.1 at noon and almost 1.0 during the night at very low altitudes. According to Fig. 53 this corresponds to variations of A between 0.1 and less than 0.01 g/cm sec or of D between 80 and less than 8 cm²/sec, values which are of the expected magnitude.

Tables 37 and 38 show that the half-life of thoron, and its decay products, is much shorter than that of radon. Radon and its decay products will thus dominate in the troposphere. The long-lived products RaD, RaE, and RaF will be removed from the atmosphere and deposited at the ground. On the average, over the entire globe, the activity of this RaD, etc., must be equal to the average activity of the uranium-238 in the soil from which the radon escapes.

Radium A and thorium A are atoms at the moment of their formation. It soon became apparent that most of these atoms are positively charged and this fact was utilized for a while to collect the decay product on a negatively charged wire. Since radon and thoron are α emitters, the positive charge is difficult to understand. In addition, it is to be expected that charged atoms will be neutralized and perhaps be recharged by recombination with small ions (Israël, 1940, p. 98 ff). It is likely that these decay products behave like small ions and form molecule clusters with water, oxygen, or perhaps other trace gases, at least as long as they carry a charge. These primary particles, as we shall call them, have a high mobility and soon become attached to aerosol particles to form secondary particles. This process is of basic importance for natural radioactivity and will be discussed in more detail.

Chamberlain and Dyson (1956) demonstrated that in the case of thoron, most ThB is attached to aerosol particles. Only a small fraction of it is present in the form of primary particles which have a diffusion coefficient of 0.05 cm²/sec. Similar values can be expected for primary particles produced by radon or by the interaction of cosmic rays with atmospheric gases. This diffusion coefficient corresponds to a particle size of about 5×10^{-8} cm radius, or twice the size of air molecules. It is the size of this diffusion coefficient and the corresponding size of the primary particles which suggest a cluster of molecules instead of a single atom.

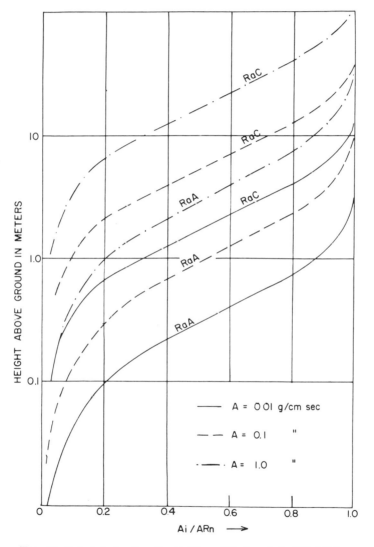

FIG. 53. Calculated ratio of activities of RaA and RaC(RaC′) to Rn as a function of altitude and of the austausch coefficient. The austausch coefficient A is related to the eddy diffusion coefficient D by $A = \varrho \cdot D$ where ϱ = air density (Jacobi et al., 1959).

Recently Lassen *et al.* (1960, 1961) made a detailed study of the process of attachment of these primary particles to aerosol particles by diffusion. Previously, Smoluchowsky's theory of coagulation had been employed (e.g., Jacobi *et al.*, 1959), in which the rate of attachment is given as

$$(du/dt)_r = 4\pi(d + d_r)\,(r' + r)n\,n_r\,dr$$

where d = diffusion coefficient of a primary particle

d_r = diffusion coefficient of an aerosol particle of radius r

r' = radius of a primary particle

n = concentration of primary particles

$n_r dr$ = concentration of aerosol particles of radius between r and $r + dr$.

In the present case $d_r \ll d$ and $r' \ll r$ and we obtain

$$(dn/dt)_r = 4\pi\,dr\,n\,n_r\,dr\,.\tag{2}$$

This expression shows a linear dependence on r, but for aerosol particles which are small compared to the free mean path length of the primary particles, one would expect a dependence on r^2. This inconsistency in Smoluchowsky's theory is due to the assumption that the flux of primary particles toward the surface of an aerosol particle is controlled exclusively by the concentration gradient at the surface of the particle. However, Lassen *et al.* point out that this flux at the surface can never become larger than $\pi r^2 \bar{v}n$, where $\bar{v}$ is the average gas kinetic velocity of the primary particles. The concentration of primary particles around an aerosol particle must, therefore, be constant within a certain distance l, which is approximately equal to the mean free path length of the primary particles. With some simplification, it can be assumed that the flux Φ of primary particles toward one aerosol particle as a function of the distance ϱ from the center of the particle is given by

$$\Phi_\varrho = 4\pi\varrho^2 d\,\partial n/\partial\varrho$$

for $\varrho \geq r + l$ and by

$$\Phi_r = 4\pi r^2 \bar{v}' n_{r+l}$$

at the particle surface where $\bar{v}' = \bar{v}/4$ is the average gas kinetic velocity component of the primary particles perpendicular to the surface of the aerosol particle. The solution of the stationary diffusion equation gives

$$\Phi_r = \pi r^2 \bar{v} n \; \frac{r + l}{r + l + \bar{v}r^2/4d}\tag{3}$$

or

$$(dn/dt)_r = \Phi_r n_r dr\,.\tag{4}$$

Chamberlain and Dyson (1956) found that for ThB, $d = 0.05$ cm²/sec. If we assume that the ThB primary particle consists of 1 ThB atom and a cluster of 10 air molecules, $\bar{v} = 1.1 \times 10^4$ cm/sec and l is approximately 1.5×10^{-6} cm. The use of these figures shows that for $r > 1.8\ \mu$ (3) and (4) give (2) (Smoluchowsky's solution), and for $r < 0.028\ \mu$, we obtain

$$(dn/dt)_r = \pi r^2 \bar{v} n_r dr \,, \qquad (5)$$

the expression expected from gas kinetic collisions. For $r \gg l$, that is for $r > 0.1\ \mu$, it follows from Eq. (3) that $(dn/dt)_r$ is proportional to $r^2/(1 + r\bar{v}/4d)$.

Lassen et al. checked these theoretical considerations by careful experiments. They produced two different aerosols with radii varying between 0.04 and 5.0 μ, mixed them, and exposed them to thoron for 10 minutes so that radioactive equilibrium was reached. They determined the ratio of the activity which became attached to these two different particle populations and compared it with their theory. The agreement was quite satisfactory and demonstrated that Smoluchowsky's theory is not valid for the particle size range considered.

We will now apply these considerations to atmospheric aerosols which may have the size distribution n_r between the limits $r_1 < r_2$. The following parameters are of interest and can be calculated:

(a) The average lifetime τ of a primary particle.

(b) The ratio of secondary to primary activity.

(c) The size distribution of the secondary activity, if its radioactive half-life is short compared to the aerosol half-life. The latter is of the order of days to weeks, depending on its height in the troposphere.

We will discuss these parameters in detail and start with τ: The total decrease of primary particles according to (4) is

$$dn/dt = 4\pi n \bar{v} \int_{r_1}^{r_2} \frac{r^2(r + l)}{r + l + \bar{v} r^2/4d}\ n_r dr \equiv 4\pi n q$$

and consequently the lifetime $\tau = 1/4\pi q$. For numerical evaluation we used the aerosol size distribution in Fig. 54, which is fairly representative of populated continental areas. The quantity dn/dt was computed for Smoluchowsky's and for Lassen's theory. By numerical integration of curves 2 and 3 we obtain $\tau_{\text{Smoluchowsky}} = 21$ sec and $\tau_{\text{Lassen}} = 80$ sec. These calculated values can be compared with measurements. Chamberlain and Dyson (1956) measured τ by separate determination of the radon or thoron activity and the concentration of primary particles. Their values range from 9 to 44 sec. The lack of knowledge about the aerosols in their experiments does not permit a distinction between the two τ values. All we can conclude is that both theories give the proper order of magnitude for τ. For maritime aerosols, we should expect τ values about 10 times larger.

The ratio of secondary to primary particles n_s/n is easy to calculate. Except for RaD, RaE, and RaF, all decay products have lifetimes

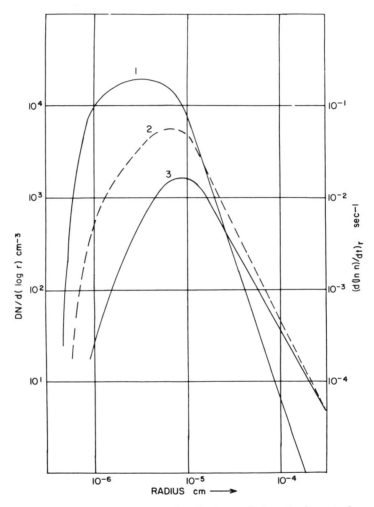

Fig. 54. Natural aerosol size distribution and the attachment of radon and thoron decay products. Curve 1, typical continental aerosol size distribution (scale on the left). This distribution is characterized by: total number of particles = 17850/cm³; Aitken particles = 16800/cm³; large particles = 1050/cm³; giant particles = 1/cm³. Curve 2, relative rate of attachment $(d \ln(n)/dt)_r$ according to Eq. (2) (Smoluchowsky's solution). Curve 3, the same for Eq. (4) (Lassen and Rau, 1960). Scales for curves 2 and 3 appear on the right.

which are short compared to the aerosol lifetime. For them the equilibrium conditions can be expressed by

$$dn_s/dt = 0 = 4\pi dnq - n_s\lambda$$

and

$$n_s/n = 4\pi dq/\lambda$$

where λ is the decay rate of the secondary activity. The distribution in Fig. 54 yields the following values:

	RaA	ThB
Smoluchowsky, n_s/n =	12.4	2.6×10^3
Lassen, n_s/n =	3.3	6.8×10^2.

We see that ThB and its daughters are almost completely attached to aerosol particles, but that this is not true of RaA. For maritime aerosols, with their low concentrations in the 0.1 μ range or at higher altitudes, considerable fractions of primary activity are to be expected under equilibrium conditions.

As we have seen in Chapter 2, up to 30% of the natural aerosol particles carry a positive or negative single charge and the question arises whether this influences the attachment process. Estimates show that these effects stay within 30% of the values given here and can therefore be disregarded for a first approximation.

In studies of atmospheric radioactivity, we are especially interested in the distribution of activity with particle size. This is important, e.g., for retention in the respiratory tract or for filter collection. For natural radioactivity, this distribution is given by the size distribution of aerosols and the attachment process expressed by Eq. (4). We use $A(r)dr$ to denote the activity attached to aerosol particles between r and $r + dr$, and $n_s(r)dr$ to denote the number of atoms which represent this activity. Equilibrium then requires

$$A(r) = n_s(r)\lambda = (dn/dt)_r,$$

where $(dn/dt)_r$ is given by Eq. (4). Except for the constant factor λ, $A(r)$ is given by curve 2 or 3 in Fig. 54. According to Smoluchowsky's theory, one should find 85% of the activity between 0.018 and 0.18 μ radius, with the peak at 0.06 μ, if the aerosol distribution is given by curve 1. The corresponding figures for Lassen's theory are 0.03 and 0.3 μ, with the peak at 0.09 μ. The two distributions of activity are not very different and the bulk of the activity is near or somewhat below 0.1 μ radius. Clearly, in continental air masses the particles with radius larger than 0.3 μ and smaller than 0.02 μ are of little importance as carriers of short-lived natural radioactivity. For maritime aerosols, one should expect the peak of activity to shift toward smaller particle sizes.

Except for Lassen's experimental investigations of the attachment process there are very few data on the size distribution of natural radioactivity. Wilkening (1952) obtained the first data and recently Jacobi *et al.* (1959) studied the question more carefully. Wilkening found that practically all activity was attached to particles smaller than 0.015 μ radius. An analysis of his collection methods indicates that particles in the important size range of 0.015 to 0.25 μ radius are hardly represented in his samples. In addition, the large fraction of small particle activity could have been overestimated due to the deposition of *primary* particles in his arrangement.

Jacobi *et al.* (1959) considered the size distribution of atmospheric aerosols and applied better methods. They collected the short-lived activities on two filters in series and measured the activities by the α radiation of RaA and/or RaC'. The retention of the filters was calibrated as a function of particle size under the flow conditions used and showed a broad minimum of about 50% between 0.015 and 0.5 μ radius. A similar value of 50% retention was found for the natural activities, and did not change on subsequent filters. They concluded from these observations that the distribution of activity did not shift very much after passing through the filters and that the area of the filter minimum thus coincided with the peak of the activity distribution. Further, by using impactors they showed that about 50% of the activity was attached to particles larger than 0.1 μ radius. Jacobi *et al.* (1959) made their measurements in outside air, indoors, and in radium mines, and found similar results in all these places. This implies that the size distribution of aerosols was reltively constant, an experience which agrees with aerosol observations discussed earlier in Chapter 2.

The main result of this study is that the activity is concentrated around 0.1 μ radius between 0.015 and 0.5 μ, in satisfactory agreement with curve 3 in Fig. 54. Pending further investigations, we think that Lassen's theory can be regarded as the best approximation for the time being.

The above considerations about the size distribution of activity are valid only for decay products whose lifetimes are short compared to the lifetime of natural aerosols, i.e., for all decay products except RaD and its daughters. Any change in the size distribution of the natural aerosols by meteorological processes will have a similar effect on the size distribution of long-lived activity. In Chapter 2 we discussed in detail those processes which are likely to affect the size distribution of natural aerosols. Most of them occur in clouds and can be very effective if the condensation and evaporation cycle is repeated. The net result will be a decrease of the concentration of the smaller particles and a growth of the particles which are activated in water vapor condensation in clouds and fog, e.g., those in continental aerosols which are larger than about 0.1 μ. Correspondingly, one should expect to find RaD and its daughters attached to larger particles than the short-lived activities. No observations are available on this question, but in Section 3.4 it will be shown that such a shift of particle size is strongly indicated for fission products within the troposphere.

So far we have not considered the possibility that radon and thoron themselves become adsorbed at the aerosol surface. Observations indicate (see, e.g., Israël, 1940, p. 115) that absorption takes place, but that the amounts are small compared to the activity of the decay products, except under conditions with high concentrations of either radon or aerosols.

The processes which modify the aerosol distribution will also remove a certain fraction of the aerosol from the atmosphere. Therefore, RaD, E, and F will be present in much smaller concentrations than would be expected from radioactive equilibrium with radon. The ratio of short-to long-lived decay products can be used to obtain information on the residence time of natural aerosols. Considerations and measurements of this kind were made by several authors (Blifford et al., 1952; Haxel and Schuman,, 1955; Schumann, 1956; Lehmann and Sittkus, 1959).

Let n_R, n_1, n_2, etc., be the concentration of radon and its daughters in atoms/cm^3 and let λ_R, λ_1, λ_2, etc., be the corresponding decay rates. If we assume that the removal rate of aerosols, λ_a, is proportional to their concentration and is also constant with time and space and, further, if we assume that n_R is constant within the atmosphere, we can write

$$dn_1/dt = n_R \lambda_R - n_1(\lambda_1 + \lambda_a)$$

$$dn_i/dt = n_{i-1}\lambda_{i-1} - n_i(\lambda_i + \lambda_a) \qquad i = 2, 3, \ldots.$$

This gives

$$n_i = n_R \lambda_R \cdot \frac{\lambda_1}{\lambda_1 + \lambda_a} \cdot \frac{\lambda_2}{\lambda_2 + \lambda_a} \cdots \frac{\lambda_{i-1}}{\lambda_{i-1} + \lambda_a} \cdot \frac{1}{\lambda_i + \lambda_a}.$$

For the short-lived daughters $\lambda_i \gg \lambda_a$ and the expression is reduced to that for equilibrium in a decay series $n_i \lambda_i - n_R \lambda_R$. For the long-lived RaD, $\lambda_{RaD} \ll \lambda_a$ and we obtain $n_{RaD} \cong n_R \lambda_R / \lambda_a$ a value which is about three orders of magnitude smaller than the radioactive equilibrium concentration. This latter expression can be used to determine λ_a, and to this end, filter collections were analyzed for RaD and for RaB, which in turn gave n_R. Blifford et al. (1952) determined RaD by chemical methods and Haxel and Schumann by less reliable observation of decay curves. Lehmann and Sittkus also determined λ_a from the ratio of RaD to RaF activity in air and in rain. The results are compiled in Table 41. The first two values by Blifford (personal communication) are probably too high by a factor of .2 and are closer to the values in Alaska and Heidelberg. With this correction the values in ground air tend to be about 1 week. Other values in the table are more or less representative of the *total* troposphere and seem to be higher. They will be discussed in Section 3.4.

TABLE 41

RESIDENCE TIMES OF NATURAL AEROSOLS IN THE TROPOSPHERE OBTAINED
FROM DATA ON ATMOSPHERIC RADIOACTIVITY

Observer	Location	Method	Residence time (days)	
Blifford et al. (1952)	Washington, D.C. Marocco Alaska	Ratio of short- to long-lived decay products of radon	15 18 4	Likely to be too high by a factor of 2
Haxel and Schumann (1955)	Heidelberg	Ratio of short- to long-lifed decay products of radon	6	
Lehmann and Sittkus (1959)	Freiburg, Br.	Ratio of short- to long-lifed decay products of radon	0.8-3.0	
		Ratio RaF/RaD in air	8-36	
		Ratio RaF/RaD in rain	33	
Goel et al. (1959)	India	Comparison of calculated and measured Be^7 production	30	
Lal (1959)	India	Ratio in rain of Be^7/P^{32}	40	
Stewart et al. (1955)	North Atlantic	Fission products from Nevada tests	32	
Burton and Steward (1960)	England	Average RaD content in the troposphere and RaD deposition by rain	17	
		Ratio FaR/RaD in rain water	22	

It should be emphasized that the values obtained from the ratio of short to long-lived radon decay products are not very reliable. Besides the inaccuracies of the measurements, the calculations are based on the assumption that n_R and λ_a are constant throughout the troposphere and that λ_a is proportional to the secondary activity.

These assumptions do not agree with the facts. The radon concentration varies by a factor of 100 from continent to ocean and considerable fluctuations must therefore be expected during the passage of air masses of different origin. Washout and rainout of aerosols, i.e., λ_a, varies with the amount of precipitation and with altitude. Consequently, it can be expected that the accuracy of the λ_a values obtained by this method is not better than a factor of 2 to 3.

Measurements of the RaE content in rain by King et al. (1956) are an indirect confirmation of the long residence time of aerosols. Their data, in Table 42, show that the difference between continent and

TABLE 42

RAIN WATER CONCENTRATION OF RaE [a]

Location	dpm/liter
Alaska	1.4
Illinois	4.6
Hawaii	2.0
Philippines	2.0
Panama	0.7
Samoa	0.4

[a] According to King et al. (1956).

ocean in the northern hemisphere is not larger than a factor of 2 in contrast to the radon concentration. Consequently, the aerosol residence time must be long compared to the 3.8 days for radon.

The source area for radon (land) in the southern hemisphere is much smaller than north of the equator. Since mixing across the equator is rather slow, lower radon concentrations must be expected in the southern hemisphere. This seems to be reflected in the correspondingly low RaE concentrations shown in Table 42 and is in agreement with the radon data in Table 40.

Vertical profiles of RaD concentrations in the troposphere and stratosphere have recently become available (Burton and Stewart, 1960; Machta, 1960) and are presented in Fig. 69. The concentration by volume decreases by a factor of about 4 from ground level to the tropopause, which is equivalent to an almost constant mixing ratio. The United States and the Great Britain stratospheric data do not agree. Burton and Stewart found a pronounced increase with altitude above the tropopause, similar to that of fission products, whereas the data given by Machta show the same mixing ratio as in the troposphere. For radioactive decay equilibrium, one would expect 1 radon atom for 2100 RaD atoms present. However, for RaD attached to an aerosol with a half-life of 20 days, this ratio would be 1 Rn atom to 5.5 RaD atoms. If we assume that horizontal distribution of Rn and RaD is uniform in the upper troposphere, the concentration of RaD in the stratosphere cannot increase by more than a factor of $6.5/5.5 = 1.2$, no matter how and at what rate the air enters the stratosphere. This estimate does not agree with the data from Great Britain. Since the RaD source from meteorites is negligible, Burton and Stewart's findings can only be explained by assuming that the stratospheric air over England is primarily of continental origin with a higher radon content than the Atlantic air and that the origin of stratospheric air is strongly dependent on the longitude.

Burton and Stewart also measured the RaF content at various altitudes and found a ratio of RaF/RaD of 0.13 near the ground, increasing to 0.65 at 14 km in the lower stratosphere. This implies that RaF with a half-lifetime of 140 days builds up in the stratosphere due to a lack of washout. This permits an estimate of the age of the stratospheric air, which can vary between 170 and 220 days, depending on the assumption for the ratio of Rn/RaD in the air entering the stratosphere. This exchange time is in approximate agreement with the result from fission product measurements.

3.3 Radioisotopes Produced by Cosmic Radiation

Cosmic radiation constantly produces a number of radioisotopes in the atmosphere by nuclear reactions with atmospheric gases. Table 43 lists those isotopes which have been detected either because their

TABLE 43
COSMIC-RAY PRODUCED RADIOISOTOPES

Radio-isotope	Calculated average total production rate (atoms/cm² tear)	Half-lifetime	Estimated steady state activity in the troposphere (disintegrations per cm² and per sec)	Detected and measured in:
Be^{10}	2.6×10^6 [a]	2.7×10^6 years	1.1×10^{-9}	Deep sea sediments [b]
C^{14}	6.3×10^7 [c]	5.7×10^3 years	—	$C^{14}O_2$, all organic materials
Si^{32}	6.3×10^3 [d]	710 years	8×10^{-9}	Marine sponges
$H^3(T)$	7.9×10^6 [e]	12.5 years	—	HTO, HT
Na^{22}	$\sim 5 \times 10^2$ [f]	2.6 years	1.7×10^{-7}	Rain
S^{35}	4.2×10^4 [g]	87 days	1.6×10^{-4}	Rain, air
Be^7	2.4×10^6 [g]	53 days	1.5×10^{-2}	Rain, air
P^{33}	2.0×10^4 [g]	25 days	2.6×10^{-5}	Rain
P^{32}	2.4×10^4 [g]	14.3 days	5.6×10^{-5}	Rain

[a] Lal *et al.* (1958);   [b] Arnold (1956);   [c] Fergusson (1960);   [d] Lal *et al.* (1960 b); [e] Craig and Lal (1961);   [f] Marquez *et al.* (1957); estimate based on observations; [g] Lal *et al.* (1960 a).

production level is sufficiently high or because their half-lives are long enough to be of meteorological interest. Those with smaller atomic weights, e.g., $H^3(T)$, Be^7, Be^{10}, and C^{14}, are formed mainly in interactions involving atmospheric nitrogen and oxygen nuclei (atomic weights 14 and 16), whereas the isotopes Si^{32}, P^{32}, P^{33}, and S^{35} are formed exclusively by interactions with atmospheric argon (atomic weight 39.9).

The production rate of radioactive nuclides by cosmic radiation depends on a variety of physical parameters, such as the energy spectrum of the radiation, its modification within the atmosphere, and the physical characteristics of the various primary and secondary cosmic-ray particles involved. The details are rather complex and the reader must be referred to the special literature (e.g., Lal et al., 1958). Most of the radioisotopes are produced by secondary, low energy neutrons, and their rate of production is approximately proportional to this neutron flux which is about 4 times higher at the geomagnetic poles than at the equator.

The distribution of the isotope production rate within the atmosphere can be calculated from data on the cosmic-ray intensity and from experimental information on the reactions involved (Lal et al., 1958). The main feature of this distribution is a broad maximum around 12-km altitude, which varies somewhat with geomagnetic latitude (see Fig. 55). This maximum layer is the result of the interaction of two phenomena: The rapid downward decrease of the low energy neutron flux with decreasing altitude, and the vertical distribution of air density. The product of these two quantities has a maximum at the indicated level and it is this product which controls the isotope formation rate. Such layers of maximum production are a basic phenomenon in the atmosphere and occur whenever a constituent is formed by absorption of extraterrestrial radiation as, e.g., ozone, atomic oxygen, etc.

Two of the radioactive isotopes, T and C^{14}, form gases and their atmospheric cycle has already been discussed in connection with H_2O, H_2, and CO_2 in Chapter 1. It is possible that S^{35} too is temporarily present as a gas, namely, as SO_2. The other isotopes will pass through the state of primary particles and become attached to aerosols in a manner similar to radon and thoron decay products. Their process of removal from the atmosphere is therefore identical to that of aerosols, i.e., by mixing from the stratosphere to the troposphere and by precipitation from the troposphere to the ground. The calculated total production rates and half-lives of all observed cosmic-ray induced isotopes are listed in Table 43.

The concentration of cosmic-ray produced isotopes in the troposphere is extremely low. An idea of the experimental difficulties involved can be obtained by an estimate of their tropospheric activity concentration assuming a tropospheric production rate one-half the total, and a residence time of 30 days for aerosols. This gives the figures listed in column 4, Table 43.

      The activity levels of S[35], Be[7], P[33], and P[32] are high enough to be measured in rain water and in fact almost all the data on these isotopes are obtained in this way. The detection of Na[22] in rain is marginal. The

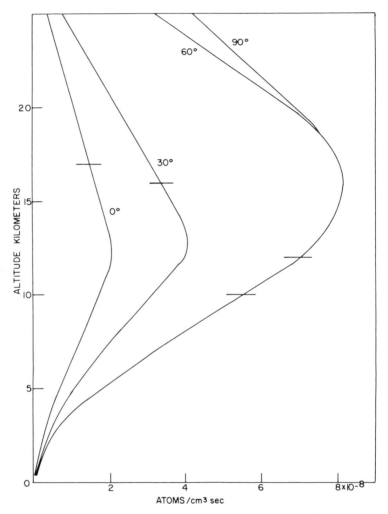

FIG. 55. Cosmic-ray production of Be[7] in the atmosphere for 0°, 30°, 60°, and 90° geomagnetic latitude as a function of altitude, based on data from Lal *et al.* (1958). The horizontal lines mark the tropopause heights for the various latitudes.

presence of Si[32] has been proven only in marine sponges, which accumulate the Si from sea water and Be[10] has been detected in pelagic sediments with very low sedimentation rates (see references in Table 43).

The isotopes T, C^{14}, S^{35}, Na^{22}, and, perhaps to a small extent, P^{32} have also been produced by atomic tests since 1954. The concentrations of artificial T and C^{14} are still considerable compared to the natural background, but the levels of S^{35} and P^{32}, with their shorter half-lifes, were returned to normal in summer 1961 since they were last produced in Pacific surface tests in spring 1958.

After these general remarks we will discuss the various isotopes in more detail. Most features of the natural occurrences of T and C^{14} have already been treated in Chapter 1 and here we shall add only a few facts about their production. The production rate of T has been calculated as 0.15 atom/cm² sec, on the basis of cosmic-ray intensities and measurements of cross sections (e.g., Suess, 1958). However, according to Libby (1959 b) and others, the few HTO measurements made prior to the production of artificial T, and their proper interpretation, seem to indicate that the total production rate of T is greater and amounts to about 2 atoms/cm² sec, as an average for all latitudes and the whole atmosphere, and to about 1 atom/cm² sec at ground level, because of stratospheric hold-up times. It was suggested that this difference could only be due to accretion from the sun. However, a new and very careful analysis by Craig and Lal (1961) reveals that most of the pre-Castle tests, which were considered uncontaminated in previous papers, already contained some synthetic tritium from earlier thermonuclear tests. The uncontaminated tritium level in precipitation was established by a comparison of deuterium and tritium concentrations of the same samples. The global mean production rate of tritium is thus found to be 0.5 ± 0.3 atom/cm² sec, which is 3 to 4 times smaller than earlier estimates. The average stratospheric residence time is 1.6 years in contrast to previous assumptions of 10 years. In correspondence to results from fission product observations, it is concluded that tritium is injected into the troposphere primarily at high latitudes.

A recalculation of the expected production rate resulted in the value of 0.25 ± 0.08 atom/cm² sec. The observed and calculated values thus agree within the limits of uncertainty.

The C^{14} produced by cosmic rays forms the basis for the dating method developed by Libby and his associates (see, e.g., Anderson, 1953). The subject was recently reviewed very thoroughly by Fergusson (1960). Carbon-14 is produced predominantly by the interaction of N^{14} with secondary neutrons, and the most recent calculations indicate a production rate of 2.0 ± 0.5 atoms/cm² sec. This can be checked by the specific activity of carbon at the earth's surface. If the cosmic-ray flux has been constant over the past 10,000 to 20,000 years (the fluctuations seem to be less than a few per cent), the total C^{14} production should equal the decay in steady state. The total decay is given by the specific activity and the total reservoir of *that* carbon with which C^{14} can exchange. The latter is close to 8 g/cm² on the average and the specific activity of carbon in the biosphere is 0.25 ± 0.02 disintegration per second and per gram, resulting in an average total decay rate of 2 atoms/cm²sec, in agreement with the above figure.

Normally it is assumed that C^{14} is oxidized to $C^{14}O_2$. Recently Pandow et al. (1960) made laboratory investigations of the oxidation of C^{14} produced by radiation in $O_2 + N_2$ mixtures and found that 90% of the C^{14} is oxidized to $C^{14}O$. No measurements of the specific activity of atmospheric CO are yet available to check this result, but all observations seem to indicate that $C^{14}O_2$ is the final form in which C^{14} is present in the atmosphere.

Because of the long half-life of C^{14}, there should be practically no difference in the specific activity of atmospheric CO_2 between stratosphere and troposphere.

Most of the nongaseous isotopes in Table 43 have been observed for only a few years. Since then they have been studied rather intensively for the dual purpose of obtaining quantitative information on their production rates and of using them as tracers for atmospheric circulation. For this latter application, it is necessary to know the spatial distribution of production rates within the atmosphere. The most reliable calculations are those by Lal et al. (1958) with some corrections based on newer observations by Lal et al. (1960 a). Figure 55 was prepared from their studies. It shows that at low latitudes the maximum of Be^7 production occurs in the upper troposphere, but that it shifts to the low stratosphere north of 30°, primarily because of the decrease in tropopause height. The variation with latitude beyond 60° is small. The fraction produced in the troposphere is of special importance for meteorological applications and is shown in Fig. 56 together with the total production rate as a function of latitude. The variation in production rate and tropopause height compensate each other in such a manner that the tropospheric production is fairly independent of latitude, whereas the total and the stratospheric component increase considerably. The production distribution of the other cosmic-ray isotopes is very similar to that shown in Fig. 56.

The natural aerosol concentration in the stratosphere is so low that the lifetimes of the primary particles are of the order of hours compared to about 1 minute for the decay products of radon near the ground. Despite these long lifetimes, most of the cosmic-ray produced activity will be attached to aerosols as secondary activity because the half-lives of the respective isotopes are so much longer than those of the short-lived radon and thoron decay products.

The estimated size distribution of stratospheric aerosols given for two altitudes in Table 28 is somewhat different from that in Fig. 26. However, the application of Lassen's theory results in a distribution of secondary activity for which the maximum is below but still close to 0.1 μ radius, not very much different from curve 3 in Fig. 54. This particle size is so small that removal from the stratosphere will be similar to that of gases. Since it can be expected that the attachment process is the same for the various isotopes, their rate of removal by rain, etc., from the troposphere will also be practically the same. This short discussion shows that natural

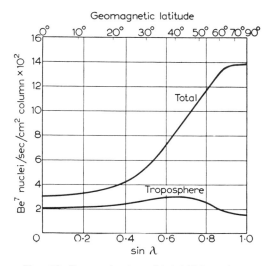

FIG. 56. Tropospheric and total Be⁷ production rates as a function of latitude (Lal *et al.*, 1958). (By courtesy of *Journal of Atmospheric and Terrestrial Physics*.)

aerosols are as important as carriers of cosmic-ray induced isotopes as they are for the decay products of emanations in the troposphere.

We shall now discuss the observational results of the non-gaseous isotopes. Most data were obtained from rain water analyses and only very few data have been published on the concentration in air which can be compared with these figures. Cruikshank *et al.* (1956) measured the Be⁷ concentration in surface air north of 55° geomagnetic latitude over a period of 14 months and found an average value of about 10 atoms/liter. The value in Table 43 is 2.6 d/cm² sec, which corresponds to 82 atoms/liter if the height of the tropopause is assumed to be 12 km. However, we know that a residence time of 30 days is only valid for the troposphere as a whole and that for ground air, values of 6 days are more likely (Table 41). This would reduce the calculated concentration from 82 to 16 atoms/liter, in satisfactory agreement with the observations. It is also of interest to note that the Be⁷ concentration showed a seasonal variation with a maximum around April and an annual amplitude of about 50 to 70% of the average value, similar to tropospheric ozone.

Recently new data on the concentration of Be^7 in surface air for 1960 and 1961 became available from England (Parker, 1962) and Sweden (Lindblom, 1962), which show a maximum in April and a minimum in the fall. The concentration varies between about 2 and 8×10^{-14} curie/kg air in both places so that the amplitude of the variation is somewhat larger than Cruikshank *et al.* found. These variations indicate that in middle and high latitudes a considerable fraction of Be^7 is of stratospheric origin. It must be expected that for lower latitudes the amplitude of the annual variation decreases markedly due to the increasing part of the tropospheric production.

Numerous data on the *stratospheric concentration* of Be^7 were obtained in the High Altitude Sampling Program of the U.S. Department of Defense (HASP, 1961). The evaluation of the data shows that the distribution with latitude and altitude within the stratosphere up to 20 km is in satisfactory agreement with the concentration calculated for radioactive equilibrium except for the area close to the tropopause because here mixing with the troposphere becomes important.

We now turn to the comparison of the calculated production rates of the nongaseous isotopes with the observed rates of their removal by precipitation. No reliable data are available for Be^{10}, Si^{32}, and Na^{22} because of the low activity levels. A rough estimate of Na^{22} production has been made by Marquez *et al.* (1957), but no calculated data are available.

For Be^7, P^{32}, P^{33}, and S^{35}, the observations are numerous enough to permit a reliable comparison with calculated values. It soon became apparent in these investigations that the deposition rates observed in low latitudes agree best with the *tropospheric* portion of the production rate, both with respect to the absolute values and to the latitude dependence (Lal *et al.*, 1958; Göl *et al.*, 1959; Peters, 1959). This agreement is particularly good for Be^7 and implies that the residence time of stratospheric air in these low latitudes is long compared to the radioactive half-life of Be^7, which is 53 days and that the southward transport of Be^7 in the troposphere is negligible. It is now generally accepted that the residence time of low stratospheric air, especially in tropical latitudes, is in fact about 1 year.

The concentration of Be^7, P^{32}, and S^{35} in rain water was measured primarily in India and all the values were recently summarized by Lal *et al.* (1960 c). These figures were multiplied by the average rainfall of the corresponding latitude belt and resulted in the deposition rates given in Table 44.

These figures can be compared with calculated production rates, corrected by factors published recently by Lal *et al.* (1960 a). Since the average tropospheric residence time of aerosols is about 30 days, a decay factor must be applied (columns 6, 7, and 8 in Table 44).

TABLE 44

ANNUAL DEPOSITION AND PRODUCTION RATES OF Be[7], P[32], AND S[35] AT TROPICAL LATITUDES FROM DATA IN INDIA IN ATOMS/CM[2] YEAR [a,b]

Radio-isotope	Measured values				Calculated values		
	Annual deposition rates at tropical latitudes			Average	Tropo-spheric production for rate	Decay factor 30 days	Deposition rate [c]
	1956	1957	1958	1956-1958			
Be[7]	4.8×10^5 (76)	4.0×10^5 (75)	4.3×10^5 (19)	4.4×10^5	7.3×10^5	0.68	5.0×10^5
P[32]	3.1×10^3 (10)	2.7×10^3 (30)	4.3×10^3 (19)	3.3×10^3	12.0×10^3	0.24	2.9×10^3
S[35]	1.3×10^5 (9)	0.31×10^5 (10)	1.5×10^5 (19)	1.0×10^5	0.15×10^5	0.73	0.11×10^5

[a] Lal et al. (1960 c).

[b] Number of rain water analyses in parentheses.

[c] These calculated deposition rates are those given by Lal et al. (1960 c), corrected by applying factors of 1.06, 1.82, and 1.83 for Be[7], P[32], and S[35], given by Lal et al. (1960 a).

For Be[7] the individual yearly values, 1956 through 1958, are fairly constant and the agreement with calculation is satisfactory, confirming that a residence time of 30 days is close to the correct figure. Agreement is also good for P[32], but the observed values are a little higher for 1956 and 1958. It is possible that in these years 10-30% of the P[32] was produced in surface water shots, by nuclear reactions with sea water constituents such as S[32], S[34], and Cl[35]. The observed S[35] values are definitely too high, particularly for 1956 and 1958, by factors from 5 to 20 due to artificial production in bomb tests.

The difficulty with rain water concentrations is the great variability of individual values. However, the *ratio* of these concentrations, e.g., the ratio of Be[7]/P[32], varies much less. Variations of this ratio cannot develop under equilibrium conditions since the spatial distribution of production rates, the attachment to aerosols, and the removal by rain are all very similar for different isotopes. They can only be explained by the *duration* of irradiation of an air mass from which the isotopes were removed by a preceding rain. Complete removal after a rainfall is certainly an extreme assumption but we may accept it as an approximation. The concentration ratio Be[7]/P[32] shortly after the beginning of the build-up should be equal to the ratio of the production rates

$$P_{Be^7}/P_{P^{32}}.$$

If equilibrium is approached, the concentration ratio becomes

$$P_{Be^7} \cdot \lambda_{P^{32}}/P_{P^{32}} \lambda_{Be^7} = 3.7 \, P_{Be^7}/P_{P^{32}}.$$

The concentration ratio thus can vary only by a factor of 3.7. Observations show that the concentration ratio in rain varies by a factor of 4, in good agreement with the theoretical value of 3.7. The average value of this ratio for individual rains corresponds best to a tropospheric residence time of about 40 days, assuming complete removal after each rainfall (Lal, 1959). The validity of this assumption is doubtful. If correct, one would expect some correlation between the absolute concentrations in rain water and their ratio, since air and rain concentrations run parallel to a certain extent, but the data do not indicate such a correlation.

3.4 Artificial Radioactivity

3.4.1 Production of Fission Products in the Atmosphere

The global distribution of fission products from atomic bomb tests has been the object of considerable public and scientific interest in recent years. Never before has it been so clear that air chemistry must consider the whole atmosphere as a unit. The principle problem which arose concerned the role of the stratosphere in the storage and world-wide distribution of such dangerous fission products as Sr^{90}. It soon became evident that the final deposition on earth of debris injected into the stratosphere cannot be controlled or can be controlled only to a small extent by the choice of the test site and time. As testing continued, a series of intensive but sometimes poorly coordinated studies was initiated to document the atmospheric distribution and deposition of fission products on a local, continental, or global scale. The basic facts about fallout began to emerge with the accumulation of data, but many details of the large-scale atmospheric transport and mixing processes involved are still not understood.

The atomic tests served as large-scale tracer experiments in the atmosphere, but the usefulness of the data was limited. The main difficulty for a satisfactory interpretation of the observations is the large number of injections and their irregularity with time, latitude, and altitude. Another difficulty is the fact that some important information about these tests is not made public. As a result we still do not know, e.g., to what extent the observed variations of the deposition rate with time and latitude are due to the timing of the tests and the location of the test sites, or to meteorological phenomena. Apparently, a satisfactory answer to this and other questions cannot be obtained with the material now available and cannot

be expected until well-planned large-scale tracer experiments are per-
formed by single injections of known characteristics.

The discussion of fallout in the literature is somewhat controversial because the data were interpreted on the basis of different concepts and assumptions. We shall therefore concentrate on summarizing
the observational facts and those conclusions which follow directly. The
observations will be treated in the natural order of events, i.e., the formation
of debris, its distribution and storage in the stratosphere, its passage through
and removal from the troposphere, and, finally, its deposition on the ground.
In separate sections we will discuss bomb-produced tritium and carbon-14,
the hih-altitude rhodium-102 tracer experiment, and the various concepts
which have been offered for stratospheric mixing and circulation.

Since our interest is primarily directed toward the meteorological aspects of fallout, we will mention here only a few basic facts about
the production of fission material in atomic tests. For more detailed information, the reader must be referred to the special literature (e.g., Katcoff,
1958).

In all nuclear tests, most radioactive isotopes are produced
by neutron-fission of U^{235}, U^{238}, and Pu^{239}. This process results in a wide
variety of primary nuclides, but in the overwhelming majority of cases
each fission results in two nuclei of unequal mass of about 100 and 140.
These primary nuclides are highly unstable and pass through a variety of
decay chains before becoming long-lived or stable isotopes. Some long-
lived isotopes are also formed directly. The fission or production yield of
a special nuclide gives its total number formed from 100 atoms of fissionable
material. All three nuclides U^{235}, U^{238} and Pu^{239} have fairly similar fission
yield curves with two peaks of about 5% at atomic weights of 100 and 140.
As a consequence, the composition of the debris cannot vary much with
the type of nuclear device. Table 45 gives a survey of the important long-
lived isotopes normally considered in fallout literature. Isotopes with half-

TABLE 45

IMPORTANT RADIOACTIVE ISOTOPES IN WORLD-WIDE FALLOUT AND THEIR HALF-LIVES

Isotope	Half-life
Cs^{137}	28.8 years
Sr^{90}	27.7 years
Ce^{144}	285 days
Zr^{95}	65 days
Sr^{89}	51 days
Ba^{140}	12.8 days

lives that are short compared to stratospheric residence times are of little importance for world-wide fallout. They may be useful for identification of fresh debris, but they cannot accumulate on the ground and thus do not constitute a biological hazard. The potential danger of longer-lived isotopes is determined by their relative amounts, by the radiation they emit, and by their tendency to accumulate within the organism, i.e., by their biological residence time. Strontium-90 is considered to be one of the most dangerous isotopes. It has a long radioactive half-life and accumulates in bones with a practically unlimited biological residence time due to its chemical similarity to Ca.

In the fireball, radioactive and inert material is present in a highly vaporized form and condenses into aerosol clouds as cooling progresses. It is important for the condensation history that some of the longer-lived nuclides have gaseous or volatile precursors:

$$\text{Kr}^{89} \xrightarrow{\ 3.2\ \text{min}\ } \text{Rb}^{89} \xrightarrow{\ 15\ \text{min}\ } \text{Sr}^{89}$$

$$\text{Kr}^{90} \xrightarrow{\ 0.55\ \text{min}\ } \text{Rb}^{90} \xrightarrow{\ 2.7\ \text{min}\ } \text{Sr}^{90}$$

$$\text{Xe}^{137} \xrightarrow{\ 3.9\ \text{min}\ } \text{Cs}^{137}$$

$$\text{Xe}^{140} \xrightarrow{\ 16\ \text{sec}\ } \text{Cs}^{140} \xrightarrow{\ 66\ \text{sec}\ } \text{Ba}^{140}.$$

Nuclides with these precursors will condense later than others and it is likely that later condensation will result in a smaller average particle size. This fractionation of activity with respect to particle size is of interest because of the possibility that the rates of sedimentation, of washout, and, eventually, of deposition at the ground will be different for different isotopes.

Fractionation was observed in filter samples collected at the tropopause over Sweden by Edvarson et al. (1959). The larger particles, which are likely to consist of early condensed material were, e.g., considerably enriched in zirconium-95 and niobium-95 and impoverished in ruthenium-103, in agreement with considerations about the volatility of the elements in the corresponding mass-chains about 20 sec after fission. Storebö (1960) found that deposits on a mountain station in Norway are somewhat enriched in short-lived fission products. This may indicate that in periods when fresh debris prevails, a substantial part of the activity is associated with particles larger than 0.5 μ and depleted in fission products with half lives shorter than 1 to 2 months.

The radioactive aerosol formed is also strongly influenced by the type of test. Three types of atomic tests are generally distinguished: detonations in the air and at or near the surface (tower), either over land or sea. In surface detonations, considerable amounts of ground material are swept up into the fireball. This material melts or evaporates and mixes with the radioactive debris of the device. A variety of particles is formed during the cooling of the fireball, depending on the ground material, the distance of the detonation from the surface, and the size of the bomb (Adams *et al.*, 1958). A considerable fraction of the material forms particles larger than 20 μ and is removed from the atmosphere fairly rapidly by sedimentation. It constitutes the local fallout. The fraction of fission products deposited in this fashion ranges from practically zero for high air bursts to almost 100% for low-yield ground bursts. Only test clouds of devices larger than about 200 kilotons TNT penetrate the tropopause sufficient to stabilize within the stratosphere (Kellogg, 1956), and thus are important for long-range fallout. Test clouds in high latitudes will reach the stratosphere easier because the tropopause is lower. It is estimated that the following fractions of fission products remain in the stratosphere: Land surface shots: 20% (Libby, 1959 a), 35-50% (HASP, 1960 a); water surface shots: 30-80% (Libby, 1959 a), 50-70% (HASP, 1960 a). These figures are important for calculating the stratospheric inventories of debris. According to the HASP Report (1960 a), the total calculated inventory of Sr^{90} for the year 1958 does not differ by more than 20%, if the assumed fractions are varied within the given ranges. A comparison with *observed* stratospheric inventories thus does not allow the indicated limits to be narrowed. It should be noted that additional assumptions enter into such computations so that in general the over-all accuracy of figures for stratospheric inventories of fission products cannot be expected to be better than 50%.

Table 46 contains a list of all high-yield tests and their stratospheric source strength insofar as it is known. The size of the device is usually given in terms of energy produced. A megaton corresponds to the energy released by 10^6 tons of TNT, and a megaton of fission energy release produces about 0.1 megacurie of Sr^{90}.

The debris which remains in the troposphere and which is not deposited as local fallout is called tropospheric fallout. It can spread over large parts of the earth's surface, primarily within the latitude belt of the respective test site (Machta, 1958). For small land surface bursts, it can amount to 25% but is considerably smaller for high-yield explosions. It is estimated that on a global scale, total tropospheric fallout in 1958 amounts to about 5% and can thus be neglected for most considerations.

Tropospheric fallout consists primarily of particles between about 1 and 10 μ, which can be carried over considerable distances before they are removed from the atmosphere. Particles of this size range are also found weeks and even months after injection in the stratosphere (Sisefsky, 1960). The larger particles in this range are still removed primarily by sedimentation, but as the particle size decreases precipitation becomes increasingly important.

Particles between 1 and 10 μ carry relatively high individual activities, up to 10^{-9} curie and their detection as so-called " hot "

TABLE 46

ESTIMATED STRENGTH OF STRATOSPHERIC SOURCE FOR HIGH-YIELD NUCLEAR TESTS [a]

Test series [b]	Period	Location	Source strength (megatons of fission)
U.S. (Ivy)	Nov. 1952	PPG [c] (11°N, 166°E)	1.4
U.S. (Castle)	Mar.-May 1954	PPG (11°N, 166°E)	20
U.S.S.R.	Aug.-Nov. 1955	(~ 52°N)	1.8
U.S. (Redwing)	May-July 1956	PPG (11°N, 166°E)	6.7
U.S.S.R.	Aug.-Nov. 1956	(~ 52°N)	2.7
U.S.S.R.	Jan.-Apr. 1957	(~ 52°N)	
U.K.	May-June 1957	Christmas Island (2°N, 157°W) Malden Atoll (4°S, 155°W)	2.7
U.S.S.R.	Aug-Dec. 1957	(~ 52°N)	
U.K.	Nov. 1957	Christmas Island (2°N, 157°W)	5.3
U.S.S.R.	Feb.-Mar. 1958	(~ 52°N) Novaya Zemlya (75°N, 55°E)	3.3
U.S. (Hardtack I)	May-July 1958	PPG (11°N, 166°E)	4.0
U.S.S.R.	Oct. 1958	Novaya Zemlya (75°N, 55°E)	12.5–15
Total			~62

[a] Martell and Drevinsky (1960).

[b] U.K. tests of 3 high-yield devices, April and September 1958, not tabulated. The stratospheric component, based on stratospheric inventory estimates of Libby assumes stratospheric injection of 20% for surface land shots, 80% for surface water shots, and 100% for air shots.

[c] PPG, Pacific Proving Ground (includes Eniwetok and Bikini Atolls).

particles on filters in places far from test sites has caused some concern (see Strahlenschutz No. 12, 1959). These " hot " particles represent only the upper end of a wide continuous size distribution of active particles formed in the fireball and their concentration increases with decreasing activity. A few months after testing, practically all particles with more than about 10^{-10} curie are removed from the atmosphere.

Particles smaller than a few tenths of a micron can remain in the stratosphere for a long time and constitute the bulk of stratospheric activity. For all practical purposes, they behave like a gas and are removed from the stratosphere by air eschange with the troposphere and from the troposphere primarily by precipitation.

3.4.2 Distribution of Fission Products in the Stratosphere

After it became apparent from early studies (e.g., Libby, 1956 a) that the stratosphere acts as a world-wide reservoir for fission products of high-yield devices, attempts were made to obtain direct measurements. The first data which became available were aircraft profiles of the gross fission activity over England and Scandinavia in the mid-fifties (see, e.g., Machta and List, 1959). They showed low concentrations throughout the troposphere and a sharp rise within the few kilometers above the tropopause covered by the flights. However, these scattered data were not much more than a qualitative confirmation of long stratospheric hold-up times. Determination and monitoring of the distribution of fission products within the entire stratosphere poses a tremendous problem. The frequency of tests before the test moratorium of November 1958 required coverage over a wide range of altitudes and latitudes within sufficiently short time intervals. The problem can be simplified by determining latitudinal profiles, at selected longitudes, on the assumption that the pronounced zonal circulation of the atmosphere eliminates longitudinal variations. This assumption is not valid until several weeks after tests. To assess the contribution of the various test series by isotope ratios, it became necessary to determine the concentration of individual isotopes and this required collection of large samples by filters for radiochemical analysis.

Essentially two programs were initiated, both in the United States. The United States Atomic Energy Commisson used high-altitude balloons to carry filter collectors which operated at four altitudes to cover the range from 15 to 28 km. From 1956 through 1958, these " Ash Can " devices were flown once a month at four stations, Minneapolis or Sioux City (45°N), San Angelo (32°N), Panama (9°N), and Sao Paulo (23°S), and since then these flights have been continued on a reduced scale at two northern stations (Holland, 1959). The filters were analyzed for the following six isotopes: Ba^{140}, Sr^{89}, Zr^{95}, Ce^{144}, Sr^{90}, and Cs^{137}, with special interest in the last two. The results are given in disintegrations per minute and per 1000 standard cubic feet.

These balloon data are not very reliable because the volumes collected and the efficiency of the filters for the important size range between 0.01 and 0.1 μ were not accurately known. The values fluctuate considerably and it is suggested that this is due in part to these methodical difficulties. From about 16 values per month it is difficult to obtain adequate average values for the entire stratosphere (Machta and List, 1959). The meridional cross sections for the periods January to June in 1957 and January to December in 1958 show higher concentrations of Sr^{90} in the northern stratosphere with a maximum at about 20-km altitude near the equator and another maximum at about 18 km in higher latitudes. Details about the ratio of the two hemispheres and about the vertical gradients in the lower stratosphere can hardly be deduced.

The second program used U-2 aircraft and began operations in late 1957 (HASP, 1960 a, b). The sampling was done approximately along 70°W extending from 67°N to 57°S and, in the last phase, over central and western North America. Unfortunately, the collection was restricted to altitudes below 20 km. The aircraft were equipped with large filter collectors, using the ram pressure for sampling. The filter efficiency and the flow rates were determined carefully so that the concentrations obtained are accurate within 20%. Laboratory measurements indicated a collection efficiency close to 100% under flight conditions. This was confirmed by the distribution of the radioactivity within the filters as a function of the distance from the face of the filter, which showed that radioactivity dropped to practically zero towards the rear of the filter.

The samples were analyzed for Sr^{90} and partly for Cs^{137} and shorter-lived isotopes such as Sr^{89} to obtain information on the age from Sr^{89}/Sr^{90} ratios. After the Hardtack series, analysis was extended to the tracers, W^{185} and Rh^{102}.

In this program the collection frequency varied from about 2 samples per day in the early phases to about 6 samples per day in 1959 and 1960. Thus, a considerable quantity of reliable data has been obtained in this unique effort. Analysis of these data is not quite completed. The major drawback of this program is the altitude limitation. Above the collection altitude, the data were extrapolated on the basis of the Ash Can data. Since the HASP data indicated that in equatorial latitudes the concentration maximum was above 20 km this extrapolation introduces some uncertainty, especially with respect to determinations of the total stratospheric burden of various isotopes.

At present the HASP data are by far the most comprehensive available documentation of the history of fission products in the stratosphere and we will discuss the results in more detail. Figures 57-59 show the average Sr^{90} distribution for three important time intervals, November 1957-December 1958, January-August 1959, and January-March 1960. The scales are the cosine of latitude and the air density so that the isopleths represent the distribution of total Sr^{90} in the atmosphere.

Figure 57 shows a distribution with strong latitudinal and vertical gradients typical of fresh injections, primarily within the tropical stratosphere. It should be noted that the figure does not adequately represent the U.S.S.R. October tests since the authors indicate that only a few samples from these tests were included. A pronounced maximum from the Hardtack series appears above the equatorial tropopause and a secondary one appears north of 43°N.

The strong vertical and horizontal gradients disappeared

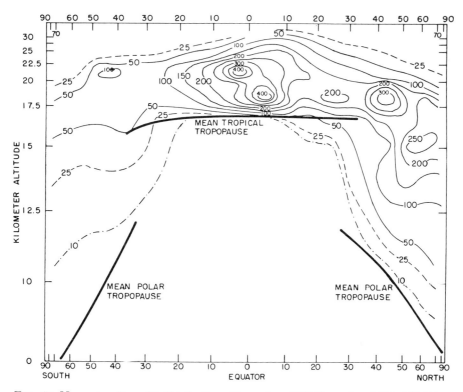

FIG. 57. Mean strontium-90 distribution, November 1957-December 1958 (HASP, 1960 b). The values above 20 km are extrapolated by limited balloon (Ash Can) data. Unit: disintegrations per minute per 1000 cubic feet STP. Latitude and altitude scales are such that the same area represents the same mass fraction of the atmosphere.

in the first half of 1959 (Fig. 58). The tropical maximum stretched hori zontally and combined with the northern one. In spring 1960 (Fig. 59), the horizontal distribution became even more uniform. All profiles show that the height of maximum concentration decreases by a few kilometers from the equator to the pole. There is an indication of a small northward movement of the concentration maximum.

This change in Sr^{90} distribution over the 1.5 years during which there were no new injections should give a clue as to whether hor izontal mixing or an organized poleward movement within the stratosphere is the main mode of transport. The data clearly show that organized mo tions, if present at all, are of minor importance and that the changes in distribution can be explained adequately by horizontal and vertical mixing along the gradients.

HASP measurements of the Sr^{89}/Sr^{90} ratio from September 1958 to October 1959 are of interest with regard to horizontal stratospheric movements of debris. Figure 60 shows that all the data north of the equator agree well from December 1958 on, irrespective of the latitude range from which the samples were taken. The slope of the curve between December 1958 and August 1959 agrees with that of the decay curve of Sr^{89} and corresponds to an effective production date of July 1958, if the production ratio Sr^{89}/Sr^{90} is assumed to be 170. This interesting result can be interpreted in two ways (Feely and Spar, 1960): Either the Soviet debris from October

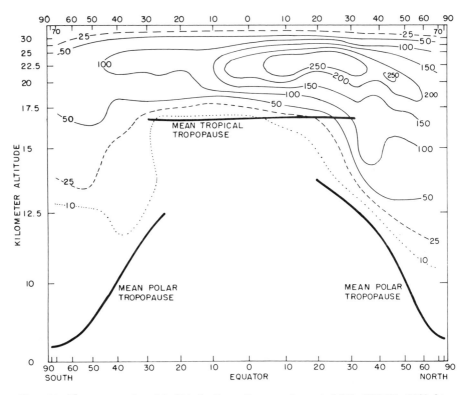

FIG. 58. Mean strontium-90 distribution, January-August 1959 (HASP, 1960 b). The values above 20 km are extrapolated by limited balloon (Ash Can) data. Unit: disintegrations per minute per 1000 cubic feet STP. Latitude and altitude scales are such that the same area represents the same mass fraction of the atmosphere.

1958 was rapidly mixed throughout the stratosphere down to the equator, contributing 27% or less Sr^{90} so that the curve represents the decay of this homogeneous mixture; or it must be assumed that virtually all debris from Soviet tests had fallen out before it had an opportunity to mix with the part of the stratosphere covered by the sampling and that the apparent age of the debris was caused by the transfer of large quantities of debris from Hardtack into the polar stratosphere. Perhaps some Soviet debris remained in the very low polar stratosphere, but only in low concentrations. The second explanation seems to be the more likely one because the data between September and October 1958 indicate a northward spreading of the debris, which was almost completed in December 1958. It is also in agreement with evidence to be discussed later, that considerable quantities of Soviet debris were removed in late winter and early spring 1959.

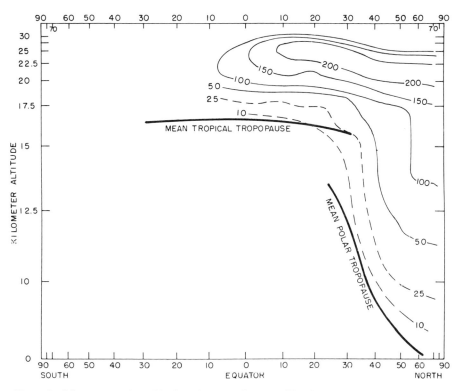

Fig. 59. Mean strontium-90 distribution, January-March 1960 (HASP, 1960 b). The values above 20 km are extrapolated by limited balloon (Ash Can) data. Unit: disintegrations per minute per 1000 cubic feet STP. Latitude and altitude scales are such that the same area represents the same mass fraction of the atmosphere.

The rate of Sr^{90} fallout should be equal to the differences in the stratospheric burden, which can be obtained by integrating the HASP latitude profiles. Let us recall that considerable parts of these profiles, i.e., those above about 20 km, are based on the less reliable Ash Can data, so that we cannot expect differences of the total burden to be very accurate. Table 47 gives some values for the period November 1958 to August 1959, which indicate an increase of the over-all residence time from 1 year to 2 and more years. Except for the last value, this increase

seems to be real and may indicate that debris of the low stratosphere is
removed faster.

TABLE 47

STRATOSPHERIC STRONTIUM-90 INVENTORIES FOR SUCCESSIVE FOUR-MONTH PERIODS [a]

Period	Sr⁹⁰ inventory (megacuries)	Per cent removed	Effective residence time (months)
Nov. 1958-Feb. 1959	1.00		
Jan.-Apr. 1959	0.83	17	12
Mar.-June 1959	0.74	11	17
May-Aug. 1959	0.72	3	67

[a] HASP (1960 a).

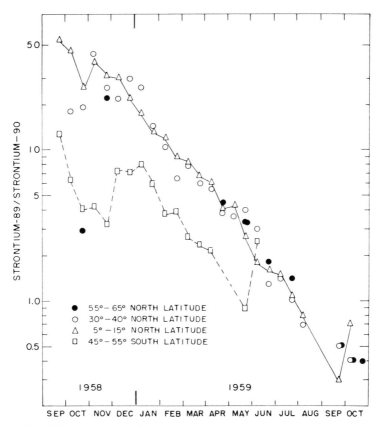

FIG. 60. Strontium-89/strontium-90 ratios in stratospheric debris
at 20-km altitude (HASP, 1960 a).

It should be emphasized here that the concept of a defined residence time τ for a natural reservoir, such as the stratosphere, is only correct if the outflow is proportional to the total content c :

$$dc/dt = -\,ac \; ; \quad c = c_0 \exp\,(-\,at) \; ; \quad \tau = 1/a.$$

This requirement is certainly fulfilled if the reservoir is well mixed, i.e., if the internal turnover time is short compared to the residence time and if the outflow is proportional to the concentration of the constituent, but this is not a *necessary* condition.

It is conceivable that, at least approximately, the above equation holds for reservoirs which are not well mixed but for which a special mechanism of exchange with surroundings results in a proportionality, or an approximate proportionality, to the content. The considerable gradients observed for all stratospheric constituents indicate that internal mixing is relatively poor and that the stratosphere does not represent a well-mixed reservoir. It is thus hard to estimate just how good or how poor the concept of a definite residence time is for the stratosphere as a whole or for portions of it. Data which will be discussed later seem to indicate that the residence time appears to increase with altitude and to decrease with latitude.

It should also be noted that if the exchange process is not of first order, the concept of a residence time for a constituent loses its meaning only for non-steady state conditions. If a steady state exists for a constituent because of a constant production rate P, we have

$$P = -\,dc/dt = ac$$

and

$$\tau = c/P.$$

This condition is perhaps realized in the stratosphere for the cosmic-ray produced isotopes. However, any spatial distribution of τ with altitude and latitude which might be obtained by such studies will have a defined meaning for this particular constituent only and cannot be applied to non-steady state conditions.

The Sr^{90} distribution in the stratosphere is a complicated mixture of a large number of injections and is not very suitable for a study of stratospheric behavior. In a number of tests made during the Hardtack series, and only then, tungsten-181 and -185 were produced in considerable quantities. These tungsten injections are the closest thing to an ideal tracer experiment, except for a single injection of Rh^{102} into very high altitudes. HASP documentation of W^{185} distribution in the stratosphere from September 1958 through 1959 shows how the equatorial cloud spreads primarily to the north along surfaces which slope down from above the sampling altitude

(20 km) at low latitudes to about 16 km at 60°. The vertical spread is not very pronounced. Apparently, the lateral spread is not constant with time, but is more rapid during the winter season of the respective hemisphere. As a result, the ratio of the tungsten burden of the two hemispheres shows a semiannual rhythm. There is no indication of an organized stratospheric circulation. During the indicated period the maximum concentration remains at the latitude of injection and the cloud seems to spread because of mixing along the horizontal gradients. These observations are in close agreement with those of Sr^{90}.

Figure 61 gives horizontal W^{185} distributions in the stratosphere, normalized for their peak values. They demonstrate the horizontal mixing process very clearly. Spar (HASP, 1960 a) used these and similar data to estimate coefficients for turbulent diffusion within the stratosphere. He approximates the cross section of debris clouds by a normal probability distribution and assumes the effective eddy diffusion coefficient D to be constant. Very little is known about D in the stratosphere and the estimates from the HASP data are perhaps among the most reliable. For lateral mixing, D seems to be between 5×10^8 and 5×10^9 cm²/sec, and for vertical mixing the data indicate values of 10^3 for the tropical and 10^4 cm²/sec for the polar stratosphere. These values are in agreement with other estimates (e.g., Brewer, 1949).

The total stratospheric inventory of W^{185} can be calculated as a function of time, if certain assumptions are made for its distribution above sampling altitudes. The decrease of the bimonthly values with time (HASP, 1960 a) is in agreement with residence times of 9 months during the winter of 1958/59, and 1.5 years and longer in the summer of 1959. These values are similar to those obtained from Sr^{90} inventories.

Before leaving the discussion of stratospheric data, let us discuss brifly the few data on the size distribution of artificial radioactivity. Stern (1959) and Jones (1960) obtained values by a two-stage cascade impactor with a back-up filter and also by simultaneous collection with various filter devices of different efficiencies. The two sets of data seem to be consistent and indicate that the average size of active particles is between 0.02 and 0.05 μ radius. However, these values must be considered tentative since in some instances much larger radii were observed, and it is not clear to what degree these variations are due to inaccuracies of the radiochemical analysis or to other reasons.

If we accept the figures given, the question arises: To what extent do the natural aerosols act as carriers for the fission products? In our discussion of cosmic-ray produced isotopes, it was pointed out that attachment of originally very small particles to the natural stratospheric aerosols would result in an activity distribution with a maximum between 0.05 and 0.1 μ radius. Values of 0.02 to 0.05 μ radius seem to indicate,

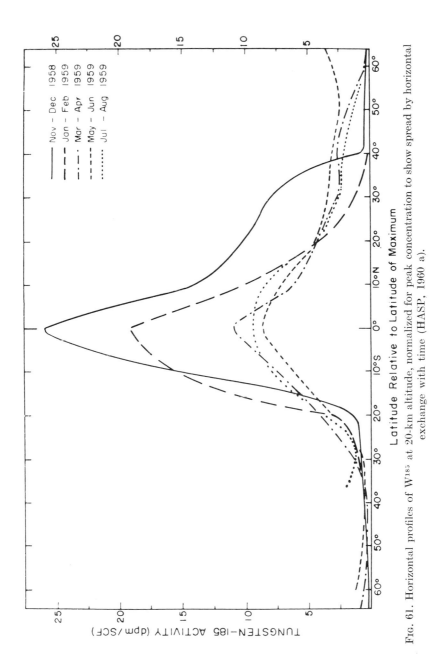

FIG. 61. Horizontal profiles of W^{185} at 20-km altitude, normalized for peak concentration to show spread by horizontal exchange with time (HASP, 1960 a).

therefore, that such an attachment did not occur to any degree and that we are still dealing primarily with the original population of particles. This is consistent with calculations which show that the rate of coagulation between particles of 0.02 μ radius and the natural aerosols in the stratosphere is so slow that agglomeration of an original particle population with natural aerosols cannot have advanced very much.

3.4.3 Distribution of Fission Products in the Troposphere

The stratospheric fission products enter the troposphere in the form in which they are present in the stratosphere, i.e., most likely as particles with an average or effective radius of 0.02 to 0.05 μ. In the troposphere these particles soon become involved in the processes of water vapor condensation, cloud evaporation, and aerosol coagulation, which were discussed in detail in Chapter 2. The net effect of these processes is a growth of the large and giant particles, and a decrease in the number concentration of the Aitken particles, due to attachment to the first two categories. Such a profound modification of the size distribution of aerosols must result in a similar modification of the distribution of fission products on their way down through the troposphere. This is clearly borne out by observation. Kalkstein *et al.* (1959) obtained distributions of the long-lived β-activity on aerosols collected 10 meters above ground with the same equipment as was used for chemical analysis of natural aerosols (Chapter 2), consisting of a two-stage cascade impactor with a back-up millipore filter. Samples of about 1 week duration were taken between July 1958 and February 1959 in air fairly unaffected by city pollution. The β-activity distribution among the three size ranges varied but little over the whole period, and the average distribution of activity was as follows:

Stage 1:	≥ 0.9 μ radius	57%	⎫
Stage 2:	0.1-0.9 μ radius	35%	⎬ β-activity.
Filter:	≤ 0.1 μ radius	8%	⎭

Most of the activity is attached to particles larger than 0.1 μ. This distribution is similar to the mass distribution of natural aerosols shown in Fig. 24 and indicates that the ratio of activity to mass does not vary much over the whole size range of natural aerosols. Rosinski and Stockham (1960) obtained a similar set of data for β-activity and Sr^{90} concentration with the following distribution:

> 1 μ radius:	19%	β-activity and 30% Sr^{90}
0.5-1 μ radius:	25%	β-activity and 24% Sr^{90}
< 0.5 μ radius:	56%	β-activity and 46% Sr^{90}.

The separation into size intervals is different and a direct comparison with the above data is not possible, but the largest particles seem to carry less, and the smallest particles more, activity. The difference may be partly due to the fact that Rosinski and Stockham collected their samples in polluted air (Chicago). However, both sets of data clearly indicate a considerable shift of the activity to larger particle sizes compared to the stratospheric distribution. This is considered to be a very basic result with respect to the dynamics of tropospheric aerosols and it would be desirable to have more and independent confirmations of this phenomenon.

The aerosol spectrum within the troposphere is modified primarily by physical processes, and, therefore, one can assume that all radioactive isotopes are affected in the same way. This, in turn, should result in the same removal rates by precipitation for different isotopes. Indication of differences in tropospheric removal rates (Storebö, 1960) imply differences in the original size distribution of stratospheric radioactive particles, i.e., a fractionation of isotopes during condensation in the fireball.

The removal of both the aerosols and the fission products from the troposphere is due primarily to precipitation, as indicated by many observations which show that dry fallout amounts to only about 10 to 20% of the total fallout at normal rainfall rates (Junge, 1958; Small 1960). It can be expected that this fraction increases in dryer climates. An ideal opportunity for determining the rate of this removal rate arose during the early U.S. tests in Nevada in which the debris remained confined to the troposphere. Stewart *et al.* (1955) documented the time variation of this debris over a period of many weeks by an aircraft sampling program over the British Isles and the Atlantic down to Gibraltar. They found a clear exponential decrease with a half-life of 20 days, or a residence time of close to 30 days. Most likely the actual lifetime is somewhat longer because the lateral spread of the fission-product cloud during its circulation around the earth was not considered. However, it was estimated that this is of no great importance after an initial period of a few weeks.

Stewart's residence time is generally accepted as the best and most reliable average value for tropospheric fallout, and applies for a constituent whose concentration increases with altitude. Table 41 shows that this residence time agrees reasonably well with values for cosmic-ray produced isotopes which have a similar vertical distribution. However, it is larger than the residence time for radon and thoron decay products, which are concentrated in the lower tropospheric layers where clouds, precipitation, and rainout and washout are more frequent. It must be expected that variations in the vertical distribution and in the particle size distribution will result in a certain range of residence times. There should also be some variation with latitude, i.e., with the lifetime of water vapor (Table 4) and with the structure and frequency of clouds. It is also not known to what extent the removal of aerosols from the troposphere is approximated by a first order process or, in other words, how good the concept of a definite residence time is.

We will now turn to the discussion of tropospheric fission products, their concentration, their variation with latitude and time, and their isotopic composition. The ease with which air and rain samples can be collected at the earth's surface has resulted in a considerable number of data from various parts of the world. It is impossible to survey these data here in detail. Sometimes they are not even comparable for technical and analytical reasons. Fortunately, this is not necessary because all the essential features can be demonstrated by the most complete and extensive set of such data obtained in the United States. In 1956 a network of 15 air sampling stations along the 80th meridian was initiated, ranging in latitude from Coral Harbor on the north side of Hudson Bay (64°N) to Punta Arenas at the southern tip of South American (53°S), (Lockhart et $al.$, 1959, 1960). Daily filter samples were analyzed for total β-activity 2 weeks after collection and for such isotopes as Sr^{90}, Sr^{89}, Ce^{144}, W^{185}, and a few others. Monthly average values of the air concentration were plotted in latitudinal cross sections, for which Fig. 62 covers an interesting period. The interpretation of these cross sections is based on the assumption that the values are representative of the entire lower troposphere, due to fairly rapid zonal and vertical mixing. Apparently, this zonal uniformity is established after about 3 to 6 weeks.

In conjunction with these profiles, we will discuss the variation of the Ba^{140}/Sr^{90} ratio obtained by Martell and Drevinsky (1960) for New England rains during the same period (Fig. 63). It can be assumed that the isotopic composition of rain is the same as that of air and is not affected by the large variations of absolute concentration due to the type of precipitation. If we deal with fresh debris from one source, the ratio Ba^{140}/Sr^{90} decreases with the half-life of Ba^{140} because it is so much shorter than that of Sr^{90}. This ratio can be used to determine the age of debris if the original production ratio is known and if debris from one source dominates. The Sr^{89}/Sr^{90} ratio can be used in a similar way. The source of the Ba^{140} component for any data point can be dated approximately by extrapolating back along a Ba^{140} decay-slope line to the intercept date corresponding to the production ratio. The inaccuracy is about 1 week and the presence of older Sr^{90} will tend to increase the apparent age of the source. The fractionation effects of the two isotopes due to short-lived gaseous precursors is minimized in high-yield nuclear tests because of the slow cooling rates in the fireball, and their chemical similarity will limit chemical fractionation, if any, in subsequent meteorological processes. Figure 63 shows that the the Ba^{140}/Sr^{90} ratio varies systematically according to Ba^{140} decay over considerable periods of time, indicating the presence of fresh debris from the same source.

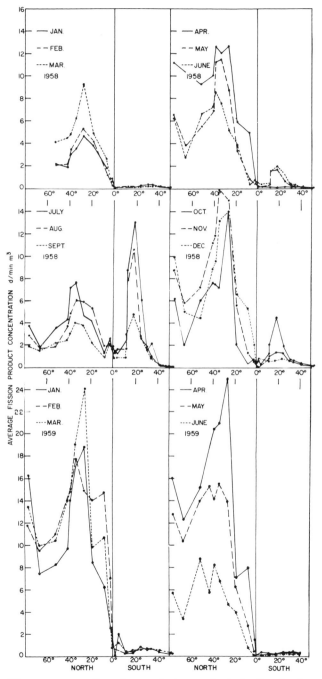

Fig. 62. Monthly average profiles of gross fission products in the air along the 80th meridian from January 1958 to June 1959. Value are given in disintegrations per minute and per cubic meter (Lockhart *et al.*, 1959, 1960).

The last high-yield tests in 1957 were those at 52°N in August-December and on the Christmas Islands in November. Figure 62 shows that beginning in January 1958 the concentration of fission activity is much higher in the northern hemisphere than in the southern hemisphere, and that there is a sharp break at the equator. The next three major test series of 1958 can be recognized clearly in both Figs. 62 and 63. By March 1958, the northern hemisphere values had risen by a factor of almost 2, with a maximum around 30°N and this continued in April and May. As Fig. 63 indicates, this rise was due primarily to the U.S.S.R. tests in February-March at 52°N. In May, debris of the U.S. Hardtack series (Fig. 62) bagan to appear in increasing values south of the equator. Figure 63 shows that from June through September, the debris in the northern hemisphere was predominantly from this source, which evidently prevailed in the southern hemisphere through November.

In October 1958 the massive U.S.S.R. test at 75°N began and soon became the primary source of north hemisphere debris (Fig. 63) and remained so throughout the first half of 1959. The concentrations south of the equator remained very low, proof that mixing across the equator within the troposphere is negligible and that no Soviet debris had reached the southern stratosphere. The sharp separation of the hemispheres within the troposphere is an important meteorological phenomenon and must be attributed to the equatorial rain belt and the trade wind circulation, but even for gases the exchange across the equator seems to be rather slow, as indicated by the distribution of tritiated methane (see Section 3.4.5).

A number of interesting features can be noted in Fig. 62. For all tests, American and Russian, a maximum in air concentration appears between 30° and 40°N, and a minimum at about 65°N. This indicates that the tropospheric distribution is caused by meteorological factors and not by the latitude of injection. These factors are the latitude of preferential stratospheric-tropospheric exchange (if any) and the latitude dependence of removal by precipitation. When Soviet debris prevails in the troposphere, a second maximum in polar latitudes is indicated. This points to a separate area of exchange between stratosphere and troposphere in high latitudes. The peak in concentration at 35°N may be caused by a preferential exchange through the tropopause gaps, and the minimum at 60° may be due to increased removal rates within the belt of west wind circulation and cyclonic activity. No attempt, however, has been made to separate these various factors.

A special feature of Fig. 63 should be mentioned. Debris from the Hardtack series showed consistently alternating Ba^{140}/Sr^{90} ratios over a period of 2 months from July to September 1958. A meteorological analysis certified that the higher values were always associated with rain in tropical air masses and the lower values with rain in polar air masses.

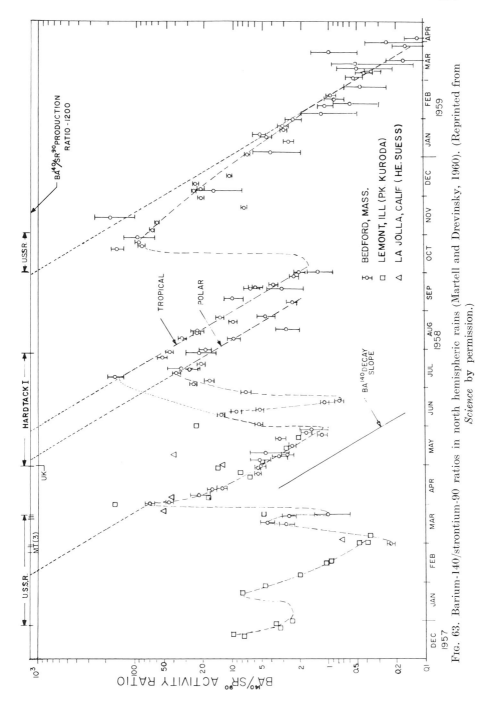

FIG. 63. Barium-140/strontium-90 ratios in north hemispheric rains (Martell and Drevinsky, 1960). (Reprinted from *Science* by permission.)

According to Martell and Drevinsky, this suggests two main areas of tropospheric-stratospheric exchange, one in polar regions and the other in southern latitudes. It also suggests that the mixing within the troposphere across the polar front or across the area of maximum precipitation in the middle latitudes is not very effective.

The spread of W^{185} from the Hardtack series was also documented by the 80th meridian network (Lockhart et $al.$, 1960). Tungsten-185

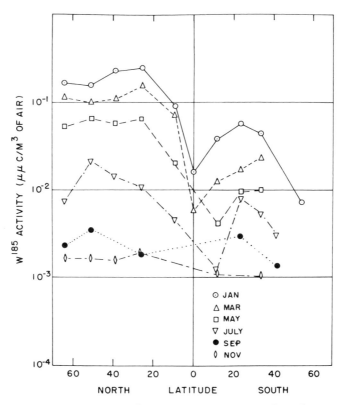

FIG. 64. Tungsten surface air activity concentrations along the 80th meridian during 1959 (Lockhart et $al.$, 1960). (By courtesy of $Journal$ of $Geophysical$ $Research.$)

first appeared near the equator in the spring of 1958, and it rapidly spread north and south in May from 34ºN to 24ºS and in June from 51ºN to 53ºS. The build-up was much the same in both hemispheres until July when the increase north of the equator became more pronounced, with a maximum again around 30º to 40ºN as in the case of Sr^{90}. Figure 64 shows the latitudinal distribution in 1959. In the beginning of the year, the decrease was more rapid in the southern hemisphere, but this was reversed in the summer of 1959 so that by the end of 1959 the concentration was about equal in both hemispheres. This semiannual rhythm was already noted in the W^{185} HASP data within the stratosphere and the phases seem to correspond to each other.

The isotopes W^{185} and Sr^{89} can be used to calculate the contribution of different test series to the total observed Sr^{90}, which is normally a mixture of older and newer debris. Martell and Drevinsky (1960) applied this method to rain samples in New England for the heavy fallout in the spring of 1959; they found that 15% of the Sr^{90} was due to the Hardtack series and 85% to the U.S.S.R. October 1958 series. Lockhart (1960) found similar values. This agrees with the conclusions drawn from Fig. 63.

Because of the placement of nuclear tests in time and latitude, it is very difficult to determine how far the observed variations of fallout are controlled by seasonal variations of meteorological factors. Stewart et al. (1957) and Machta (1958) think that the major part of each peak in late winter-early spring is caused by increased exchange between the stratosphere and troposphere, similar to the tropospheric variation of ozone (see Fig. 16). Martell (1959) and Martell and Drevinsky (1960) employed isotope ratio data to demonstrate that most spring peaks are dominated by debris from high latitude tests in the preceding fall.

What is the evidence for true seasonal variations? Let us start with the southern hemisphere. All stratospheric activity in the southern hemisphere stems from U.K. tests right at the equator or from U.S. test debris that has mixed southward across the equator. This is reflected in the HASP data by a more pronounced drop of the concentration south of the equator than north of it. The tropospheric air concentrations of Sr^{90} and W^{185} along the 80th meridian in the southern hemisphere show no or only minor indications of a southern spring maximum, which *cannot* be explained by the timing of the tests. It appears from this that stratospheric sources in low latitudes do not cause a marked seasonal variation. However, it should be considered that both hemispheres do not behave symmetrically in circulation and in exchange between stratosphere and troposphere. Surface and total ozone data from Antarctica (Wexler et al., 1960) and from other places south of the equator, e.g., indicate that the maximum occurs already during the winter rather than in late winter or early spring as in the northern hemisphere.

In the northern hemisphere one should distinguish between debris from low and from high latitude injections. There is evidence of a seasonal variation of U.K. and U.S. debris in the long series of New York City Sr^{90} rainfall data (U.S. Atomic Energy Commission, 1958). These data show a regular spring maximum in deposition even is spring 1955 after only very small U.S.S.R. tests had been conducted in the preceding fall. Other evidence is the 1959 spring maximum of W^{185} concentration in New

England rains. Martell and Drevinsky (1960) showed that this increase in deposition was primarily associated with rains in polar air masses, whereas rains in tropical air masses did not show a variation in activity. The concentration of W^{185} in air in the north temperate latitudes during the same period exhibits only one broad maximum from September 1958 to June 1959 (Lockhart et al., 1960) and the phase difference between the two hemispheres during the 1959 decrease is not very marked (Fig. 64). However, spring maxima of fallout do not seem to occur at all longitudes. Miyake et al. (1960) measured the deposition of Sr^{90} in Tokyo from 1956 through 1959 and found no regular spring peak. It is possible that the location of Japan with respect to the permanent upper air trough is responsible for this different behavior. Ozone data from Japan seem to point in the same direction. However, it should always be kept in mind that the total deposition by rain is influenced by both the amount of rainfall and the air concentration, and that the air concentration in the troposphere in turn is influenced by injection rate from the stratosphere and the deposition rate at the ground. The occurrence of a spring maximum is positively ensured only if both rainfall and rain concentration (or air concentration) show a maximum.

The deposition of debris injected into the stratosphere at *high* latitudes shows a pronounced seasonal variation. Martell (1959) and Martell and Drevinsky (1960) demonstrated that debris from Soviet tests at northern latitudes is removed within 3 to 9 months. The release of this material is apparently controlled by the same processes in late winter and early spring which cause the downward transport of ozone. The actual holdup time depends on the time interval between injection and spring release. Removal seems to be rapid and fairly complete for high-altitude injections in late fall, as demonstrated by the dramatic fallout in early 1959 from the U.S.S.R. tests in October 1958.

A small but distinct spring maximum was observed during 1960, e.g., by Bleichrodt et al. (1961) who measured the specific activity of surface air in Holland. This maximum was caused by meteorological factors exclusively and was not affected by the French tests, February 13 and April 1, 1960. The amplitude was about a factor of 2 similar to tropospheric ozone. Since it can be assumed that at this time the stratospheric debris was aready fairly well mixed, this agreement is significant.

These observations are still tentative, but they point to the following general picture: The *amplitude* of the seasonal variation of stratospheric fallout is high for material in the polar stratosphere and decreases considerably for stratospheric material in lower latitudes. The *residence times* are of the order of $\frac{1}{2}$ year for the low polar stratosphere, about 1 year for the low tropical stratosphere, and perhaps several years for tropical injections into the higher stratosphere (30 km), such as the Castle tests.

These differences in the fallout of stratospheric material are important for the rate and density of deposition on the earth's surface. The fallout of high latitude injections will be confined to one hemisphere and released at a faster rate. Tropical injections, on the other hand, will spread over both hemispheres and will be released at lower rates. Since most of the U.S. high-yield tests were land or water surface bursts with considerable local fallout, the contribution of fallout per megaton of test source for U.S. tests is even further reduced. Martell and Drevinsky (1960) estimate that on a per megaton basis the concentration of Sr^{90} activity in rains in middle latitudes is higher by a factor of 10 to 50 for high latitude tests than for tropical tests. This estimate may be too high (Peirson and Stewart, 1961; Martell and Drevinsky, 1961), but there can be little doubt that injections into the lower polar stratosphere represent a relatively higher potential hazard for temperate latitudes. This is increased even more by a larger contribution from short-lived fission products, due to *faster* deposition.

3.4.4 Deposition of Fallout on the Earth's Surface

Measurements in temperate latitudes indicate that precipitation accounts for 80 to 90% of the fallout deposition, similar to the removal of other particulate material. It is likely that in areas of ittle rainfall, the percentage of dry fallout will be greater. The best data on this subject were reported recently by Small (1960). He compared air concentrations of fission products and fallout rates on dry and rainy days for the period 1956 to 1959 in southern Norway. Monthly average values of both dry and wet deposits show a good correlation with the air concentration. The average deposition velocity is 50 meter/day for dry days and 3000 meters/day for rainy days. A deposition velocity of 50 meters/day corresponds to an effective particle radius of about 2 μ and seems to support the indication that most artificial activity is concentrated on rather large particles, at least in the lower troposphere. The dry deposit amounts to 16% of the deposit on rainy days. This figure is in good agreement with previous observations (e.g., Stewart *et al.*, 1959).

In single rains the concentration of fission products, like other constituents, varies considerably. If average values over a period of a month or longer are formed, these variations are largely smoothed out and the rain concentrations become fairly uniform, at least within areas of similar climatological conditions. In other words, within such areas the local deposition of long-lived fission products is proportional to the rate of precipitation (e.g., Collins and Hallden, 1958; Martell, 1959). Figure 65 shows the Sr^{90} deposition as a function of rainfall for the southern and northern U.S., revealing a linear relationship. The slope of the curves, which is equivalent to the average rain concentration, varies with the climatological area and also with the season. The southern U.S. stations include primarily those from the S.E. with high rates of rainfall. Ohta (1960) showed that in England and Japan the highest concentrations are observed in winter and spring. The rule that the deposition is proportional to rainfall emerged

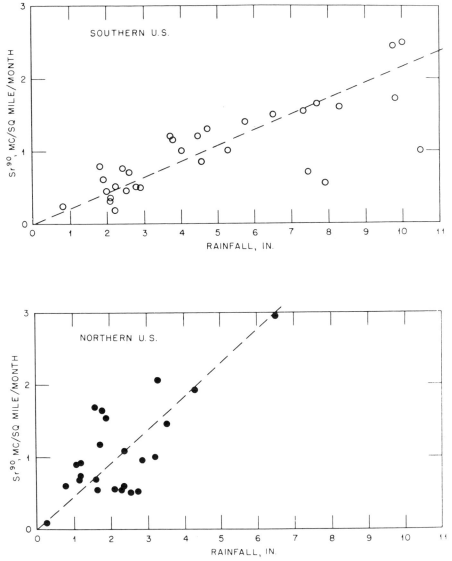

FIG. 65. Relation between the total monthly deposits of strontium-90 and the monthly amounts of precipitation for a number of stations in southern and northern United States.

from a large number of data obtained in different parts of the world and is of basic importance for air chemistry, especially for fallout studies. The average concentration in rain water, and its variation with climate and season, depends on the average concentration of the constituent in air and on the characteristics of the rain-producing clouds, particularly their liquid-water content and their vertical structure. In general, the concentration in rain water will be lower for clouds with a high liquid water content, as for example convective clouds, but this will be discussed in more detail in Chapter 4.

Another important observation which was reported by several observers is that the concentration in rain water is roughly proportional to the concentration in air. In his long series of homogeneous data, Small (1960) finds that the ratio of ground air to rain concentration (both expressed in the same units) varies only within rather narrow limits, i.e., from 0.25×10^{-6} to 2.1×10^{-6}, with an average of 0.9×10^{-6}. This average value is close to that found in other places, e.g., Holland or Germany (Hinzpeter, see Strahlenschutz No. 12, 1959). The physical significance of this ratio is discussed in Section 4.2.2 and it can be expected that it varies to some extent with the climatological area and the season. It is likely that this rule of a fairly constant ratio is valid only for constituents which have a rather uniform vertical distribution like that of the fission products, but that it cannot be applied to constituents which vary considerably with altitude, like sea-salt particles over the ocean.

Most of the Sr^{90} in rain is present in soluble form. In contact with soil it becomes almost completely adsorbed and this adsorption is so strong that it remains concentrated within the upper layers of the soil for many years. Walton (1960) has recently reviewed this subject very carefully. He finds that in over 10 different investigations on the vertical distribution of Sr^{90}, in a variety of soil types, 62-80% of the total Sr^{90} is contained in the upper 5 cm of the soil. Of course, this is valid only for uncultivated soils, or soils whose upper layers have not been disturbed by other processes. Generally, the Sr^{90} penetrates somewhat further in sandy soils, and less deep in soils which are rich in loam.

Of great interest is the *latitudinal* deposition of fission products, primarily Sr^{90}. Because of its long half-life, Sr^{90} gives a fairly representative picture of the total deposition of fission products. Walton (1960) compiled the best data available on Sr^{90} in soil and used them for the global estimate given in Fig. 66.

The density of deposition (Fig. 66 b) is based on direct soil analyses, primarily on the unique set of data obtained by Alexander (1959). The average data for the latitude belts were obtained by assuming proportionality for rainfall and Sr^{90} deposition for those areas where no soil data were available. We see that Sr^{90} fallout has a maximum between

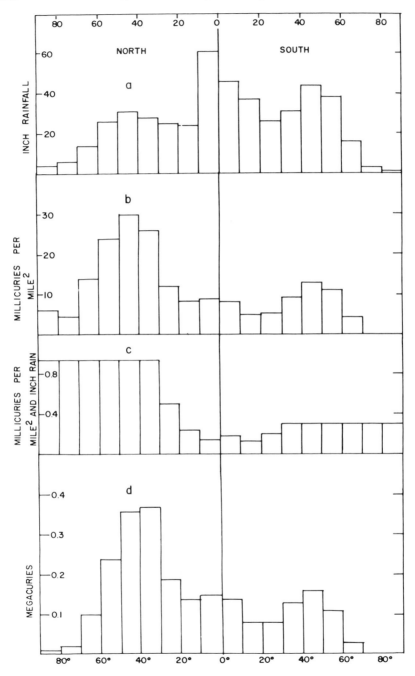

FIG. 66. The latitudinal deposition of Sr^{90} (Walton, 1960). a, Average rainfall; b, average density of Sr^{90} deposit on soil by July 1958; c, average Sr^{90} concentration in rain during 1958; d, total global deposit of Sr^{90} by July 1958.

40° and 50°N and a smaller secondary maximum south of the equator. These maxima must be due to meteorological factors because the amount of *tropospheric* fallout is considered to be less than 5% and because local fallout is not included in Fig. 66 b. Any incidental inclusion of *local* and *tropospheric* fallout would tend to minimize the maximum since the latitudes of the test sites are located north (Soviet) and south (U.S.; U.K.) of the northern maximum. The latitudinal distribution of average rainfall (Fig. 66 a) shows maxima at the same latitudes, but these are much less pronounced. The high rainfall rate at the equator, on the other hand, corresponds to rather low Sr^{90} deposition.

The average rain concentration (Fig. 66 c) shows a pronounced minimum at the equator and almost constant values at latitudes higher than 30°. These rain concentrations are based on independent observations during 1958 and, therefore, do not agree with values calculated from Figs. 66 a and b. Figure 66 d gives the integrated total for the entire earth's surface and shows that most Sr^{90} is deposited in north temperate latitudes.

The higher amounts of Sr^{90} deposit in the northern hemisphere are due to a higher fraction of the U.S. debris plus the total of the Soviet debris. It is to be noted that the latitude of the deposition maximum does not correspond to the maximum of air concentration at 30°N (Fig. 62). The peak in rainfall in both hemispheres also does not coincide with the minimum in air concentration at about 65° (Fig. 62), or with a minimum in rain concentration. The relationships between the latitudinal variation of the deposit, the rain concentration, the rainfall intensity, and the air concentration are not clear, and no attempt has been made to explain them quantitatively. The concurrence of high rainfall and low air and rain concentrations at the equator are at least qualitatively understandable. It is likely that most of the Sr^{90} and other fission products in the tropics are supplied from higher latitudes by the trade winds and it can be expected that removal by rain in the ascending air at the thermal equator will be fairly complete.

As of July 1958 the global fallout of Sr^{90} is given by the following figures (Fig. 66):

Northern hemisphere	1.58 megacuries	⎫
Southern hemisphere	0.73 megacuries	⎬ ratio 2.3
	⎭
Total fallout	2.31 megacuries.	

We can compare the ratio of the two hemispheres with the figures in Table 46 if we assume that by June 1958 everything was deposited which was injected before the U.K. tests in November 1957, that all U.S.S.R. debris remained in the northern hemisphere, and that the source strength is equally divided between the U.K. and the U.S.S.R. tests in the two cases where only the total amount is given. The observed ratio of 2.3 is then obtained by splitting the U.S. and U.K. tests by 3 : 2 between the northern and southern hemispheres. This appears to be reasonable in view of the HASP data and the latitude of the test sites.

In conclusion we may give some figures on the world-wide Sr^{90} budget. Walton (1960) arrived at the following figures for July 1958:

Total surface burden, 2.3 megacuries. This figure may be in error by $\pm 30\%$, primarily due to uncertainties in the precipitation data.

Total stratospheric burden, 1.0 megacuries, based on HASP and Ash Can data.

Total Sr^{90} present, 3.3 megacuries.

Total stratospheric injection, 3.6 megacuries. This is the total estimated production minus local and tropospheric fallout. The accuracy of this figure is perhaps not better than $\pm 50\%$ due to uncertainties in production and local fallout. The tropospheric fallout amounts to only a few per cent.

We see that both values for total Sr^{90}, 3.3 and 3.6, agree satisfactorily for the given limits of accuracy.

3.4.5 Artificial Carbon-14 and Tritium

In contrast to the previously discussed isotopes, C^{14} and T form gases. This difference in their final phase after formation is the reason for a different behavior in their atmospheric distribution and warrants separate discussion.

Natural C^{14} is produced by cosmic radiation at an average rate of two atoms per cm^2 and per second (Table 43). It is in exchange with all the carbon reservoirs listed in Fig. 9 and again in Table 48. Since the residence time in these reservoirs is short compared to its radioactive lifetime of 8000 years, the specific activity of about 14 to 15 dpm/g carbon is approximately uniform throughout these reservoirs. The " slow " carbon cycle of the sedimentary rocks, on the other hand, is of the order of 3×10^5 years or about 30 times longer than the C^{14} lifetime and the amounts of C^{14} in the reservoirs of this cycle are negligible (Brown, 1957).

Artificial C^{14} is produced in considerable quantities by neutrons which escape from the fireball and are absorbed by atmospheric nitrogen. Experiments indicate that at first $C^{14}O$ is formed rather than $C^{14}O_2$ (Pandow et al., 1960), but the fact that atmospheric CO_2 has the required specific activity forces one to conclude that the final form under natural conditions in $C^{14}O_2$.

Several estimates have been made of the C^{14} produced per megaton TNT equivalent (e.g., Libby, 1956 b; Pauling, 1958). This quan-

TABLE 48

AVERAGE DATA FOR ARTIFICIAL C^{14} BY MID-1959

	Carbon reservoir [a] (g/cm²)	Natural C^{14} [b] inventory (atoms/cm²)	Artificial C^{14} inventory (atoms/cm²)	Increase by mid-1959 (%)
Stratosphere	0.024 [c]	1.4×10^9	$\sim 2.9 \times 10^9$ [d]	~ 210
North troposphere	0.051	3.0	0.8 [e]	27
South troposphere	0.051	3.0	0.5 [e]	17
Terrestrial biosphere	0.06	3.5	0.06 [e]	1.7
Humus	0.21	12.4	—	—
Ocean above thermocline	0.15	8.8	0.3 [e]	3.4
Ocean below thermocline	7.30	430	—	—
Total [f]	7.85	460×10^9	$\sim 4.6 \times 10^9$	~ 1.0

[a] See also Fig. 9.

[b] Specific activity of cyclic carbon assumed to be 14 dpm/g, equivalent to 5.8×10^{10} atoms C^{14} per gram carbon.

[c] Average tropopause height assumed to be 12 km.

[d] Hagemann et al. (1959).

[e] Brocker (1959), Münnich and Vogel (1959), Fergusson (1959).

[f] Earth's surface is 5.10×10^{18} cm² for conversion to total amounts on earth.

tity depends on the type of device and on whether the explosion takes place near the ground or in the atmosphere. In the former case only 50% of the neutrons are absorbed in the air. The most recent average figures are 1×10^{26} atoms per megaton of total (fission and fusion) weapon yield for a ground burst and 2×10^{26} for an air burst. This gives estimates from 10 to 50×10^{27} atoms for the total production by 1959. Measurements of the stratospheric burden result in an estimated total of 25×10^{27} atoms (Hagemann et al., 1959) which value is used in Table 48. The tropospheric values in Table 48 are based on data from Brocker (1959) and Münnich and Vogel (1959) for the northern hemisphere and Fergusson (1959) for the southern hemisphere. Both values show a persistent difference over years, indicating poor mixing in the troposphere *and* stratosphere.

The increase over the natural background is substantial in the stratosphere (last column, Table 48), 20-30% in the troposphere, and only a few per cent in the biosphere and the upper ocean. The value for the biosphere refers to an average whereas newly formed portions of the biosphere will have values close to those of the troposphere. If no further testing of atomic weapons takes place, the C^{14} will slowly spread uniformly throughout the exchangeable reservoirs, with a final increase of about 1% before decay becomes appreciable. For an over-all residence time of about

5 years for atmospheric CO_2, one would expect a small increase of tropospheric $C^{14}O_2$ for a few years until the exchange with the ocean becomes the controlling factor and the concentration begins to decrease again.

Our information on the C^{14} distribution in the stratosphere is based on a program of air collections at the same four stations (Minneapolis, Minnesota, 45°N; San Angelo, Texas, 32°N; Canal Zone, Panama, 9°N; Sao Paulo, Brazil, 23°S) at which the Ash Can program was operated. Samples were obtained with balloon equipment at four altitudes between 15 and 30 km beginning in 1954/55 (Hagemann et al., 1959). The C^{14} increase in the lowest level at 15 km was found to be small, but considerable amounts and fluctuations were observed in higher layers, indicating poor vertical and horizontal mixing even within 1 year after injections. The latitude-altitude cross section based on data collected during the summer of 1955, is of special interest since all major injections prior to this time occurred at 11°N, primarily in two series in 1952 and 1954, and since in 1955 one year had elapsed for mixing. This cross section shows the following features:

(1) The mixing ratio of C^{14} with air increases at all latitudes up to the peak sampling altitude of 29 km. This suggests that a maximum of more than 5×10^7 atoms/g of air was located *beyond* 29 km in the summer of 1955. The Sr^{90} profiles a few years later show a definite maximum below this altitude (see Figs. 57-59).

(2) The values are generally lowest above the tropical tropopause and increase towards higher latitudes at each altitude level. This fact is surprising because all injections occurred at 11°N and because corresponding Sr^{90} cross sections show the maximum above the latitude of injections.

(3) Except for a few not very reliable values at peak altitude, mixing ratios are higher in the northern hemisphere. This corresponds to the findings in the troposphere given in Table 48.

Almost all these features are different from those observed for Sr^{90}, and later for W^{185} and other isotopes. The reason for this discrepancy is not clear, but somehow a large-scale fractionation between particulate material and gases such as $C^{14}O$, $C^{14}O_2$, or THO and TH must be involved. Although the greatest lateral extent of the visible test clouds in the stratosphere may have been below 29 km, the gases could have passed to higher altitudes while the particulate material sank down by gravitation. An indication of such fractionation is given by tropospheric C^{14} data from 1954 and 1955 by Patterson and Blifford (1957). They found practically no increase of C^{14} in 1954 despite considerable fallout of fission products. The C^{14} concentration in tropospheric air did not increase markedly until April 1955, due to release from the stratosphere.

However, this fractionation would not account for the fact that the lowest concentrations are found in the latitude zone of injection. Hagemann *et al.* (1959) offered two tentative explanations. First, the material in the tropical stratosphere is bodily removed by a Brewer-type circulation (Brewer, 1949), with the air ascending in the equatorial stratosphere, spreading north and south and subsiding in higher latitudes. This explanation, however, is not in agreement with the Sr^{90} and W^{185} profiles (Figs. 57-59). The second possibility assumes that the material was injected into altitudes above 29 km and that it diffuses downward. If this downward diffusion is less efficient in equatorial latitudes, and if horizontal exchange in the lower stratosphere is somewhat restricted, the observed distribution could result. A similar distribution is observed for the high-altitude injection of Rh^{102}, which will be discussed in the next section. Slow mixing across the equator in the higher stratosphere may account for higher mixing ratios in the northern hemisphere.

The removal rate of stratospheric C^{14} would be of interest, but the stratospheric inventories are not accurate enough for an estimate. In fact, the inventory seems to be almost constant over the period from 1955 to 1958. At the same time, there is a general increase in tropospheric $C^{14}O_2$ concentration, which amounts to about 25% of the stratospheric inventory, after a correction is made for exchange with the ocean and the biosphere. This is equivalent to a 5-year residence time, which is longer than the estimates for Sr^{90} and W^{185}, but the C^{14} is concentrated in higher stratospheric layers than the other isotopes are and the result may indicate a general increase in residence time with altitude.

The specific activity of tropospheric CO_2 and also of fresh plant material shows a general increase with time up to the time for which data are published (fall, 1959; Münnich and Vogel, 1959). Seasonal variations with a minimum in winter are superimposed. Since all sinks for atmospheric CO_2, e.g., the ocean, work rather slowly, the winter minimum must be local and is perhaps due to dilution of the C^{14} concentration by fuel consumption in the heavily populated areas of West Germany.

Most of the *tritium* produced in atomic tests is oxidized to HTO. Synthetic tritium in rain water first became noticeable after Operation Ivy in 1952, and Craig and Lal (1961) showed that the natural conditions must have been affected already during this time. The Castle tests in early 1954 and subsequent tests generated such considerable quantities that by now most of the T found in the interchangeable reservoirs is artificial and will remain so for quite some time even without further testing. This is demonstrated in Tables 49 and 50, which are compiled from data by Begemann and Libby (1957) and Libby (1959 b, 1961).

The behavior of the tritium fallout from the Castle tests, and perhaps also from other water surface shots, was entirely different

TABLE 49

TRITIUM CONCENTRATIONS IN TRITIUM UNITS (10^{-18} T/H) [a]

	Pre-Castle, considered natural background, prior to Craig and Lal [b]	1955 Post-Castle	1959/1960
Rains			
Northern hemisphere			
Continental (Chicago)	2-15; av. 8	10-50; av. 20	68
Maritime (West Caost)	—	8	18
Southern hemisphere	3–7	—	9
Mississippi River	5	44	119
Ocean surface water			
Northern hemisphere	0.2-2; av. 1	1.5-4.0; av. 3	8
Southern hemisphere	1	1	4

[a] Data from Begemann and Libby (1957) and Libby (1959 b, 1961).

[b] According to Craig and Lal (1691), most of these values must already be considered contaminated by synthetic tritium.

from that of all other isotopes, including C^{14}. In a period of several months, up to the end of 1954, huge amounts of T were deposited as THO by rains in the northern hemisphere, but none was deposited south of the equator (Table 49). The fallout of tritium had practically stopped during 1955. The concentration in surface waters of northern oceans rose by a factor of about 3, with perhaps a small decline during 1955, and the concentration in Mississippi river water rose by a factor of 10. The deposition rate of tritium during 1954 corresponded to a residence time of about 40 days, which is much shorter than the stratospheric residence time of Sr^{90} and longer than the 10-day tropospheric lifetime of water vapor. It is suggested that this specific behavior is caused by the considerable amounts of sea water which were engulfed in the fireball and rose high into the stratosphere. Most of this water condensed to ice particles which settled down into the troposphere at a rate corresponding to a 40-day residence time and carried with them the larger portion of the T produced and burned to HTO. Rough estimates for the northern hemisphere give $200 \times 10^7 - 50 \times 10^7 = 150 \times 10^7$ atoms/cm^2 removed (Table 50) and about $50 \times 10^7 - 7 \times 10^7 \cong 40 \times 10^7$ remaining in the stratosphere. This latter value is rather uncertain. The first value was obtained from the observed 2 tritium unit increase in ocean water above the thermocline, on the assumption that mixing did not penetrate very much below the thermocline (Libby, 1959 b). The stratospheric value is based on the C^{14} inventories obtained by Hagemann et al. (1959) and discussed earlier. Their simultaneous C^{14} and T

TABLE 50

TRITIUM INVENTORIES IN AVERAGE NUMBER OF ATOMS PER cm² OF EARTH'S SURFACE

Inventory	Natural	Post-Castle	1959/1960
Stratosphere	7×10^7 [a]	50×10^7 [b]	100×10^7 [c]
			20×10^7 [d]
Troposphere [e]			
North of equator	0.05×10^7	0.10×10^7	0.20×10^7
South of equator	0.05×10^7	0.05×10^7	0.10×10^7
Surface ocean waters [f]			
North of equator	50×10^7	200×10^7	350×10^7
South of equator	50×10^7	50×10^7	130×10^7

[a] Stratospheric production rate 0.25 atom/cm² sec and a residence time of 1 year for the lower stratosphere (Craig and Lal, 1961).

[b] Estimated from a 1955 C^{14} burden of 1.6×10^9 C^{14} atoms/cm² and a ratio of $T/C^{14} = \frac{1}{3}$ (Hagemann et al., 1959).

[c] Estimated from a 1959 C^{14} burden of 2.9×10^9 C^{14} atoms/cm² (Table 48) and a ratio $T/C^{14} = \frac{1}{3}$.

[d] Estimate, Libby (1961). This value seems to be more reliable than 100×10^7.

[e] Average precipitable water, 2.5 cm.

[f] Depth of thermocline, 75 meters.

data show a good correlation corresponding to an average ratio of $C^{14}/T = 3$ for most samples at all altitudes from 1955 through 1959. The amount of 40×10^7 T atoms/cm² at the end of 1954 remained at a similar altitude as the C^{14} and was apparently too high to cause any tritium fallout during 1955.

Throughout 1955 the tritium concentration remained essentially constant in ocean surface water, in rain water, and in Mississippi water. This was interpreted by Begemann and Libby (1957) to indicate that mixing above the thermocline and within the ground water reservoir, at least of the Mississippi Valley, was rather rapid. The resulting 1955 plateau of all concentrations represented thus a quasi-steady state of the T distribution. This offered a unique opportunity to obtain information on the continental water budget. An average T deposition of about 200×10^7 atoms/cm² in the northern hemisphere and an increase of the Mississippi T concentration from 4 to 44 T.U. (Table 49) requires an average exchangeable ground water reservoir of 8 meters, if rapid mixing is assumed. Eriksson (1958), however, points out that the assumption of rapid mixing is unrealistic for ground water and shows that a constant tritium content of river water can also be explained by the fact that the passage time of water through the ground varies over a wide range. The net effect for river water composition would be similar to rapid mixing, but the estimate of the ground water reservoir is seriously affected and could be as small as one-third of the above value. The average precipitation rate of 77 cm in the Mississippi Valley would indicate an average residence time of ground water of 3 to 10 years, and it is thus understandable that the Mississippi water changes its composition very slowly.

The fact that the tritium concentration in the Chicago rains was only 20 T.U. during the same period (Table 49) indicates, according to Libby (1959 b), that the atmospheric water vapor was composed of two-thirds maritime water and one-third reevaporated continental water. Libby draws further interesting conclusions about the North American water budget which we cannot discuss in detail here, but which show the potentialities of tritium as a tracer in meteorology and hydrology.

Further T fallout occurred from 1956 through 1959 and the concentrations in rain, river, and ocean water increased irregularly. The large 1959 spring peak in Sr^{90}, caused by the Soviet tests in October 1958, was paralleled by a similar peak in T fallout (Libby, 1961). This suggests that in land or air bursts, tritium behaves like the other isotopes and that the peculiar features of the Castle tritium are restricted to water surface shots. Since 1956 there has also been tritium fallout in the southern hemisphere (Table 49), but the amounts were only half as large as in the northern hemisphere, similar to Sr^{90} and C^{14}.

Most of the estimates listed in Table 50 are based on a small and insufficient number of data and are rather uncertain. This is demonstrated by the discrepancy between the estimates of stratospheric tritium in 1959 by Libby (1961) and by C^{14} inventories. However, it appears quite certain that by 1960 most of the T injected into the stratosphere had already been deposited on the ground. We would like to mention that a spring peak of T in 1960 in rain water from the west coast of Ireland is another proof of seasonal variations of stratospheric removal rates (Libby, 1961).

Artificial tritium is present not only in water but also in atmospheric hydrogen. Reliable data recently became available through Gonsior (1959), Bishop and Taylor (1960), and, primarily, Begemann and Friedman (1959). Their main results can be summarized as follows.

(1) The HT content of air did rise considerably after the Ivy tests, but was hardly affected by Operation Castle. We recall that water tritium behaved exactly the opposite way. It is possible that differences between Ivy and Castle, with respect to HT, are partly due to different types of devices tested.

(2) From 1955 on, the increase of the T concentration is considerably accelerated. By 1958 the tritium level is 30 times the natural level. Bishop and Taylor think that the general trend is approximately

exponential, with a doubling time of 1.5 years. The numerous data of Begemann and Friedman show that this approximation is only very rough and that considerable fluctuations are superimposed.

(3) There is very little correlation between the variations of tritium in water and in hydrogen.

(4) From 1954 to 1956, Begemann and Friedman made parallel measurements of tritium and deuterium in atmospheric hydrogen and found a marked positive correlation. This is of special interest since the amount of deuterium added in atomic tests is relatively small compared to the natural deuterium level.

It is clear that considerable amounts of HT were formed by thermonuclear tests, but the accelerated build-up of the HT level after the test moratorium is remarkable. The correlation between deuterium and tritium is not easy to explain. The natural sources of hydrogen are too small to account for considerable fluctuations in the isotopic composition, although it is known that, e.g., hydrogen produced in biological processes can have different D/H ratios (Chapter 1). Exchange of T and D between water and hydrogen is much too slow at normal temperatures to account for any fluctuations. Begemann and Friedman suggest that the variations are caused by hydrogen sources which have a tritium level similar to that of water, but whose D/H is 20-30% lower. These sources must be rather local and should result in corresponding fluctuations of the total H_2 concentrations.

Recently tritium has also been observed in a third constituent of the atmosphere, namely, in methane. Bishop et al. (1961) collected methane samples from the northern and southern hemispheres at the ground and by aircraft up to 15 km. Their results can be summarized in the following way.

(1) An average latitude-altitude cross section for the period September 1957 to February 1959 shows the highest values of 22×10^3 T.U. (1 T.U. corresponds to a T/H ratio of 10^{-18}) in the northern troposphere, 10-14 $\times 10^3$ T.U. over the equator, and about 8×10^3 T.U. in the southern troposphere and in the lower stratosphere for both hemispheres. This cross section implies that the source cannot be stratospheric, but must be located in the northern troposphere. All the data show that the specific activity of CH_4 is considerably higher than that of water, but lower by a factor of about 15 than that of hydrogen.

(2) The data in the southern hemisphere from 1953 through 1958 show an increase from 0.9×10^3 T.U. (1953) to 9×10^3 T.U. (1958), which can be approximated by an exponential curve, with a doubling time of 1.5 years.

(3) Thirty samples from England between October 1958 and March 1959 show short-term fluctuations between 15 and 33 $\times 10^3$ T.U.

This points to rather local sources, and air trajectories indicated the sources in a direction northwest of England.

A natural source of the tritiated CH_4 is excluded because of its increase with time and the differences in distribution between the hemispheres in view of a residence time of methane of about 50 to 100 years and a radioactive half-life of tritium of 12.5 years. The lower concentrations in the stratosphere make it very unlikely that tritiated CH_4 was produced in thermonuclear tests. An exchange with tritiated water is equally unlikely because of the much lower specific activity of water.

Bishop et al. checked the possibility that the tritiated methane is produced in biological processes, by measuring sewage methane, which showed a tritium content of less than 0.1×10^3 T.U. At the present time it is not possible to give a plausible source for this methane, but the evidence points to industrial production. As mentioned earlier, Bishop and Taylor (1960) found that HT also increases approximately exponentially, with a doubling time of 1.5 years. This suggests a similar source for both constituents since an exchange of T between HT and CH_4 is unlikely at normal temperatures.

The specific activity of atmospheric HT is about 15 times higher than that of methane. Since the concentration ratio CH_4/H_2 is about 2.5, the total tritium content in methane is about 0.17 times that in hydrogen. Nothing is known about an exchange of tritium between HT and CH_4.

Irrespective of the source of the radioactive methane, the data by Bishop et al. provide a unique opportunity to estimate the exchange rate between the two hemispheres. Assuming the source in the northern hemisphere we can write the following budget equations:

$$T_2 = b_2 \cdot e^{at},$$

and

$$dT_2/dt = k(T_1 - T_2),$$

where T_1, T_2 = reservoir of tritium in methane in the northern and southern hemispheres (atoms),

      k = exchange rate between the hemispheres (year^{-1}), and

      a = 0.46 (year^{-1}).

This gives

$$T_1 = b_1 \cdot e^{at}$$

and

$$\frac{b_1}{b_2} = \frac{a + k}{k} = \frac{21 \times 10^3 \text{ T.U.}}{8 \times 10^3 \text{ T.U.}} = 2.6$$

and results in an exchange time of

$$\tau = 1/k = 3.5 \text{ years.}$$

This is a first figure for the net exchange between the two hemispheres and must still be considered tentative. It appears to be rather long compared to stratospheric residence times, but seems to be consistent with the observed persistent differences in C^{14} content of the two hemispheres (Table 48).

3.4.6 The Rhodium-102 High-Altitude Tracer Experiment and Stratospheric Mixing and Circulation

One of the important meteorological problems for air chemistry is the exchange between stratosphere and troposphere and also the exchange *within* the stratosphere and mesosphere. We have already touched on these questions several times in the sections on H_2O, O_3, Sr^{90}, W^{185}, C^{14}, and THO. Before we enter into a more detailed discussion, we will present the results of a high-altitude tracer experiment which provides some important insights into the exchange mechanism within the higher stratosphere and mesosphere.

Large amounts of rhodium-102 were produced in the Orange shot of the Hardtack series, August 11, 1958, which was an air burst at about 40-km altitude near the equator (Kalkstein, 1961). It is very likely that the major part of the rhodium went up in the fireball to altitudes above 100 km and that the material injected into these altitudes was almost molecular dispersed. Based on the thermal structure of the high atmosphere, we can make the following considerations about the possible fate of this material in the higher atmosphere: The theory of atmospheric diffusion (see, e.g., Lettau, 1951) shows essentially two terms: One is concerned with the flux produced by molecular and eddy diffusion along gradients of the mixing ratios; it results in the horizontal and vertical spreading of gas or particle clouds. The other term represents the sedimentation in the gravitational field. This second term is very important at high altitudes and to a large extent determines the vertical movement of a cloud. Since the molecular weight of Rh^{102}, its oxides, or any aggregate, is larger than that of air, sedimentation starts immediately. It can be estimated that most of the Rh^{102} should have arrived at about 80 km after $\frac{1}{2}$ year with or without turbulence in layers above this altitude. Below 80 km sedimentation becomes exceedingly slow, but between 60 and 80 km the thermal structure of the atmosphere shows an average lapse rate of $-5°C/km$, so that considerable turbulence can be expected. This turbulence will generate a constant mixing ratio with the result that in terms of *absolute* values most of the material will be concentrated above the mesopeak at about 60 km. While the material descends, there will be sufficient horizontal mixing to spread the Rh^{102} fairly uniformly over all latitudes. Thus, we estimate that about a year after injection, most of the Rh^{102} was located in a widespread layer at about 60-km altitude. Below 50 km, within the mesoincline, the thermal stratification is extremely stable and downward mixing would be very slow unless a special mechanism provided a faster transport. Thus it can be expected that the hold-up time of finely dispersed material injected into altitudes above 80 km does not depend much on the actual injection height, but is primarily controlled by the exchange mechanism within the meso-incline and the upper stratosphere.

There are strong indications that deep vertical exchange processes take place over the winter pole, within the polar vortex (e.g., Hare, 1960). Compared with the very stable conditions over the summer pole, the stratospheric temperature fluctuations over the polar regions of the winter pole are very pronounced and are observed over a wide range of altitudes of the stratosphere and mesosphere. They are most likely due to high-reaching vertical movements and show a climax in the well-known "explosive" warmings observed in January and February when the polar winter vortex starts to break down.

Unfortunately, there are no data on Rh^{102} above 20 km to use as a direct check on the suggested ideas. Most of the data on Rh^{102} concentrations were obtained by aircraft collection up to 20 km, and the results are presented in Fig. 67. We see that in October 1958, shortly after the injection, some rhodium was found in both hemispheres, with much higher values north of the equator. This rhodium may have been produced in small amounts in earlier tests or may have been part of the material left behind in the stem of the rising fireball. In October 1959, a full year later, a sudden increase occurred in the northern hemisphere, spreading from north to south in the course of the winter. Obviously, the material was brought down into the lower stratosphere, preferentially over the polar region. It is tempting to link this phenomenon to the meteorological processes discussed above, in particular to the vertical motions indicated in the dynamic warmings and coolings found in radiosonde and rocket soundings in high latitudes over the winter pole. These temperature fluctuations start in October-November and have their maximum in the beginning of the year. The same processes are indicated in ozone observations (Allington et al., 1960).

This vertical exchange process was already known for the lower stratosphere from the ozone data and it was suggested that the same process is responsible for bringing water vapor to higher altitudes (see Chapter 1). The Rh^{102} experiment gives striking evidence of the importance of the large-scale and high-reaching vertical mixing processes over the winter pole for interstratospheric exchange. Later data on the stratospheric rhodium concentrations at 20 km, which are not included in Fig. 67, show that the higher concentrations of about 0.1 $\mu\mu c/m^3$ STP are maintained in both hemispheres after spring 1960, but only at latitudes higher than 30°, while lower concentrations persist over the equatorial regions. This distribution has some similarity to the C^{14} cross sections and is likely due to some restriction in the horizontal and vertical mixing, as indicated previously in the C^{14} discussion.

Estimates of the total amount of Rh^{102} produced and the amounts observed in the stratosphere indicate hold-up times in the mesosphere of about 10 years.

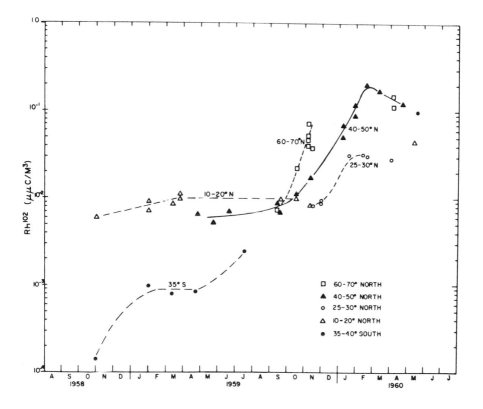

FIG. 67. Rhodium-102 concentrations at 20 km (corrected to August 12, 1958) as a function of time and latitude (Kalkstein, 1961). (By courtesy of Dr. M. Kalkstein.)

We will now survey and summarize all the important evidence for mixing processes within the stratosphere and across the tropopause obtained from various tracers. It should be kept in mind that in almost all cases we register only net decreases or increases in the concentration of constituents. Without detailed information on the eddy diffusion constants or air movements involved, these net effects do not allow us to distinguish between eddy diffusion fluxes along gradients or true one-way air circulations. Figure 68 gives a schematic diagram of all exchange processes which are backed by observations. In case this exchange mechanism is mixing or in case there is not sufficient support for an organized circulation, double-pointed arrows are used. The possibility of an organized

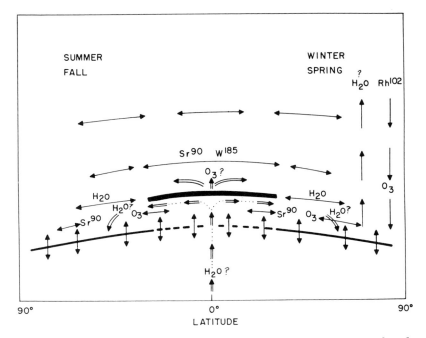

FIG. 68. Schematic diagram of the stratospheric exchange processes based on observations of various tracers. Double pointed arrows indicate mixing. Broad arrows for H_2O and O_3 indicate possible circulation.

circulation for water vapor and perhaps for ozone above the tropical tropopause is indicated by broad arrows. On the basis of this figure, we will now summarize for the various constituents the facts insofar as they are important for stratospheric mixing and circulation.

H_2O: The persistent minimum of the water vapor mixing ratio at about the altitude of the tropical tropopause over a wide range of latitudes (Fig. 1) requires either a fairly rapid and effective horizontal exchange between tropical and higher latitudes, or an organized meridional circulation with rising air at the equator up to or through the tropical tropopause, and with slowly descending air motion within the stratosphere over middle and high latitudes as proposed by Brewer (1949).

If air from the equatorial tropopause spreads north and south there will be an upward flux of water vapor into this dry layer. This flux must be rather small or otherwise it would be impossible to observe persistent frost point temperatures in higher latitudes similar to those of the tropical tropopause. Brewer assumed eddy diffusion coefficients of the order of 2000 cm^2/sec above the tropopause in temperate latitudes, which are in approximate agreement with other estimates, e.g., by Spar (HASP, 1960 a) from Sr^{90} data. However, vertical turbulent mixing of this intensity would require that the poleward drift has to be unreasonably fast and for that reason Brewer suggested a general subsidence of the order of 25 to 50 meters/day in the lower mid-latitude stratosphere.

Brewer also suggested that rising air at the equator penetrates through the tropical tropopause to an unspecified height and it is this part of his circulation model which is difficult to reconcile with other facts. We pointed out that the Sr^{90} and W^{185} data, and, to some extent, also the increase in water vapor above 16 km are not consistent with this circulation. We think that the poleward spreading, if any, occurs at or close to the level of the tropical tropopause. This is closer to the version of this circulation model given by Dobson (1956) and seems to agree better with the observation from other constituents. It should be noted that the literature refers mostly to the Brewer-Dobson model and that this implies circulation *through* the tropical tropopause. However, we feel that it is justified to distinguish between these two circulation models.

The conclusions about the subsidence in the low stratosphere in temperate latitudes are not modified very much if the organized poleward drift at the level of the tropical tropopause is replaced by an effective large-scale horizontal two-way air exchange.

O_3: The ozone distributions and variations (see, e.g., Fig. 12), strongly suggest a downward flux of ozone in winter and spring in high latitudes and a subsequent southward spread in the lower stratosphere (Dobson, 1956). Mixing into the troposphere is achieved through a variety of means, most likely through the tropopause gaps, but also over cyclones and troughs in middle latitudes and to some extent by small-scale turbulence. A puzzling phenomenon is the ozone-free layer below 20 km above the tropical tropopause as indicated in Fig. 12. It is now reported from various places (Congo, India 17°N, and Panama; unpublished data) and, if considered by itself, suggests a Brewer circulation. Corresponding profiles of Sr^{90} and W^{185} show a linear increase of concentration directly above the tropical tropopause. This discrepancy with the Sr^{90} and W^{185} profiles is striking and no explanation has been offered. It is not excluded that chemical destruction of ozone in the lower tropical stratosphere is involved.

Sr^{90} and W^{185}: Ash Can and HASP profiles clearly indicate that horizontal and vertical mixing are the main processes by which material is distributed within the lower stratosphere (Spar, see HASP, 1960 a). These data are not compatible with a Brewer circulation and are only to some degree, compatible with a Dobson circulation. Spar was able to estimate the coefficients of horizontal and vertical mixing (Section 3.4.2) and these values agree with other meteorological considerations. There is indication of a seasonal variation of the intensity of this exchange.

It was suggested that the discrepancy between the O_3 and the fission product profiles over the tropical tropopause is due to a slow upward movement which just balances the sedimentation rate of the particulate material. The sedimentation rate of 0.03 μ radius particles is about 10^{-3} cm/sec and a rise of 5 km from 16 to 21 km would take 5 years. The adjustment time of photochemical equilibrium for O_3 is 30 years at 15 km, 3 years at 20 km, and 0.3 year at 25 km. A comparison of these figures shows that ozone could hardly be reformed below 20 km at the required rate. However, it is unlikely that the sedimentation rate would match the rising air motion so exactly.

Rh^{102}. The rhodium data suggest a large-scale downward transport over the winter pole, starting perhaps at altitudes as high as 60 km. On the basis of meteorological observations, it is likely that the compensating upward air movements also occur over the winter pole and not over the summer pole. These ascending air motions, indicated by dynamic coolings (e.g., Hare, 1960) or by ozone variations (Allington et al., 1960), could be responsible for the upward transport of water vapor.

The picture presented in Fig. 68 is consistent with the major features of stratospheric exchange derived from atmospheric composition studies at the present time. There is very little indication of closed organized circulations. We cannot exclude entirely the possibility of their existence for the water vapor minimum at 15 km and perhaps in other cases too, but their importance may have been overemphasized. During summer and fall, mixing throughout the stratosphere seems to be primarily horizontal with some small-scale vertical exchange at all altitudes. However, during winter and spring, interactions between horizontal and vertical air motions in the polar stratosphere become important for stratospheric exchange processes. The tropopause gaps and the upper tropical troposphere are other areas where such interactions are of similar importance, in this case for the exchange between stratosphere and troposphere. It should be mentioned that vertical profiles of Aitken nuclei over India (17°N) indicate that the tropical troposphere above 13 km is not well mixed with the lower part of the tropical troposphere. This is supported by temperature profiles which show a smaller temperature gradient beyond 13 km, indicating some extension of the tropopause of temperate latitudes into the tropical zone (Fig. 68.)

Libby and Palmer (1960) used a circulation proposed by Goldie to explain long residence times near the equator and shorter residence times in polar regions. This circulation assumes that the air rises *within* the tropical stratosphere, spreads north and south at high altitudes, and descends over the polar regions. However, the entire circulation is supposed to occur exclusively at altitudes above 52 km and therefore cannot be checked by presently available data (Machta, 1961; Libby and Palmer, 1961).

Figure 68 is based to a great extent on the model of horizontal and vertical mixing given by Spar (HASP, 1960 a; Feely and Spar, 1960). It can be combined to some extent with the Dobson (1956) model, but not with the Brewer model. The suggested high-reaching vertical exchange processes over the winter pole are primarily based on the Rh^{102} results, but are also consistent with other observations.

Figure 68 supports the concept that stratospheric residence times increase with increasing altitudes and with decreasing latitudes. It is not unlikely that the most stagnant zone in our atmosphere is between 30°S and 30°N and between altitudes of 30 and 50 km. However, it is clear from this discussion that we are just beginning to acquire a qualitative understanding of the main features of stratospheric exchange and that much work must be done to make this picture quantitative as well.

List of Symbols

a = activity; rate of production of nuclei by radioactive decay; rate of outflow from reservoir; rate of exponential increase of CH_3T

A = activity on aerosols

b = constant

c = concentration of emanation; content of reservoir

d = diffusion coefficient of particle

D = eddy diffusion coefficient

E = exhalation rate

h = altitude above ground

k = hemispheric exchange rate

l = distance from particle center

n = number concentration of radioactive nuclides; concentration of primary particles

n_r = concentration of aerosol particles

P = production rate of nuclides by cosmic radiation

q = parameter

r = radius of aerosol particle

r' = radius of primary particle

t = time

T = content of CH_3T in hemisphere

$\bar{v}$ = gas kinetic velocity of primary particle

$\bar{v}' = \frac{1}{4}\bar{v}$

z = depth below ground

λ = radioactive decay rate

Φ = flux of primary particles

ϱ = distance from particle center

τ = radioactive or other lifetime

Subscripts:

s = soil; secondary activity (attached to aerosol particles)

a = atmosphere; aerosols

r = radius

ϱ = distance ϱ from center of particle

R = radon

REFERENCES

ADAMS, C. E., FARLOW, N. H., and SCHELL, W. R. (1958). Compositions, structure and origins of radioactive fallout particles. U.S. Naval Radiological Defense Laboratory Technical Report USNRDL-TR-209.

ALEXANDER, L. T. (1959). Strontium-90 distribution as determined by the analysis of soils. Hearings, Joint Committee on Radiation, Congress United States, Vol. I, pp. 278-371.

ALLINGTON, K., BOVILLE, B. W., and HARE, F. K. (1960). Midwinter ozone variations and stratospheric flow over Canada, 1958-1959. *Tellus* **12**, 266-273.

ANDERSON, E. C. (1953). The production and distribution of natural radiocarbon. *Ann. Rev. Nuclear Sci.* **2**, 63-78.

ARNOLD, J. R. (1956). Beryllium-10 produced by cosmic rays. *Science* **124**, 584-585.

BEGEMANN, F., and FRIEDMANN, I. (1959). Tritium and deuterium content of atmospheric hydrogen. *Z. Naturforsch.* **14a**, 1024-1031.

BEGEMANN, F., and LIBBY, W. F. (1957). Continental water balance, ground inventory and storage times, surface ocean mixing rates and world-wide water circulation patterns from cosmic ray and bomb tritium. *Geochim. et Cosmochim. Acta* **12**, 277-296.

BISHOP, K. F., and TAYLOR, B. T. (1960). Growth of the tritium content of atmospheric molecular hydrogen. *Nature* **185**, 26-27.

BISHOP, K. F., DELAFIELD, H. J., EGGLETON, A. E. J., PEABODY, C. O., and TAYLOR, B. T. (1961). The tritium content of atmospheric methane. Symposium on the Detection and Use of Tritium in the Physical and Biological Sciences. Vienna, 1961, Paper No. TTS/79.

BLEICHRODT, J. F., BLOK, J., and DEKKER, R. H. (1961). On the spring maximum of radioactive fallout from nuclear test explosions. *J. Geophys. Research* **66**, 135-144.

BLIFFORD, I. H., LOCKHART, L. B., Jr., and ROSENSTOCK, H. B. (1952). On the natural radioactivity in the air. *J. Geophys. Research* **57**, 499-509.

BLIFFORD, I. H., FRIEDMAN, H., LOCKHART, L. B., and BAUS, R. A., (1956). Radioactivity of the air. NRL Report 4760. pp. 1-35. Naval Research Laboratory, Washington, D. C.

BREWER, A. W. (1949). Evidence for a world circulation provided by the measurements of helium and water vapor distribution in the stratosphere. *Quart. J. Roy. Meteorol. Soc.* **75**, 351-363.

BROCKER, W. S. (1959). Data presented at the Oceanographic Congress, New York, 1959.

BROWN, H. (1957). The carbon cycle in nature. *In* "Fortschritte der Chemie organischer Naturstoffe" Vol. 14, pp. 317-333. Springer-Verlag, Wien.

BURTON, W. M., and STEWART, N. G. (1960). Use of long-lived natural radioactivity as an atmospheric tracer. *Nature* **186**, 584-589.

CHAMBERLAIN, A. C., and DYSON, E. D. (1956). The dose to the trachea and bronchi from the decay products of radon and thoron. *Brit. J. Radiol.* **29**, 317-325.

COLLINS, W. R., and HALLDEN, N. A. (1958). A study of fallout in rainfall collections from March through July 1956. Environmental contamination from weapon tests. *U.S. Atomic Energy Comm.* HASL-42, 339-354.

CRAIG, H., and LAL, D. (1961). The production rate of natural tritium. *Tellus* 13, 85-105.

CRUIKSHANK, A. J., COWPER, G., and GRUMITT, W. E. (1956). Production of Be[7] in the atmosphere. *Can. J. Chem.* 34, 214-219.

DOBSON, G. M. B. (1956). Origin and distribution of the polyatomic molecules in the atmosphere. *Proc. Roy. Soc.* A236, 187-193.

EDVARSON, K., LÖW, K., and SISEFSKY, J. (1959). Fractionation phenomena in nuclear weapons debris. *Nature* 184, 1771-1774.

ERIKSSON, E. (1958). The possible use of tritium for estimating groundwater storage. *Tellus* 10, 472-478.

FEELY, H. W., and SPAR, J. (1960). Mixing and transfer within the stratosphere. Progress Report on HASP, Defense Atomic Support Agency, Washington, D. C., DASA 1222 (Dec. 31, 1960), pp. 1-73.

FERGUSSON, G. J. (1959). Paper presented at the Oceanographic Congress, New York, 1959.

FERGUSSON, G. J. (1960). Radiocarbon from nuclear tests. UN Scientific Committee on the Effects of Atomic Radiation. Report of the Secretariat, 6 July 1960.

GOEL, P. S., NARASAPPAYA, N., PRABHAKARA, C., RAMA T., and ZUTSHI, P. K. (1959). Study of cosmic ray produced short-lived isotopes P[32], P[33], Be[7], and S[35] in tropical latitudes. *Tellus* 11, 91-100.

GONSIOR, B. (1959). Tritium-Anstieg im atmosphärischen Wasserstoff. *Naturwissenschaften* 46, 201-202.

HAGEMANN, F., GRAY, J., Jr., MACHTA, L., and TURKEVICH, A. (1959). Stratospheric carbon-14, carbon dioxide, and tritium. *Science* 130, 542-552.

Handbuch der Physik (1956). Vol. XLVII, pp. 295 ff., Springer, Berlin.

HARE, F. K. (1960). The disturbed circulation of the arctic stratosphere. *J. Meteorol.* 17, 36-51.

HASP (1960 a). High altitude sampling program. Defense Atomic Support Agency, Washington 25, D. C., DASA 532, (June 1, 1960), pp. 1-262.

HASP (1960 b). High altitude sampling program. Defense Atomic Support Agency, Washington 25, D. C. (September 1, 1960), pp. 1-34.

HASP (1961). High altitude sampling program. Defense Atomic Support Agency, Washington 25 D.C., DASA 539b (August 1, 1961,), p. 117 ff.

HAXEL, O., and SCHUMANN, G. (1955). Selbstreinigung der Atmosphäre. *Z. Physik* 142, 127-132.

HOLLAND, J. Z. (1959). Stratospheric radioactivity data obtained by balloon sampling. Hearings, Joint Committee on Radiation Congress United States, Vol. I, pp. 592-606.

ISRAËL, H. (1940). "Radioaktivität." Johann Ambrosius Barth-Verlag, Leipzig.

ISRAËL, H. (1951). Radioactivity of the atmosphere. *Compendium Meteorol.*, pp. 155-161.

ISRAËL, H. (1958). Die natürliche Radioaktivität in Boden, Wasser und Luft. *Beitr. Phys. Atmosphäre* **30**, 177-188.

ISRAËL-KÖHLER, H., and BECKER, F. (1936). Die Emanationsverhältnisse in der Bodenluft. *Gerlands Beitr. Geophys.* **48**, 13-58.

JACOBI, W., SCHRAUB, A., AURAND, K., and MUTH, H. (1959). Über das Verhalten der Zerfallprodukte des Radons in der Atmosphäre. *Beitr. Phys. Atmosphäre* **31**, 244-257.

JONES, S. (1960). Tenth progress report, upper atmosphere monitoring program. U.S. Atomic Energy Commission Contract AT(11-1)-401.

JUNGE, C. E. (1958). Atmopsheric chemistry. *Advances in Geophys.* **4**, 1-108.

KALKSTEIN, M. I. (1961). Personal communication.

KALKSTEIN, M. I., DREVINSKY, P. J., MARTELL, E. A., CHAGNON, C. W., MANSON, J. E., and JUNGE, C. E. (1959). Natural aerosols and nuclear debris studies. Progress Report II, GRD Research Notes, No. 24, pp. 1-36.

KATCOFF, S. (1958). Fission product yields from U, Th and Pu. *Nucleonics* **16**, 78-850.

KELLOGG, W. W. (1956). Atomic cloud height as a function of yield and meteorology. *U.S. Atomic Energy Comm.* AECU-**3403**.

KING, P., LOCKHART, L. B., BAUS, R. A., PATTERSON, R. L., FRIEDMAN, H. and BLIFFORD, I. H. (1956). RaD, RaE, and Po in the atmosphere, *Nucleonics* **14**, 78-84.

KOSMATH, W. (1930). Der Gehalt der Freiluft an Radiumemanation und deren vertikale Verteilung in der Nähe des Erdbodens. *Gerlands Beitr. Geophys.* **25**, 95-117.

KOSMATH, W. (1935). Die Exhalation der Radiumemanation aus dem Erdboden und ihre Abhängigkeit von meteorologischen Faktoren. *Gerlands Beitr. Geophys.* **43**, 258-279.

LAL, D. (1959). Cosmic ray produced radioisotopes for studying the general circulation in the atmosphere. *Indian J. Meteorol. Geophys.* **10**, 147-154.

LAL, D., MALHORTA, P. K., and PETERS, B. (1958). On the production of radioisotopes in the atmosphere by cosmic radiation and their application to meteorology. *J. Atmospheric and Terrest. Phys.* **12**, 306-328.

LAL, D., ARNOLD, J. R., and HONDA, M. (1960 a). Cosmic ray produced rates of Be[7] in oxygen, and P[32], P[33], S[35] in argon at mountain altitudes. *Phys. Rev.* **118**, 1626-1632.

LAL, D., GOLDBERG, E. D., and KOIDE, M. (1960 b). Cosmic-ray produced silicon-32 in nature. *Science* **131**, 332-337.

LAL, D., RAMA, T., and ZUTSHI, P. K. (1960 c). Radioisotopes P[32], Be[7] and S[35] in the atmosphere. *J. Geophys. Research* **65**, 669-674.

LASSEN, L., and RAU, G. (1960). Die Anlagerung radioaktiver Atome an Aerosole (Schwebestoffe). *Z. Physik* **160**, 504-519.

LASSEN, L. and WEICKSEL, H. (1961). Die Anlagerung radioaktiver Atome an Aerosole (Schwebestoffe) im Grössenbereich 0.7-5 μ (Radius). *Z. Physik* **161**, 339-345.

LEHMANN, L., and SITTKUS, A. (1959). Bestimmung von Aerosolverweilzeiten aus dem RaD und RaF-Gehalt der atmosphärischen Luft und des Niederschlages. *Naturwissenschaften* **46**, 9-10.

LETTAU, H. (1951). Diffusion in the upper atmosphere. *Compendium Meteorol.* pp. 320-333.

LIBBY, W. F. (1956 a). Radioactive strontium fallout. *Proc. Natl. Acad. Sci. U.S.* **42**, 365-390.

LIBBY, W. F. (1956 b). Radioactive fallout and radioactive strontium. *Science* **123**, 657-660.

LIBBY, W. F. (1959 a). Radioactive fallout particularly from the Russian October series. *Proc. Natl. Acad. Sci. U.S.* **45**, 959-976.

LIBBY, W. F. (1959 b). Tritium in hydrology and meteorology. *Researches in Geochem.* pp. 151-168.

LIBBY, W. F. (1961). Tritium Geophysics; recent data and results. Paper presented at the American Geophysical Union Meeting, May 1961.

LIBBY, W. F., and PALMER, C. E. (1960). Stratospheric mixing from radioactive fallout. *J. Geophys. Research* **65**, 3307-3317.

LIBBY, W. F., and PALMER, C. E. (1961). Author's reply to the preceding discussion. *J. Geophys. Research* **66**, 1593.

LINDBLOM, G. (1962). Determination of concentration of cesium-137 in precipitation and ground-level air in Sweden. *Nature* **193**, 866-867.

LOCKHART, L. (1960). Atmospheric radioactivity in South America and Antarctica. *J. Geophys. Research* **65**, 3999-4005.

LOCKHART, L. B., BAUS, R. A., KING, P., and BLIFFORD, I. H. (1959). Atmospheric radioactivity studies at the U.S. Naval Research Laboratory. Hearings Joint Committee on Atomic Energy, Congress United States Vol. 1, pp. 561-574.

LOCKHART, L. B., PATTERSON, R. L., Jr., SAUNDERS, A. W., Jr., and BLACK, R. W. (1960). Fission product radioactivity in the air along the 80th meridian (West) during 1959. *J. Geophys. Research* **65**, 3987-3997.

MACHTA, L. (1958). Discussion or meteorological factors and fallout distribution. Environmental contamination from weapon tests. *U.S. Atomic Energy Comm.* HASL-**42**, 310-325.

MACHTA, L. (1960). Paper presented at the International Symposium on Air Chemistry, Helsinki, 1960.

MACHTA, L. (1961). Discussion of paper by W. F. Libby and C. E. Palmer, stratospheric mixing from radioactive fallout. *J. Geophys. Research* **66**, 1592.

MACHTA, L., and LIST, R. J. (1959). Analysis of stratospheric strontium-90 measurements. *J. Geophys. Research* **64**, 1267-1276.

MARQUEZ, L., COSTA, N. L., and ALMEIDA, J. G. (1957). The formation of Na^{22} from atmospheric argon by cosmic rays. *Nuovo cimento* [10] **6**, 1292-1295.

MARTELL, E. A., (1959). Atmospheric aspects of strontium-90 fallout. *Science* **129**, 1197-1206.

MARTELL, E. A., and DREVINSKY, P. J. (1960). Atmospheric transport of artificial radioactivity. *Science* **132**, 1523-1531.

MARTELL, E. A., and DREVINSKY, P. J. (1961). Letter to the editor. *Science* **133**, 1645-1647.

MIYAKE, Y., SARUHASHI, K., KATSURAGI, K., and KANAZAWA, T. (1960). Radioactive fallout in Japan and its bearings on meteorological conditions. *Papers Meteorol. and Geophys. (Tokyo)* 11, 1-8.

MÜNNICH, K. O., and VOGEL, J. C. (1959). Variations in C^{14} content during the last years. Paper presented at the International C^{14} Symposium in Groningen, 1959.

OHTA, S. (1960). Sr^{90} deposition and meteorological factors. *Papers Meteorol. and Geophys. (Tokyo)* 11 (1), 1-6.

PANDOW, M., MacKAY, C., and WOLFGANG, R. (1960). The reaction of atomic carbon with oxygen: significance for the natural radio-carbon cycle. *J. Inorg. Nuclear Chem.* 14, 153-158.

PARKER, R. P. (1962). Beryllium-7 and fission products in surface air. *Nature* 193, 967-968.

PATTERSON, R. L., Jr., and BLIFFORD, I. H., Jr., (1957). Atmospheric carbon-14. *Science* 126, 26-28.

PAULING, L. (1958). Genetic and somatic effects of carbon-14. *Science* 128, 1183-1186.

PEIRSON, D. H., and STEWART, N. G. (1961). Letter to the editor. *Science* 133, 1643-1645.

PETERS, B. (1959). Cosmic ray produced radioactive isotopes as tracers for studying large-scale atmospheric circulation. *J. Atmospheric and Terrest. Phys.* 13, 351-370.

ROSINSKI, J., and STOCKHAM, J. (1960). Preliminary studies of scavenging systems related to radioactive fallout. Summary Report ARF 3127-12, Armour Research Foundation under Contract No. AT(11-1)-626, pp. 1-51.

SCHUMANN, G. (1956). Untersuchungen der Radioaktivität der Atmosphäre mit der Filtermethode. *Arch. Meteorol. Geophys. u. Bioklimatol.* A9, 204-223.

SISEFSKY, J. (1960). Autoradiographic and microscopic examination of nuclear-weapon debris particles. Försvarets Forskningsanstalt, Stockholm, FOA 4 Rapport A 4130-456, pp. 1-37.

SMALL, S. H. (1960). Wet and dry deposition of fallout materials at Kjeller. *Tellus* 12, 308-314.

STERN, S. (1959). The sampling of radioactive debris in the stratosphere. Paper presented at the AMS Symposium on Stratospheric Meteorology, Minneapolis, Minnesota, 1959.

STEWART, N. G., CROOKS, R. N., and FISHER, E. M. R. (1955). The radiological dose to persons in the U.K. due to debris from nuclear test explosions. Report for the M.R.P. Committee on the Medical Aspects of Nuclear Radiation A.E.R.A., Harwell, 1955.

STEWART, N. G., OSMOND, R. G. D., CROOKS, R. N., and FISHER, E. M. (1957). The world-wide deposition of long-lived fission products from nuclear test explosions. *Atomic Energy Research Estab. (Gt. Brit.) Publ. No.* AERE HP/R 2354.

STEWART, N. G., OSMOND, R. G. D., CROOKS, R. N., FISHER, E. M. R., and OWERS, M. J. (1959). The deposition of long-lived fission products from nuclear test explosions. *Atomic Energy Research Estab. (Gt. Brit.) Publ. No.* AERE HP/R 2790.

STOREBÖ, P. B. (1960). Meteorological fractionation of nuclear bomb debris. *Tellus* **12**, 293-297.

STRAHLENSCHUTZ No. 12 (1959), "Schriftenreihe des Bundesministeriums für Atomkernenergie und Wasserwirtschaft." pp. 1-204. Gersbach and Sohn, Braunschweig.

SUESS, H. (1958). The radioactivity of the atmosphere and hydrosphere. *Ann. Rev. Nuclear Sci.* **8**, 243-256.

U. S. ATOMIC ENERGY COMMISSION (1958). Environmental contamination from weapons tests. Health and Safety Lab. Publ. No. HASL-42.

WALTON, A. (1960). Stratospheric strontium-90 on the earth's surface. pp. 1-37. Report Isotopes Inc., New Jersey,

WEXLER, H., MACHTA, L., PACK, D. H., and WHITE, F. D. (1956). Atomic energy and meteorology. *Proc. Intern. Conf. Peaceful Uses Atomic Energy, Geneva 1955* **13**, 333-344.

WEXLER, H., MORELAND, W., and WEYANT, W. S. (1960). A preliminary report on ozone observations at Little America, Antarctica. *Monthly Weather Rev.* **88** (2), (1960).

WILKENING, M. H. (1952). Natural radioactivity as a tracer in the sorting of aerosols according to mobility. *Revi. Sci. Instr.* **23**, 13-16.

WILKENING, M. H. (1959). Daily and annual courses of natural atmospheric radioactivity. *J. Geophys. Research* **64**, 521-526.

4. *Chemistry of precipitation*

4.1 Introduction

Precipitation is the most important mechanism by which many natural and artificial contaminants are removed from the atmosphere. The enormous quantities of water which cycle continuously through the atmosphere are essential for life not only because they supply the necessary moisture over land but also because they keep the atmosphere clean. The significance of this fact is well appreciated by people who live in highly polluted areas.

Precipitation is an efficient process by which trace substances are removed from the atmosphere and concentrated into a small volume of liquid. Almost all trace substances present in the atmosphere are also present in rain. The convenience of this natural collection mechanism of atmospheric trace substances and the relative ease of water analyses gave rise to many studies. It is very tempting to use all these data on the composition of rainwater for obtaining information on the origin and the source areas of the constituents. However, the interpretation of rainwater data in terms of *concentration* of the constituent *in the atmosphere* is difficult and little is known about the collection mechanism itself, its efficiency, and the variation of its efficiency from constituent to constituent. Therefore, in the first part of this chapter we will discuss in detail the physical and chemical processes involved and those observations which can help to elucidate them.

It is convenient to distinguish between rainout and washout. Rainout comprises all processes within the clouds, and washout, the processes of removal by the rain below the clouds. Both mechanisms together represent the wet removal or removal by precipitation. It should be emphasized here that precipitation is only one of the processes by which substances can be removed from the atmosphere. These processes can be listed as follows:

Aerosols:

(a) Wet removal by precipitation

(b) Dry removal by sedimentation

(c) Dry removal by impaction on obstacles at the earth's surface

Gases:

(a) Wet removal by precipitation

(b) Absorption or reaction at the earth's surface

(c) Conversion into aerosols or other trace gases by chemical reaction within the atmosphere

(d) Escape into space

Our knowledge of these processes is rather vague and certain aspects of the ideas surveyed or presented here are still tentative or speculative. However, some broad and general rules seem to emerge from the numerous observations, which are in agreement with theoretical considerations and which permit a more sensible interpretation of the data than was possible a few years ago. The discussion will be concerned primarily with wet removal, because it is especially important and best studied. However, for certain constituents, such as sea salt or SO_2, other removal mechanisms, e.g., sedimentation, impaction, or absorption, can be just as efficient.

The second part of this chapter will deal with observations of the chemical composition of precipitation. The emphasis will be on a comprehensive and critical survey of the essential and large-scale phenomena, and their implications with respect to the sources and sink areas of the individual constituents. This discussion will supplement the previous chapters to a certain extent, but the special features and the importance of precipitation chemistry requires that it be treated separately. Some of the points reviewed in this discussion are still controversial and therefore the treatment reflects the opinion of the author to some extent.

This chapter does not include further data on natural or artificial radioactivity in precipitation, except in a few instances. These observations were already discussed in the context of Chapter 3.

The concentration of constituents in rainwater is generally expressed in milligrams per liter (mg/liter), which is numerically equivalent to $\mu g/cm^3$. Some authors prefer to give the deposition of a constituent by precipitation for a certain time period, usually 1 year. These deposits are expressed in kilograms per hectare (kg/ha) and are related to the concentration k by

$$k = (kg/ha) \times 10^2/h \text{ (mg/liter)},$$

where h is the amount of rainfall in that time period in millimeters (mm).

4.2 Physico-Chemistry of Wet and Dry Removal from the Atmosphere

4.2.1 Rainout of Aerosols

Rainwater can receive its constituents either by processes *within* the clouds, which are generally called *rainout*, or by processes *below* the clouds, which are called *washout*. If c is the concentration of a constituent in air ($\mu g/m^3$ STP), k_1 its concentration in cloud water due to rainout (mg/liter), ε the fraction of c which enters the cloud water, i.e., the rainout efficiency ($0 \leq \varepsilon \leq 1$), and L the total amount of water which condenses in cloud air (g/m^3 STP), we can write

$$k_1 = c \cdot \varepsilon \cdot /L . \tag{1}$$

The rainout efficiency ε represents the net effect of the following processes by which atmospheric aerosol particles can enter the cloud droplets:

(1) the consumption of condensation nuclei, ε_n,

(2) the attachment of aerosol particles, primarily Aitken particles, to the cloud elements by Brownian motion, ε_b, and

(3) the attachment of aerosol particles, primarily Aitken particles, by the water vapor gradient (Facy-effect), ε_f.

The quantity ε refers either to the total aerosol mass or to the total mass of a certain constituent and we can write

$$\varepsilon = \varepsilon_n + \varepsilon_b + \varepsilon_f .$$

No measurements of ε are available, but some estimates can be made. Figure 24 shows that in continental aerosols most of the mass is contained in the radius range 0.1 to 10 μ and that the numerous Aitken particles do not contribute very much. For marine aerosols, most of the mass is concentrated between 1 and 10 μ radius. According to the discussion in Section 2.2.3 concerning the activation of aerosol particles in water vapor condensation, the following ε_n values can be expected: for continental aerosols of high concentrations, 0.5; for continental aerosols of low concentrations, 0.8; for maritime aerosols and tropospheric aerosols with a total particle concentration of less than 200 to 300/cm³, 0.9 to 1.0. These estimates refer to the total mass of aerosols or to constituents of the same relative distribution. Since most constituents will have different distributions, the value of ε_n and also the subsequent estimates of ε_b and c_f can be quite different, and they have to be considered on an individual basis. Figure 54, e.g., suggests that for radon decay products in continental air, ε_n may be smaller than 0.2.

The effect of coagulation due to Brownian motion can be calculated with the help of the expressions of Smoluchowsky and Lassen, discussed in Sections 2.2.2 and 3.2.2. In the present case, we are dealing with rather large particles, so that the Smoluchowsky formula is a satisfactory approximation. If we assume for simplicity that the Aitken particles and the cloud droplets have uniform radii r and r_c, and if n and d designate the concentrations and the diffusion coefficients, we have

$$dn/dt = -4\,\pi(d + d_c)\,(r + r_c)n\,n_c.$$

Since $d_c \ll d$ and $r \ll r_c$, we obtain

$$dn/dt = -4\,\pi\,d\,r_c\,n\,n_c,$$

or a half-life of

$$\tau = 0.69/4\,\pi\,d\,r_c n_c.$$

As a numerical example, let us take $r_c = 10\ \mu$ and $n_c = 200/\text{cm}^3$, which are representative for the base of cumuliform clouds (Weickmann and Aufm Kampe, 1953); we obtain the following figures:

$r =$	0.01	0.03	0.10	μ
$\tau =$	0.64	3.8	38	hours

For a cloud which lasts half an hour and for an average aerosol radius of 0.03 μ, this results in an ε_b of the order of 0.01. Unless the specific constituent is concentrated primarily in the particle range below 0.1 μ, the contribution of ε_b to ε seems to be negligible. This estimate will not change much if the electrical charges normally encountered on aerosols and cloud droplets are taken into consideration.

Facy (e.g., 1958) observed that particles suspended in a mixture of water vapor in air will move along the vapor pressure gradient because of the force exerted on them by the diffusing vapor molecules. The theory for this mechanism is similar to that for the radiometer effect and shows that velocity of the particles is independent of their size and proportional to the vapor gradient. Goldsmith et al. (1961) made quantitative measurements of this velocity for particles between 0.03 and 0.1 μ and obtained

$$v = 2 \cdot 10^{-4}\,G\ \ (\text{cm/sec}),$$

if the vapor gradient G is expressed in mb/cm. In a cloud in which 100 droplets/cm³ grow to 10 μ radius, less than 10^{-3} of the unactivated aerosol material will be captured. The conclusion that the Facy effect is quite unimportant for rainout and even less efficient than Brownian motion was verified by them in experiments with radioactively marked particles captured by growing droplets in a cloud chamber.

Some observations, however, seem to indicate a much higher rate of attachment. Kumai (1951) evaporated snow crystals at subzero temperatures collected at altitudes of 1 km, and he examined the residue in an electron microscope. Besides the big "central nucleus" on which crystal growth started, he found a large number of small particles. The size distribution of these particles showed a maximum at a radius of 0.025 μ, similar to natural aerosols. The particles were equally distributed throughout the crystal, with a concentration of 1 per μ^3. A snow crystal of 1.6 mm diameter and a thickness of 10 μ thus contains about 10^7 particles with a total mass of about $5 \cdot 10^{-10}$ g. This mass corresponds to an aerosol particle of 5 μ radius and is comparable to that of the "central nucleus." This observation indicates a considerable collection efficiency for Aitken particles and is hard to reconcile with the previous considerations, unless exceptional conditions or high electrical charges are assumed.

Thus, the estimates of ε show that the condensation process itself is the most efficient rainout mechanism for total mass in the case of natural aerosols, but that Brownian motion and/or the Facy effect may become more important for constituents that are concentrated on particles smaller than 0.1 μ.

In general, the combination of the various processes will result in a dependence of ε on the radius of the aerosol particles. For a continental aerosol, for instance, condensation and rainout will result in high removal efficiencies for radii larger than 0.2 μ. On the other hand, the attachment of aerosol particles to cloud droplets by Brownian motion results in high efficiencies for particles smaller than about 0.02 μ radius. Therefore, one should expect a minimum in the rate of wet removal for particles between 0.05 and 0.1 μ radius. Greenfield (1957) arrives at similar conclusions in a theoretical study for particle removal from clouds of atomic tests, but he considers only two effects: the attachment by Brownian motion and washout. Therefore, his calculations should be amended before they are applied to natural conditions.

The other quantity of interest in Eq. (1) is the liquid water content L. It may be somewhat larger than the observed values in raining clouds because part of the water may have already been dropped out. The liquid water content of raining clouds appears to be fairly constant and varies between about 1 and 2 g/m³ (see, e.g., Mason, 1957). It must be smaller than the amount of water determined by the moist adiabat, which is about 4 g/m³ in temperate latitudes. In Section 1.2.2 it was pointed out that the depletion of oxygen-18 in rainwater by values of $\delta_{O^{18}} = -7$ may indicate that considerable fractions of the precipitable water vapor are indeed removed in rainfalls. However, evaporation of fresh water over land and/or depletion by previous rains in the same air mass have the same effect, so that it is impossible to draw definite conclusions with respect to L from these observations. We think that the actual values of L will be close to those observed in raining clouds.

There are only a few data available which can be used to check the basic Eq. (1) for rainout. These are simultaneous measurements of the concentration of fission products in rain and air. In contrast to natural aerosols, the fission product concentration increases with altitude. This has the advantage that the effect of washout will be minimized for these data. Washout below the clouds can be considerable if the aerosol concentration below the clouds is higher than in cloud air, as we shall see in the next section. Therefore, natural constituents are not very suitable for a comparison, especially such constituents as $SO_4^=$, which also involves the gas phase.

Small (1960) reports data from Norway which give $c/k_1 = L/\varepsilon = 0.25$ to 2.1 with an average of 0.9. Hinzpeter (1959) gives corresponding data for a wide range of daily rainfall rates: Rain: 0.8 for 0.1 mm/day, 1.4 for 1.0 mm/day, 2.5 for 10 mm/day. Snow: 0.9 for 0.15 mm/day, 1.6 for 1.0 mm/day, 3,4 for 10 mm/day.

The data from Norway and Germany agree fairly well but seem to be too low, even if we assume that ε is close to 1 and that L is not larger than 1 to 2 g/m³. However, it is likely that for fission products ε is smaller than 1 and that in general L is close to 2 or larger so that the discrepancy becomes even larger. On the other hand, it should be kept in mind that the concentration c of fission products in ground air is lower than at cloud level, and that washout and evaporation of raindrops below the clouds tend to increase k_1. Both these effects will minimize the observed values of $c/k_1 = L/\varepsilon$, but no estimate can be given for their magnitude.

Woodcock (1960) recently compared observations of the chloride concentration in orographic rains in the trade winds on the slopes of the Island of Hawaii with the theoretical value $k_1 = \varepsilon\, c/L$. The concentration c of chloride in air was taken from aircraft observations at cloud base level and L was calculated on the assumption that the air rises on the average by half of the observed cloud thicknes from the cloud base. This value of L corresponds to the average theoretical liquid water content of the clouds according to the wet adiabate. The calculated values $k_1 = \varepsilon\, c/L$ agree with the observed ones within 30% for $\varepsilon = 1$. This study represents the best quantiative proof of Eq. (1) so far available.

Equation (1) does not imply that all cloud droplets have the same concentration. This is to be expected only if they are formed by random collision. Kuroiwa (1953) investigated the evaporation residues of cloud droplets and did not find any correlation between the size of the cloud droplets and the size of the residue. However, Woodcock and Blanchard

(1955) conclude that in orographic showers in Hawaii the largest drops *in* the cloud form around the largest salt nuclei and that a one-to-one relationship exists between the number of raindrops and the number of salt nuclei. By coordinating the observed size distribution of raindrops with that of the salt nuclei, they find a characteristic dependence of the chloride concentration upon the size of the droplets, with a minimum around 1 mm diameter. Such a variation of the chloride concentration with droplet size was actually observed by Turner (1955) at the base of orographic showers in Hawaii. Woodcock and Blanchard infer that either the drops in these showers grow only by condensation and not by coagulation or, if coagulation is involved, the majority of the small cloud droplets do not grow around sea salt nuclei and therefore do not alter the chloride content of the raindrops. This last conclusion would be in line with the finding that even over the oceans the Aitken nuclei and some of the large nuclei do not consist of sea salt. According to Tables 30 and 31, not more than 10% of the droplets in a cloud of 200/cm³ can have grown around sea-salt particles.

It was assumed hitherto that c is independent of the amount and history of rainfall. In areas or in air masses with frequent rainfalls, c will be smaller than for isolated showers. Georgii and Weber (1960), e.g., find that the concentration of several constituents in rainwater is roughly twice as high in rainfalls after a dry period of at least 3 days than in rainfalls after a dry period of less than 12 hours. The observed decrease of concentration in rain with the amount of rainfall (Fig. 71) may also be partly due to a decrease of c in large rainstorms.

4.2.2 Washout of Aerosols

When the rain droplets leave the cloud base, they pick up large aerosol particles and start to evaporate on their way down. Both processes result in an increase of the rainwater concentration k, which can be determined by extending Eq. (1) as follows:

$$k = f \cdot k_1 + k_2. \tag{2}$$

The factor $f \geq 1$ represents the effect of evaporation and k_2 accounts for the rainout. Strictly speaking, k_2 is also partly affected by evaporation. If the cross section of a falling raindrop $\pi\, r_c^2$ collects aerosol particles of radius r, size distribution $n(r)dr$, and collection efficiency $\eta \leq 1$, we obtain

$$k_2 = \frac{\pi\, H}{r_c} \int \eta \cdot r^3 \cdot n(r)dr, \tag{3}$$

where H is the height of the cloud base.

The quantity η was calculated by Langmuir and others (see Mason, 1957) and the values differ somewhat depending on the approximations used, but the essential features are the same: For a wide range of raindrops between about 50 and 2000 μ radius, η is practically equal to 1 for nuclei of 10 μ radius. With decreasing r, η decreases rapidly and is about 0.5 for 5 μ and 0.1 for 2 μ. Particles smaller than 1 μ can hardly be collected by falling raindrops and thus washout is restricted to the giant particles.

Assuming a continental size distribution of completely soluble particles in Fig. 23, and $H = 1000$ meters, we obtain the values in Table 51 for k_2 as a function of r_c. These are of the same order as the observed

TABLE 51

CONCENTRATION k_2 IN RAINWATER DUE TO WASHOUT FOR A CONTINENTAL AEROSOL SIZE DISTRIBUTION AND A HEIGHT OF THE CLOUD BASE $H = 1000$ METERS AS A FUNCTION OF DROPLET RADIUS r_c

$r_c = 0.1$	0.2	0.4	0.8	1.6 mm
$k_2 = 71$	45	29	15	7.5 mg/liter

concentrations and indicate the importance of washout for rain chemistry. For a comparison with observed concentrations of individual constituents, one should consider that only a fraction of the aerosol material in continental aerosols is soluble and that the giant particles below the cloud are removed rather rapidly.

Expression (3) shows that k_2 is inversely proportional to r_c. The only measurements available with which to check this are those of Turner (1955), who measured the chloride concentration in raindrops of different sizes. We have already mentioned his result from Hawaii in and at the cloud base, which indicated a relationship between k_1 and r_c. Since one would expect the concentration of sea salt in air below the clouds to be rather high at the coastal sites in Australia where Turner made his measurements, his k values can be regarded as representative of k_2. Figure 68 shows a few of his results for various conditions. In general, the exponent $\varkappa$ in

$$k \propto r_c^{-\varkappa}$$

is about 1, as predicted by (3), but can be as high as 2.6. Turner attributes the high values to the evaporation of the droplets. The smaller droplets decrease in size and thus gain in concentration more rapidly than do the larger ones and his calculations can account for this increase. Turner also calculated absolute values of k_2 and found reasonable agreement with his observed k data. This confirms our previous conclusion that for sea salt, washout is an important removal process over the ocean or near the coast, and that this must be so for all aerosols which are concentrated in the layers below cloud base and in which the giant particles carry almost all the mass.

Landsberg (1954) measured the pH value of individual rain-drops and found values between 3 and 5.5. These values are a little lower than the normal pH in rain and may be influenced by the vicinity of Boston. The smallest droplets had the lowest values, which seems to indicate either that most of the material which influences the hydrogen ion concentration was collected below the cloud or that evaporation was involved.

In interpretating the observations made in Section 4.3.1, it is useful to estimate how fast aerosols below the cloud are removed by washout. We assume a simple model of *stagnant* air beneath a cloud which rains at a constant rate removing a homogeneous soluble aerosol of radius r and initial concentration n_0. The concentration k_2 in rainwater due to this washout, as a function of the height of rainfall h, is given by

$$k_2 = \frac{4\pi}{3h} H n_0 r^3 \left[1 - \exp\left(-\frac{3\eta h}{4 r_c} \right) \right].$$

For purpose of demonstration let us assume average particle sizes of 4 and 8 μ, and calculate the height of precipitation h_1 and h_2 at which the concentration in *rainwater* and the concentration of *particles* below the cloud, respectively, have been reduced to one-half. Table 52 shows that the giant

TABLE 52

HEIGHT OF RAINFALL h_1 AND h_2 NECESSARY TO REDUCE THE INITIAL CONCENTRATION IN THE RAINWATER AND THE INITIAL CONCENTRATION OF PARTICLES BELOW THE CLOUD TO ONE-HALF AS A FUNCTION OF RAINDROP RADIUS r_c AND PARTICLE RADIUS r

r_c		0.1	0.2	0.4	1.0	2.0 mm
h_1	$r = 8\ \mu$	0.32	0.56	1.0	2.6	5.5 mm
	$r = 4\ \mu$	1.2	1.3	1.7	4.1	6.5 mm
h_2	$r = 8\ \mu$	0.20	0.35	0.63	1.6	3.5 mm
	$r = 4\ \mu$	0.75	0.81	1.1	2.5	4.1 mm

particles are removed rather efficiently. After a certain amount of rain has fallen, the exponential term in k_2 becomes negligible, indicating that all the aerosol particles are rained out so that the subsequent rainfall merely results in further dilution and $k_2 \propto h^{-1}$.

One can hardly expect that this washout model can be veri-
fied by observations, since these give k and not k_2 and since it is likely that
on the average k_1 is more important than k_2. It is also questionable whether
the assumption of a stagnant air mass below the cloud is valid, since rainstorms are dynamic and not static systems. Nevertheless, model calculations
of this type will be helpful in the discussion of observations in Section 4.3.1.

The expression $\int \eta \cdot r^3 \cdot n(r)dr$ in Eq. (3) is, to some extent,
proportional to the air concentration c of aerosols and thus, on the basis of
relation (2), we can expect the same for k. The proportionality constant
between k and c depends only on meteorological factors, and average values
over sufficiently long periods should be constant. This means that under
such conditions the total deposit of a constituent will be proportional to
the average air concentration and the total amount of rainfall. The discussion of strontium-90 data in Section 3.4.4 provided evidence for this rule,
which can, of course, be considered only approximate but which is quite
useful for budget considerations in air chemistry and geochemistry. Fission
products like Sr^{90}, which become permanently absorbed in the soil and
which can be distinguished from soil material, serve as an excellent tracer
for studying this relationship. Natural rainwater constituents either are
soluble and constantly removed by river runoff under steady state conditions or are insoluble but indistinguishable from soil material.

4.2.3 Removal Rate of Aerosols in the Troposphere

In Sections 3.2.2 and 3.4.3 and Table 41, we discussed observations of the residence time of natural aerosols and radioactivity in
the troposphere. We shall now present a simple model which allows us to
make an approximate computation of this important parameter from cloud
and precipitation data (Junge and Gustafson, 1957).

Let us assume a vertical column of air of 1 cm^2 cross section
which contains a layer of precipitating clouds a cm thick, with an average
amount L g/cm^3 of condensed water. If this cloud layer produces h cm of
rain, we can write

$$a = \varrho \, h/L$$

where $\varrho = 1$ is the density of water. This corresponds to a volume fraction
of tropospheric air of a/H', if H' is the tropopause height. The fraction of
aerosols removed is then

$$\alpha = \varepsilon \cdot h \cdot \varrho/L \cdot H' \qquad (4)$$

where ε is the rainout efficiency. It is assumed here that the aerosol has a
uniform vertical distribution within the troposphere.

Since the relation between α and h is linear, we can substitute average values $\bar{\alpha}$ and $\bar{h}$. Let us now consider an air mass or an area of continental dimensions in which $\bar{h}$ is the average daily rainfall rate. Then expression (4) is valid provided all the rain falls at the same time. However, convective showers and other rain-producing cloud systems are more or less local, particularly in summer and in southern latitudes, and there will be considerable mixing of the troposphere between rainfalls. If the average daily rainfall $\bar{h}$ within a large air mass is the result of ν independent rainfalls, the average fraction of aerosols removed by rainout per day is

$$\bar{\alpha}' = 1 - (1 - \bar{\alpha}/\nu)^r$$

which can be replaced by

$$\bar{\alpha}' = 1 - \exp(-\bar{\alpha})$$

for large ν. Under normal conditions, in temperate latitudes, we can assume $h = 0.25$ cm, $L = 2$ g/m³, and $\varepsilon = 1$, and obtain

$$\bar{\alpha}' \cong 0.1 .$$

Now we have to consider washout. If we assume the average cloud base to be at 2 km, the fraction of total aerosol mass removed cannot be larger than

$$\gamma = 2 \times 10^5/H' .$$

This washout will be more important for a large number of small showers than for a small number of large showers. On the average it rains every fourth day during the summer in the eastern U.S., so that on a per day basis and for $H' = 12$ km, the fraction removed by washout will be

$$\bar{\gamma} = 2 \times 10^5/4 \times 12 \times 10^5 = 0.04 .$$

For aerosol constituents with particles smaller than 1 μ radius, which cannot be removed by washout, $\bar{\gamma}$ will be accordingly smaller, e.g., one-half the value for total aerosol mass in continental air.

These estimates indicate that γ is smaller than α. To include washout we can, therefore, correct the rainout by a factor of $\varphi \cong 1.2$ and obtain for the amount of aerosols *left* in the air after t days,

$$1 - \bar{\alpha}' = \exp(-\varphi \, \varepsilon \, \bar{h} \, \varrho \, t/LH'),$$

and for the average residence time of the aerosols,

$$\tau = LH'/\varphi \varepsilon \bar{h} \varrho .$$

Numerical values are given in Table 53. For average conditions of $\bar{h}$ and L, τ is about 8 days. For aerosols formed at the earth's surface and concentrated

TABLE 53

CALCULATED RESIDENCE TIMES τ IN DAYS OF TROPOSPHERIC AEROSOLS, DUE TO WET
REMOVAL AS A FUNCTION OF LIQUID WATER CONTENT OF CLOUDS, L, AND AVERAGE
DAILY RAINFALL RATE, $\bar{h}$, FOR $\varphi \cdot \varepsilon = 1$ AND $H' = 12$ km

$\bar{h}$ (cm)	L (g/m³)		
	1	2	3
0.12	8.3	16.6	24.9
0.25	4.0	8.0	12.0
0.50	2.0	4.0	6.0

primarily in the lower layers of the troposphere, i.e., for those not uniformly distributed in the vertical as assumed in our calculations, the effective value of H' will be smaller, perhaps 0.3-0.5 H', reducing τ to 2 to 4
days. The shorter residence times for radon decay products, e.g., Table 41,
and the considerations by Machta discussed below, point in this direction.
For aerosols which are concentrated primarily in the upper part of the troposphere, as e.g., fission products, the effective H' will be greater and τ
longer. For aerosol constituents in the size range from about 0.05 to 0.1 μ
radius in continental air, ε is certainly smaller than 1 and τ is correspondingly
longer. However, reliable data on all these parameters are still missing and
all we can say at present is that the agreement between the observed figures
in Table 41 and those in Table 53 is encouraging.

Recently Machta (1960) made an interesting study to explain
the observed vertical distribution of RaD and Be[7]. In a one-dimensional
model he assumes steady state between production of these constituents,
mixing, and removal, but considers the more realistic case of a decrease of
the removal rate with altitude. With reasonable values for mixing and removal rates, he obtains by trial and error a satisfactory match with the observed profiles. Figure 69 shows the results for RaD. The left-hand side
gives the British and the United States data on the specific activity of RaD
in air and indicates the considerable discrepancy in the stratosphere already
discussed in Section 3.2.2. The parameters used in the model are presented
in the center of the figure. An eddy diffusion coefficient of 2×10^5 cm²/sec
in the troposphere is assumed and 2×10^4 cm²/sec in the lower stratosphere.
The resulting removal rates decrease rapidly with altitude, namely, 40%
per day between 0 and 1 km, 10% between 1 and 3 km, 4% between 3 and
5 km, and no removal above 5 km. This decrease in removal rates reflects
the trend of the rain production with altitude. The negligible removal rates
above 5 km are somewhat surprising, but seem to be in agreement with other

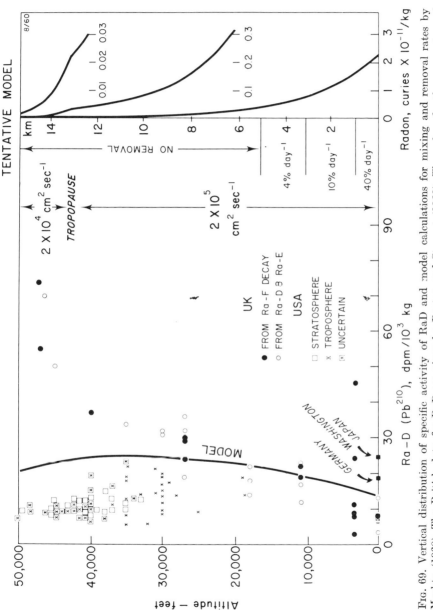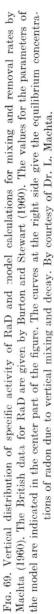

FIG. 69. Vertical distribution of specific activity of RaD and model calculations for mixing and removal rates by Machta (1960). The British data for RaD are given by Burton and Stewart (1960). The values for the parameters of the model are indicated in the center part of the figure. The curves at the right side give the equilibrium concentrations of radon due to vertical mixing and decay. By courtesy of Dr. L. Machta.

phenomena, e.g., the vertical profiles of Aitken nuclei in Figs. 45 and 46, which show little decrease of their mixing ratio with altitude in the upper troposphere.

The vertical profile of RaD in Fig. 69 calculated with this model approximates the observed RaD profiles satisfactorily except for the British data above the tropopause. This supports our earlier conclusions that the stratospheric air over England must be of continental origin with originally high radon contents. At the right-hand side of the figure, steady state concentrations of radon due to vertical mixing and radioactive decay are calculated for the same model.

The agreement of this model with the Be^7 data is of similar quality. This model also allows us to calculate how rapidly material disappears by mixing and actual removal when injected at different altitudes. Machta obtains the following figures for the time it takes for the concentration to decrease by 50%:

Altitude (km)	0	2	6	12	14
Time (days)	3	5	18	33	70.

We can conclude from this discussion that both the observations and theoretical considerations are still tentative, but by and large they agree and give a consistent picture.

4.2.4 Removal of Gases by Precipitation

Rainout of gases can occur in three different ways:

(1) By simple solution in cloud water according to Henry's law; examples are N_2O, CH_4.

(2) By solution with subsequent reversible hydration and dissociation; examples are CO_2, NH_3.

(3) By solution and subsequent irreversible conversion or reaction with other materials in cloud water; examples are SO_2, NO_2.

The absorption coefficient δ of gases in water gives the volume of the dissolved gas per unit volume of water and is independent of the partial pressure for gases in category one (Henry's law). To find the ratio of total dissolved to undissolved gas in cloud air, one has to consider the volume ratio of liquid water to cloud air, which is given by L/ϱ, where ϱ is the density of water and L is the liquid water content of the cloud expressed in g/cm^3 instead of the usual g/m^3. L/ϱ is numerically identical to L and the ratio of total dissolved to undissolved gas is thus $\delta \cdot L$. Since L is of the order of 10^{-6}, it is clear that only gases with δ values larger than 10^4 can be removed to any extent from cloud air. For gases of category

(1), δ is usually in the range 0.01-0.1 at normal temperatures. In addition, the removal of these gases from the atmosphere will only be temporary because the dissolved gas remains in exchange with the air and is released whenever the water evaporates.

The δ values for gases of category (2) can be much larger and the removal by rain can be of importance. These gases form ions in solution and the solubility is strongly dependent on the pH value. Only the undissociated part of the dissolved gas obeys Henry's law. A well-known example is CO_2. If $[CO_2]$ is the concentration in air and $[H_2CO_3]$ the concentration of the undissociated part in water, all expressed in moles per liter, we have in the absence of other ions (e.g., Harvey, 1955)

$$[CO_2] = \beta_1 \cdot [H_2CO_3]$$

$$K_1 = \frac{[H^+] \times [HCO_3^-]}{[H_2CO_3]}$$

$$K_2 = \frac{[H^+] \times [CO_3^=]}{[HCO_3^-]}$$

$$K_3 = [H^+] \times [OH^-]$$

and

$$[H^+] = [OH^-] + [HCO_3^-] + 2 [CO_3^=].$$

This gives

$$[CO_2] = \frac{\beta_1([H^+]^3 - K_w \cdot [H^+])}{K_1([H^+] + 2K_2)}.$$

For pH < 6.5 there are hardly any carbonate ions present and we can simplify to

$$[CO_2] = \beta_1[H^+]^2/K_1.$$

For atmospheric air and 10°C we have the following numerical values:

$$[CO_2] = 1.34 \times 10^{-5} \text{ mol/liter} = 300 \text{ ppm}$$
$$\beta_1 = 1.2$$
$$K_1 = 3.4 \times 10^{-7} \text{ mol/liter}$$
$$K_2 = 3.2 \times 10^{-11} \text{ mol/liter}$$
$$K_3 = 3.6 \times 10^{-15} \text{ mol}^2/\text{liter}^2,$$

which result in the following concentrations in pure rainwater:

$$\text{pH} = 5.6$$
$$[H_2CO_3] = 0.71 \text{ mg/liter (calc. as } CO_2)$$
$$[HCO_3^-] = 0.14 \text{ mg/liter}$$
$$[CO_3^=] = 0.19 \times 10^{-5} \text{ mg/liter}.$$

pH values in the range 5-6 are common in rain (e.g., Barrett and Brodin, 1955), but the considerable fluctuations observed indicate that CO_2 is not the controlling factor. It will become apparent in the course of this chapter that the mineral acids H_2SO_4, HCl, and HNO_3 are largely responsible for lowering the pH in rain and that the value is only adjusted by CO_2. The value 5.6 is expected to separate the original alkali from the acid droplet solutions. For the gases of category (2), the undissociated part of the solution obeys Henry's law and is not affected by a change in pH. However, the ion concentrations $[HCO_3^-]$ and $[CO_3^=]$ will increase by a factor of 10 and 100, respectively, for every unit increase of the pH.

Another example is the system NH_3-H_2O. If $[NH_3]$ is the concentration in air and $[NH_4OH]$ the concentration of the undissociated part in water, both in moles per liter, the ion concentration is determined by:

$$[NH_3] = \beta_2[NH_4OH]; \qquad\qquad \beta_2 = 3.6 \times 10^{-4}, \ 10°C$$
$$K_4 = [NH_4^+] \cdot [OH^-] / [NH_4OH]; \qquad K_4 = 2.0 \times 10^{-5} \ \text{mol/liter}, \ 10°C.$$

For instance, in the absence of other constituents, an NH_3 concentration of 3 $\mu g/m^3 = 1.75 \times 10^{-10}$ mol/liter gives a pH of 8.9 and only about 1% of the gas goes into solution for a liquid water content of 1 g/m^3. For a pH of 5.6, on the other hand, 97% of the 3 $\mu g/m^3$ of NH^3 would be dissolved, resulting in 2.9 mg/liter of NH_4 in cloud water. It is clear that the small amounts of NH_3 usually found in the troposphere will have an effect on the pH comparable to that of CO_2. If both systems are considered together, an original concentration of 3 $\mu g/m^3$ NH_3 and $L = 1$ g/m^3 will result in the following:

$$
\begin{aligned}
\text{pH} \quad &= 7.0 \\
[NH_4OH] \quad &= 1.2 \times 10^{-3} \ \text{mg/liter} \\
[NH_4^+] \quad &= 2.6 \ \text{mg/liter} \\
[NH_3] \quad &= 0.4 \ \mu g/m^3 \\
[H_2CO_3] \quad &= 0.71 \ \text{mg/liter} \\
[HCO_3^-] \quad &= 3.3 \ \text{mg/liter} \\
[CO_3^=] \quad &= 1 \times 10^{-3} \ \text{mg/liter.}
\end{aligned}
$$

Under these conditions, 87% of the NH_3 will be dissolved and the solution will be almost neutral. Since pH values of 5 to 6 are common in rains, they must, in the presence of NH_3 be determined by constituents other than CO_2 and should result in a considerable removal efficiency of NH_3. However, observations do not seem to indicate exceptionally high removal for NH_3 compared to other gases like SO_2 and NO_2. Georgii (1960), for instance, measured the concentration of these gases in air just before and after rain (Table 54) and found little differences. But it is not certain to

TABLE 54

AVERAGE DECREASE OF AEROSOL AND GAS CONCENTRATIONS IN GROUND AIR DUE TO
RAIN FOR VARIOUS CONSTITUENTS IN FRANKFURT/MAIN, JUNE 1956-MAY 1957 [a]

	Aerosols			Gases			
	NH_4^+	NO_3^-	$SO_4^=$	NH_3	NO_2	SO_2	Cl
Air concentration, $\mu g/m^3$							
Before rains	6.7	6.0	16.7	21.6	11.9	328	14.3
After rains	4.7	1.6	9.7	11.0	9.1	212	5.3
% decrease	70	27	58	52	76	64	39

[a] Georgii (1960).

what extent such data can be used for this comparison because they refer
to ground air and not to cloud air and because they may also be modified
by a change in air mass during rain.

The system SO_2-H_2O is more complicated and was studied
by Junge and Ryan (1958). In the absence of any catalyst in the solution,
oxidation of SO_2 to $SO_4^=$ is negligible, but concentrations of metal salts like
$MnCl_2$, $CuCl_2$, $FeCl_2$, etc., of the order of 1 $\mu g/cm^3$ are already very efficient
catalysts. These metals are well known for this property. Junge and Ryan
found that the amount of $SO_4^=$ formed in these catalytic solutions reaches
a saturation value which is proportional to the SO_2 concentration. However,
these $SO_4^=$ concentrations are rather small, of the order of 10^{-2} mg/liter for
SO_2 concentrations of 10 $\mu g/m^3$, and cannot account for the observed levels
of $SO_4^=$ in rain. This saturation concentration of $SO_4^=$ is, however, determined by the pH of the solution and as long as the pH value is kept above
the critical value, for instance by adding NH_3, oxidation will continue unlimited. In the presence of NH_3, SO_2 will thus be oxidized until most of the
NH_3 is used up, resulting in the formation of $(NH_4)_2SO_4$. Since under normal circumstances the natural concentration of NH_3 is smaller than that of
SO_2, NH_3 will act as the controlling factor for SO_2 oxidation in rainwater.
The amount of SO_2 converted also depends on the liquid water of the cloud.
Estimates indicate that this process can explain the observed levels of
$SO_4^=$ concentration in rain.

Absorbtion of NH_3 is not the only way in which the pH
value can be raised. Calcium or other earth alkali or alkali metals present
in the condensation nuclei can of course also promote SO_2 oxidation. It is
also possible that there are still other processes by which SO_2 can be converted to SO_4 *in solution*, and it should be mentioned that chemical reactions

of aerosol constituents with gases such as SO_2 and NO_2 are not restricted to water droplets in clouds, i.e., to rainout, but can also occur for dry aerosols as was already discussed in Chapters 1 and 2.

One would expect that ε in Eq. (1) is smaller for gases like SO_2 and NH_3 than for aerosols. The data in Table 54 do not seem to indicate such a difference, but they may not be representative for *rainout*. Table 55

TABLE 55

RANGE OF c/k VALUES OBSERVED IN SCANDINAVIA, CENTRAL EUROPE, AND SWITZERLAND FOR VARIOUS GASES AND THE CALCULATED RANGE OF ε IF L VARIES BETWEEN 1 AND 2 g/m^3 [a]

	NH_3/NH_4^+	NO_2/NO_3^-	$SO_2/SO_4^=$
c/k	4.5–8.3	2.5–5.5	6.7–20
ε	0.12–0.44	0.13–0.60	0.03–0.20

[a] Georgii (1960).

gives c/k values for simultaneous measurements of gases in ground air and the corresponding constituents in rainwater (Georgii, 1960) which can be compared with c/k values for fission products in aerosols given in Section 3.4.4. Although in neither case is it known how representative these data are for the processes *within* the clouds, the values for ε in Table 55 seem to be smaller than those for aerosols by a factor of 2 to 5. Since the observed rainwater concentrations for NH_4^+, NO_3^-, and $SO_4^=$ include the aerosol component, the actual values of ε for gases are likely to be even smaller than those in Table 55. If ε should prove to be smaller for gases than for aerosol constituents, the higher concentration for gases in air will compensate this to some extent with respect to the actual net removal by rainout for gases and aerosols.

Washout of gases will occur if the gas concentrations below the cloud are higher than those within the cloud and/or if the reaction within the cloud is only partially completed.

The exceptional behavior of $SO_4^=$ in rains over Frankfurt (Fig. 70 and Section 4.3.1) is very likely due to washout of SO_2. Figure 17 shows that the concentrations of SO_2 in Frankfurt are about 10 times higher in winter than those of the other gases or the natural background. The differences between Frankfurt and the Taunus Observatory for the other constituents in Fig. 70 may also include washout of gases, but the effect cannot be distinguished from the washout of aerosols.

4.2.5 Dry Removal of Aerosols and Gases

Very little information is available with which to assess the role of dry deposition in comparison to wet removal. Sedimentation of aerosols can be estimated easily if their size distribution is known. Under normal meteorological conditions, turbulence near the ground is large enough to establish an almost constant concentration with height above ground, so that the rate of sedimentation at the earth's surface can be cal-

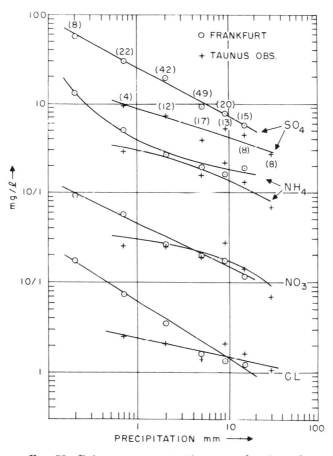

FIG. 70. Rainwater concentration as a function of rainfall amounts for various constituents. The curves with the circles are obtained in Frankfurt in a polluted atmosphere and the curves marked by crosses are obtained at the Taunus Observatory located 800 meters high and 25 km north of Frankfurt and not seriously affected by air pollution (Georgii and Weber, 1960).

The number of rainfalls are in parentheses.

culated with reasonable accuracy from concentration measurements above the ground. Sedimentation upon horizontal surfaces has in fact been used successfully to determine the concentration and size distribution of natural aerosols (Junge, 1953). The residence time of a tropospheric aerosol due to sedimentation alone can be calculated if its vertical distribution is known. For an estimate we will ignore eddy diffusion and assume that the aerosol is contained in a layer of height $\overline{H}$ with a homogeneous concentration equal to that at the ground. The residence time is then

$$\tau = \overline{H}/v$$

where v is the fall velocity. Table 56 gives values for v and τ as a function of particle size for $\overline{H} = 5$ km and a particle density of 2 g/cm³. For sea salt

TABLE 56

FALL VELOCITY AND RESIDENCE TIME OF SPHERICAL AEROSOL PARTICLES OF DENSITY 2 g/cm³ AND FOR A HOMOGENEOUS HEIGHT $\overline{H} = 5$ km

Particle radius, μ	1	2	4	6	8	10	15	20
Fall velocity, cm/sec	0.026	0.10	0.38	0.88	1.6	2.7	6.0	10
Residence time, days	220	58	15	6.6	3.6	2.1	0.96	0.58

over the ocean, $\overline{H}$ will be smaller, 1-2 km, and for aerosols which increase in concentration with altitude, $\overline{H}$ can be larger than the tropopause height.

We see that the residence time for sedimentation is long compared to wet removal if the radii are smaller than 2 μ. For constituents in the range of the giant particles, on the other hand, removal by sedimentation can be appreciable. Woodcock's data of the size distribution of sea-salt particles over the ocean give an effective sedimentation velocity of 0.7 cm/sec, which corresponds to an effective radius of 5 μ (Eriksson, 1959). This value will decrease rapidly inland, due to preferential loss of the largest particles, but no quantitative data are available on this subject.

One way to compare the efficiency of the various removal processes is to compute the "deposition velocity" defined by

$$v = D/c$$

where D is the rate of deposition, often expressed in kg/ha year, and c is the air concentration. The total deposition rate is given by

$$D_t = D_p + D_s + D_i$$

where the subscripts p, s, and i refer to precipitation, sedimentation, and impaction, respectively, Correspondingly, we have

$$v_t = v_p + v_s + v_i.$$

v_p can conveniently be calculated by

$$v_p = 3.16 \times 10^{-3} \cdot k \cdot h/c$$

where k is given in milligrams per liter, h in millimeters of precipitation per year, and c in $\mu g/m^3$.

The chloride data for Scandinavia are sufficiently complete to warrant calculations of this type. Eriksson (1960) determined the average distribution of c, D_p, and D_t over Scandinavia from data of the air chemistry network. The total deposition rate D_t can be obtained from maps of the river runoff, because the production of Cl^- by weathering in rocks and soil is negligible. The rain collection funnels received an unknown fraction of D_s and in the absence of better information on this point we assume that D_p includes $\frac{1}{2} D_s$. If the southwestern coastal areas are excluded, one obtains the following average values for Sweden: $v_t = 1.4$ cm/sec, $v_p + \frac{1}{2} v_s = 0.4$ cm/sec, $v_i + \frac{1}{2} v_s = 1.0$ cm/sec. v_s was found to be 0.7 cm/sec over the ocean and may decrease to 0.2 cm/sec inland. The comparison of these figures clearly indicates that impaction is dominant for sea salt over Scandinavia. Eriksson (1960) finds a rather constant ratio

$$(D_p + \tfrac{1}{2} D_s)/D_t = (v_p + \tfrac{1}{2} v_s)/v_t$$

of about 0.3 over all Scandinavia and suggests that this ratio may be applied to other areas for budget estimates of Cl^-.

The importance of impaction for dry removal of chloride over Scandinavia is somewhat unexpected. It is probably due to a combination of favorable conditions, as e.g., the large overage size of sea salt particles, the humid climate, the morphology of the country, and its coverage with forests. Pine trees should, for aerodynamical reasons, scavenge surface air quite effectively at normal wind speeds. These suggestions are supported by the observation (Madgwick and Ovington, 1959) that the concentrations in rainwater are higher in samples collected under trees than in the open. Georgii (1962) made similar measurements for over half a year and found the following average values for the ratio of "under trees" to "in the open":

amount of rainfall,	0.54
concentration,	3.60
total deposition,	1.95.

However, any generalization for other areas should await further studies. Gorham (1961) points out that for Australian river waters, the agreement between the observed concentrations of chloride and those calculated from rainfall analyses and river discharges is very good, suggesting little dry fallout or capture of salt particles by vegetation. It is clear that this question is of importance for all budget considerations, as for instance for the deposition of Sr^{90} on soil. So far, the soil analyses for Sr^{90} agree reasonably well with the deposition by rain, but the soil samples have been taken in open country and a comparison with the chloride data is not conclusive. Another factor is the particle size distribution. Further studies of this problem would be very desirable.

The question of dry deposition becomes further complicated for constituents like sulfur which form solid and gaseous compounds.

Dry deposition of gases occurs by adsorption or chemical reactions at the soil surface. In this case, the concentration c_0 in the boundary layer near the ground is lower than the concentration c above, in contrast to aerosols, and a diffusion flux toward the surface is established. This flux can be controlled either by the absorption rate at the soil surface or by the rate of eddy diffusion. In the first case, c_0 is only slightly smaller than c; in the second case c_0 is small compared to c.

Only a few scattered data are available on deposition velocities for gases. These are found in Johansson's (1959) work on SO_2 in pot experiments (see also Section 1.5.1) and in the work of Chamberlain and Chadwick (1953) on radioactive I_2. The following values are given: I_2 vapor over pastures, 2 cm/sec; SO_2 over bare soil, 1.5 cm/sec; SO_2 over soil with plants, 2 cm/sec. The velocities of SO_2, e.g., are about one order of magnitude larger than those of $SO_4^=$ in precipitation. Under average conditions, it can be assumed that for $SO_4^=$ $k = 1$ mg/liter, $c = 10$ $\mu g/m^3$, and $h = 500$ mm/year, which results in a v_p of 0.1 cm/sec.

Direct uptake of gases by the soil can, therefore, be an important factor and has to be included in budget considerations. Maps of *rain deposit* and *river runoff* of $SO_4^=$ in Scandinavia (Eriksson, 1960) agree approximately, in contrast to the corresponding maps of Cl, as discussed above. This means that the release and absorption of sulfur gases from the earth's surface are also approximately equal. How far this conclusion can be applied to other areas, as was done, e.g., in the estimation of the sulfur budget in Fig. 20, is still an open question.

It should be emphasized that the concept of a deposition velocity for gases or for any constituent which shows a vertical gradient above the earth's surface is only an approximate, though convenient, way of expressing average conditions. Average values of v, even over long-time intervals, depend on the altitude z at which c is measured and on the effective eddy diffusion coefficient between the earth's surface and z, which varies considerably with meteorological and microclimatological conditions.

The other removal processes for gases, mentioned in the Introduction, i.e., the conversion of gases into aerosols or into other gases, and the escape into space, have already been treated in connection with specific compounds and will not be discussed here further.

4.3 Chemical Composition of Precipitation

4.3.1 Concentration as a Function of the Amount and Type of Precipitation

Before we enter the discussion of the chemical composition of rainwater, we would like to consider some observations which are closely related to the processes of rainout and washout. Most of the rainwater data in the literature refer to average values over a certain time period, e.g., a month or a year. The reason for this is that concentrations in individual rainfalls vary so considerably with time and amount of rainfall that it is difficult to correlate them in a meaningful way with other meteorological parameters.

The scatter of values is particularly large for small amounts of rainfall h and decreases rapidly with increasing h. Gerogii and Weber (1960) found, for instance, that the ratio of maximum to minimum concentration is more than 20 for $h = 1$ mm, about 10 for $h = 10$ mm, and about 5 for $h = 20$ mm. This decrease of the ratio is due almost completely to a decrease of the *maximum* concentrations, whereas the *minimum* concentrations are fairly independent of h. The large variability for small rainfalls is caused by the influence of washout and especially of evaporation of rain droplets, by which the concentration can increase indefinitely. These effects become negligible for large rainfalls because *rainout* becomes the controlling factor and because higher humidities will reduce evaporation.

The value of the *minimum* concentration in individual rainfalls, on the other hand, is set within certain limits by the lowest air concentration and the maximum liquid water content, and can be associated with any value of h. For instance, a small amount of rain may be caused either by a light isolated shower or by the last few droplets of a large passing rainstorm.

A result of these effects is a decrease of the *average* concentration of rainwater with increasing *amount* of rainfall. To separate the effects of rainout and washout, Georgii and Weber (1960) analyzed rainfalls in Frankfurt and at the Taunus Observatory, which is located 800 meters higher on a mountain ridge about 25 km north of Frankfurt. Because of the geographical situation, it can be expected that rainout will be the same for both places, but that washout below the clouds will be important only in Frankfurt, where it occurs moreover in the polluted ground air of the

Rhein-Main valley. Figure 70 gives their data for four constituents. The concentrations of NH_4^+, NO_3^-, and Cl^- are higher in Frankfurt for rainfall amounts smaller than 2-6 mm, but approach those of the Taunus Observatory for larger amounts. This would mean that washout is more or less completed for rainfalls of 5 mm, at least for constituents with vertical distributions and particle sizes similar to those of NH_4^+, etc. The curves demonstrate that the influence of local pollution in large rainfalls becomes small for most constituents. However, the picture looks different for $SO_4^=$ for which the values for Frankfurt remain higher, though less pronounced, even in high rainfalls. This is probably due to washout of SO_2 which has markedly higher concentrations than the other gases (Fig. 17) although an effect of the higher $SO_4^=$ concentrations in aerosols may also be included.

It is interesting that the decrease in concentration for the Taunus Observatory is rather similar for all constituents. This implies that the meteorological factors of rainout and evaporation are responsible, a view which is further supported by Fig. 71. This figure compares data of various investigators and covers most of the relevant data available in the literature. Curves 1 and 2 are average values of all the data in Fig. 70, dominated by the high concentrations of $SO_4^=$. Curves 3 and 4 were obtained by Hinzpeter (1959) for rain and snow on the basis of a rather homogeneous set of data on long-lived fission products from a network of 10 stations in West Germany. Each point is represented by about 60 individual rainfalls and the average scatter around these values is about 30%. Since the air concentration of fission products increases with altitude, washout for these curves is of little importance, as in the case of curve 2 with which they agree quite well. It is important to note that the *air concentrations* measured simultaneously with curves 3 and 4 in ground air remained almost constant over the whole precipitation range.

Gorham (1958 b) measured rainfall concentrations at 280 m above sea level in the English Lake District and he presents curves 5 and 6 for $SO_4^= + NO_3^+$ (calculated here as $SO_4^=$, since NO_3^- is of less importance) and for Cl^-. The agreement with the previous curves is quite good and the slope can be approximated by a power law $h^{-0/3}$.

Curves 7 and 8 were obtained for NO_3^- and NH_4^+ in Sweden. They show a somewhat steeper slope for higher rainfalls, similar to curve 12 for Cl^- which is based on only a few data from Japan and consequently not very representative. Curves 9 and 10 for Cl^- and NO_3^- were obtained in Central Europe during the IGY and curve 11 for $NO_3 + NO_2^-$ in Australia. The latter behaves quite differently from the others in that the concentration is inversely proportional to the amount of rainfall.

Except for curve 11, all the observations show a similar trend which seems to reflect a rather basic correlation. Under average conditions, it can be expected that higher amounts of rainfall are associated with deeper

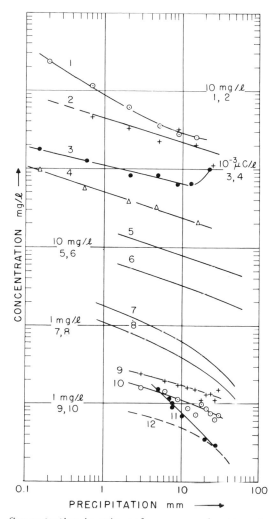

FIG. 71. Concentration in rain and snow as a function of amount of precipitation. Curves 1 and 2 are average concentrations of 4 constituents, $SO_4^=$, NH_4^+, NO_3^-, Cl^- (see Fig. 70) for Frankfurt (1) and Taunus Observatory (2), 800 meters high (Georgii and Weber, 1960). Curves 3 and 4 are average concentrations of long-lived fission product activity for rain (3) and snow (4) from a 10-station network, Germany (Hinzpeter, 1959). Curves 5 and 6 are average concentrations of $SO_4^=$ + NO_3^+, calculated as $SO_4^=$ (5) and of Cl^- (6), North England (Gorham, 1958 b). Curves 7 and 8 are average concentrations of NO_3^- (7) and NH_4^+ (8), Sweden (Ångström and Högberg, 1952 a). Curves 9 and 10 are concentrations of Cl^- (9) and NO_3^- (10), Czechoslovakia (Macku et al., 1959). Curve 11 is the average concentration of NO_3, tropical air masses, spring and autumn, Australia (Anderson, 1915). Curve 12 is the average concentration of Cl^-, Japan (Sugawara et al., 1949). Curves 5, 6, 7, 8, and 12 replotted from average curves given without data.

cloud layers and/or horizontally more extended cloud systems. In such systems the air rises to higher levels, resulting in larger amounts of the total condensed water and the evaporation of cloud and raindrops will be reduced. On the other hand, horizontally extended storm systems may cause some depletion of the constituents in the center. However, the fact that in the case of curves 3 and 4 the air concentration remained constant for all rainfall amounts seems to indicate that the latter effect is not so important and that the evaporation and the value of L in Eq. (1) are the controlling factors for the correlation between k and h. If we assume, e.g., that light rainfalls start with an L of 1 g/m³, the trend of the curves in Fig. 71 can be explained by an increase to 5 or 8 g/m³, which is not unreasonable. Any effects of evaporation will support this trend. The unusual increase of curve 3 for very large h may be regarded as further support of this concept. Hinzpeter suggests that it is due to high reaching clouds which came in contact with upper tropospheric air of higher specific activity.

The relation between L and h, plus the effect of evaporation, will depend to some extent on the average structure of raining clouds or cloud systems and should thus differ with latitude and climate. It can also be expected from Figs. 70 and 71 that *within individual* rainfalls, the concentration decreases with time or amount in a similar way. The few published observations of the concentration as a function of time during rain (e.g., Gorham, 1958 b) show a general decrease but with considerable irregularities. Such irregularities are, of course, eliminated in Figs. 70 and 71 by averaging.

Georgii and Weber (1960) also investigated the variation in concentration of different particle sizes in ground air during rainfalls due to washout. In a few cases they recorded the number of Aitken nuclei, large particles (0.5 to 1.2 μ radius) and giant particles (larger than 1.2 μ radius). So far their data show, in general, some decrease of all these constituents and no pronounced difference in behavior between the particles larger or smaller than 1 μ. It can, of course, hardly be expected that the simple model of washout in a stagnant air (discussed in Section 4.2.2.) can be applied to actual conditions, since it must be assumed that horizontal advection of different air masses in connection with the passage of frontal rains or variations in vertical mixing and other meteorological phenomena are likely to obscure the effects of washout. Further studies are needed to establish general relationships.

We will conclude this section with a comparison of the different types of precipitation. The results are not very consistent and seem to vary with the constituent and the locality. Macku *et al.* (1959) found that the concentration of Cl⁻ in Czechoslovakia is higher during drizzle and light rain than during showers, but the other ions did not show such a difference. Most of the ions had higher concentrations in snow than in rain, particularly Cl⁻, but nitrate, e.g., did not.

In Frankfurt (Georgii and Weber, 1960) there was practically no difference between *rains* and *showers* for NH_4^+, NO_3^-, and Cl^-, but the rains had about twice the concentration of $SO_4^=$. A comparison between snow and rain gave a similar result, with higher concentrations in snow for $SO_4^=$ only, and here we may also recall the exceptional behavior of $SO_4^=$ in Fig. 70. It is suggested that these differences are due in part to the longer exposure below the clouds of small droplets or snow flakes to pollutants of high concentration or high production rates, such as SO_2 or HCl. However, the dispersion, and the chemical nature of the constituent, as well as its vertical distribution, will also be of some influence.

4.3.2 Rarely Observed Constituents and Chloride

In Sections 4.3.2 through 4.3.5. we will present *observations* on the chemical composition of precipitation and its geographical and seasonal variations. Studies of the constituents in rainwater have been made for more than a hundred years and the literature on this subject is quite voluminous. The field was thoroughly reviewed by Drischel (1940), Eriksson (1952 a, b), and again by Eriksson in 1959 and 1960 for chloride and sulfate. Our discussion will be based in part on these reviews and will emphasize the basic and large-scale phenomena and their interpretation.

The following rainwater constituents and parameters have been measured and discussed in the literature:

(a) Frequently determined compounds:
    Anions: Cl^-, $SO_4^=$, NO_3^-, NO_2^-, HCO_3^-;
    Cations: Na^+, K^+, Ca^{++}, Mg^{++}, NH_4^+;
    pH and the electrical conductivity.

(b) Rarely determined compounds:
    P_2O_5, I, H_2O_2, CH_2O, and total organic and insoluble material.

In most cases the electrical conductivity calculated from the total sum of the anions and cations listed above under (a) agrees well with the measured conductivity. Larson and Hettick (1956), e.g., found agreement within 10 to 20% for rains in Illinois, U.S.A., execept for very acid rainfalls, and Gorham (1957) found even better agreement, within a few per cent, in rains collected on the west coast of Ireland. This indicates that for a wide variety of geographical conditions these ions represent most of the dissolved inorganic material. An unknown number of minor constituents will always be present, such as those listed under (b) which have been measured occasionally. Several observers found P_2O_2 in concentrations between 0.1 and 1.0 mg/liter (Eriksson, 1952 b). In Holland near the coast, Heymann (1927) found iodine concentrations between 0.001 and 0.01 mg/liter with an average value of 0.0035 mg/liter. The Cl/I ratio was higher than in sea water and there was no correlation between the Cl and I values. This is not surprising with respect to our discussion on the origin of iodine in Europe discussed in Section 1.8.

In Japan, Matsui (1949) observed hydrogen peroxide in concentrations between 0.08 and 0.86 mg/liter with a maximum in June and a minimum in January. It may be formed by ultraviolet radiation, and its presence is of interest with respect to oxidation processes. Formaldehyde was found by Dhar and Ram (1939) in concentrations between 0.1 and 1.0 mg/liter, with a mean of 0.5 mg/liter. They suggest that it is formed by the action of sunlight on a solution of organic substances in water, but it is also found in polluted atmospheres (see Section 1.9.2).

Only in a few cases has total soluble and organic material been measured. Table 57 shows that in and around Berlin the total amount of

TABLE 57

COMPOSITION OF RAINWATER FOR VARIOUS DISTANCES FROM THE CENTER OF BERLIN. AVERAGE VALUES FOR THE YEAR (Y), SUMMER (S), AND WINTER (W) IN mg/liter [a]

Location	Total insoluble Matter			Total soluble Matter			Cl^-			$SO_4^=$			NH_4^+		
	Y	S	W	Y	S	W	Y	S	W	Y	S	W	Y	S	W
Center of Berlin	84	50	46	87	70	110	6.0	4.1	9.2	25	12	42	0.60	0.62	0.61
Dahlem, 15 km SW	37	35	41	67	58	85	4.4	3.4	6.3	19	6	42	1.0	1.1	0.9
Muncheberg, 50 km E	23	13	37	28	24	34	3.5	2.5	5.4	10	7	14	0.4	0.5	0.4

[a] Liesegang (1934)

insoluble material is quite substantial and about equal to the amount of soluble material. Both are apparently affected by human activities in a similar manner. In corresponcence with the aerosol composition listed in Tables 33 and 34, the amount of organic substances, e.g., the ignition loss of evaporation residues, is also considerable. Herman and Gorham (1957) reported from Nova Scotia precipitation the accompanying tabulated values (in milligrams per liter):

Ignition loss	13	rain	2.7	snow
Ignition residue	10		4.3	
Total residue	23		7.0	

Here, the organic material is of the same order as the total soluble and insoluble material taken together. The most careful and recent study of organic and total material was made by Neumann *et al.* (1959). They found a fairly uniform distribution of organic carbon in precipitation over Sweden with the following values:

Rain	1.7 to 3.4 mg/liter;	average 2.5 mg/liter
Snow	0.8 to 1.9 mg/liter;	average 1.3 mg/liter

The ratio of carbon to inorganic matter varied from 0.28-1.03, in rough agreement with the data mentioned previously. It can be assumed that the total organic content is about twice that of carbon.

These data show that *organic* and *insoluble* materials in precipitation are equally as abundant as *soluble inorganic* constituents. However, the latter ones, which we will discuss now, are much more thoroughly studied, primarily because of simpler analytical methods and partly because of their potential importance to plant nutrition.

The following discussion of the ionic composition of rainwater will be based essentially on recent data obtained by networks of stations. The first large-scale network of this kind was established in Scandinavia in 1954 (see, Egnér and Eriksson, 1955) and later was extended over Western and Central Europe. The data are regularly published in *Tellus*. A sampling network of 60 stations in the U.S. was operated from July 1955 to 1956 (Junge and Gustafson, 1956), and a small network in Czechoslovakia was established during the IGY (Macku *et al.*, 1959).

The data from these networks can be presented in the form of maps. Most investigators prefer maps of the concentration because, as our previous discussion on the mechanism of rainout and washout indicated, the conconcentration in rainwater is highly reflective of the concentration in air, which in turn reflects the areas of production and removal. Other authors use maps of the deposition rate, expressed, e.g., in kg per hectare per year. Such maps are useful for budget considerations or in connection with problems of soil chemistry and plant nutrition but are less appropriate for our considerations since the distribution of the deposition rate is a function of *both* the concentration in rainwater and the rate of rainfall.

Figures 72 and 73 show the distribution of chloride concentration over Europe and the U.S. It is obvious that the ocean is the predominant source of chloride in precipitation. The isolines of concentration follow the coast rather closely and their spacing indicates that the decrease inland is approximately exponential. However, at a certain distance from the coast, this decrease stops and a plateau, or an area of fairly uniform concentration, is reached. This is particularly evident over the U.S., where the geographical dimensions are large enough and the spacing of the stations farther inland more uniform. The plateau concentration seems to be higher by a factor from 5 to 10 over Central Europe than over the U.S., but there is an indication that the concentration decreases farther south in Austria and Switzerland.

The distribution of chloride as a function of the distance from the coast is of special interest to air chemistry and will be discussed in more detail. To obtain a better comparison, we plotted in Fig. 74 typical profiles

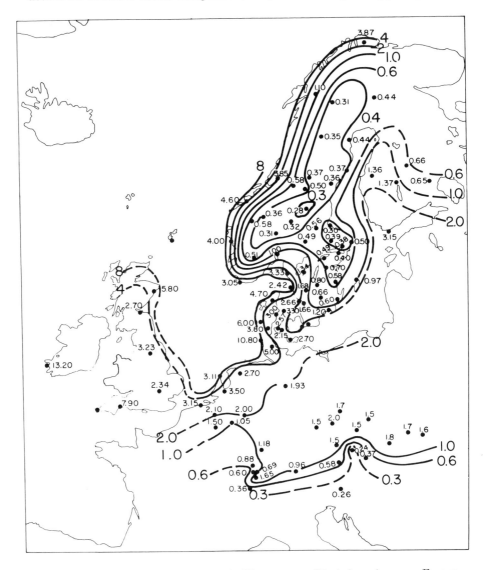

Fig. 72. Average Cl⁻ concentration (milligrams per liter) in rain over Europe, 1957/1958. Calculated from the current network data published in *Tellus*.

derived from various studies in England, Holland, southern Sweden, Australia, and the U.S. In all these cases, the drop in concentration is rather sharp within the first 10 to 20 km from the shore line, but decreases farther inland. It is easy to show that this decrease near the coast is not caused by rainout and washout as was generally believed to be the case. For example, if we assume an atmospheric residence time of 3 days for sea salt and an

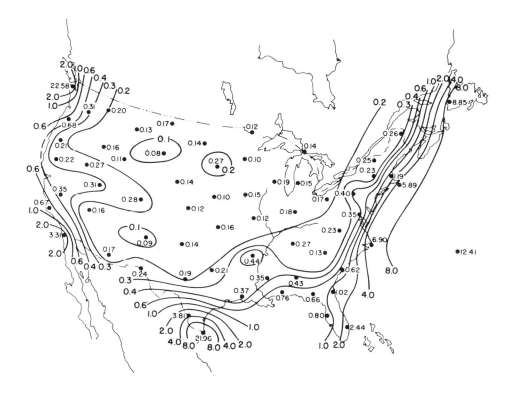

FIG. 73. Average Cl⁻ concentration (milligrams per liter) in rain over the U.S. July 1955-June 1956 (Junge and Werby, 1958). (By courtesy of *Journal of Meteorology*.)

average wind component of 25 km/hour perpendicular to the coastline, we obtain the rate of decrease with distance from the coast given by line W in Fig. 74. This estimate shows that wet removal of sea spray, even if supported by a similar rate of dry removal, is obviously not sufficient to explain the observations. Junge and Gustafson (1957) pointed out that maritime air masses will be subject to intense convective mixing when they move inland and that this vertical mixing will result in a considerable decrease

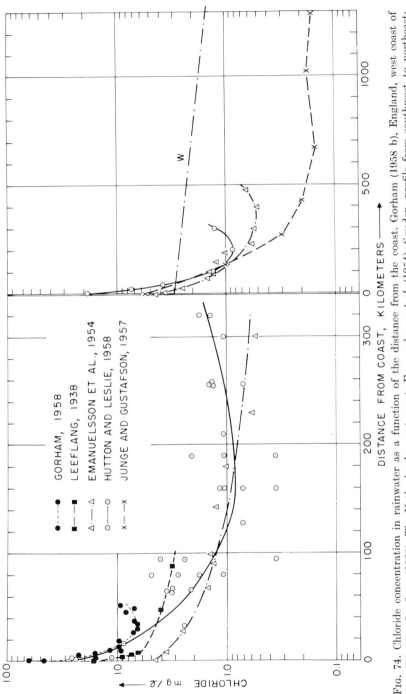

Fig. 74. Chloride concentration in rainwater as a function of the distance from the coast. Gorham (1958 b), England, west coast of Lake District; Leeflang (1938), The Netherlands, west coast; Emanuelsson *et al.* (1954), Sweden, profile from southwest to northeast; Hutton and Leslie (1958), Australia, south coast of Victoria; Junge and Gustafson (1957), United States, east coast from Cape Hatteras westward. The profiles are plotted at two different scales to cover the wide range of distances. Curve W is an estimated decrease inland for an aerosol residence time of 3 days and winds of 25 km/hour.

of the salt content in the subcloud layer and consequently in rain, if the original vertical profile of sea salt is similar to that found by Woodcock over the subtropical ocean (Fig. 36). In such a profile an eddy diffusion coefficient of 4×10^5 cm^2/sec, e.g., would reduce the concentration near the ground to 25% in 12 hours. The dilution of sea salt will cease when the vertical distribution has become sufficiently uniform. The distance from the coast where the Cl plateau starts can be interpreted on this basis as the distance at which vertical mixing is more or less completed under average conditions. This explanation implies that the amount of decrease from the coast to the plateau depends on the original vertical salt profile over the sea: The dilution in surface air is large if the sea salt layer is shallow and it it is small if the air masses are already well mixed over the ocean.

This concept is strongly supported by Fig. 36, which compares vertical profiles of large sea salt particles over the subtropical ocean and in the interior of the U.S. In Section 2.3.2 we estimated that for both sets of data the total number of sea salt particles in a vertical column is not much different which suggests that the removal over land is not very rapid. However, the effect of vertical mixing is clearly demonstrated and the concentration in the layer, where most rain is formed, decreases by a factor of about 10 over land, in approximate agreement with the decrease of chloride concentration from the coast to the center of the U.S. in Fig. 73. From this, one may conclude that most of the Cl$^-$ found in the interior of the U.S. is of oceanic origin. It is possible that land sources, e.g., pollution, are involved but the data do not allow us to judge whether and to what extent land sources contribute.

Figure 74 shows that the plateau concentrations are quite different for the individual profiles. One gets the impression that it is the value of this concentration which determines the point at which the decrease ceases, so that there is a relationship between the distance at which this occurs and the plateau concentration. The approximate figures in the accompanying tabulation are taken from Fig. 74:

England	30 km and 7 mg/lliter
Holland	50 km and 3.5 mg/liter
Australia	150 km and 1 mg/liter
Sweden	300 km and 0.4 mg/liter
U.S.A.	600 km and 0.15 mg/liter

The increase at 500 km in Sweden is due to the influence of the Baltic, which appears at this point in this SW-NE profile. The Australian data were obtained in the southern coastal area of Victoria. The data for England refer to the Cl$^-$ concentration of water in tarns in the English Lake District on the west coast. These waters are influenced but little by the ground and receive practically all constituents from the air. Thus, except for a small increase in concentration due to evaporation, their composition is essentially identical to that of the average rainfall.

On the basis of our previous discussion, one would expect that the higher plateau concentrations in Europe and Australia are due to better vertical mixing of sea salt within the maritime air masses, so that the subsequent dilution in ground air over land is less pronounced. Unfortunately, there are no data on vertical profiles of sea salt over the northern Atlantic and the southern Pacific oceans with which to check this. However, the fact that the concentrations are higher in England and Central Europe than in Scandinavia (Fig. 72) suggests that land sources of Cl^- may be involved in raising the level above the sea salt background. For Europe, the most likely source is pollution. Gorham (1958 a), e.g., found a highly significant correlation coefficient between Cl^- and acidity for a pH < 5.7 in urban precipitation samples of the Sheffield and Manchester area in England, whereas this was not the case with $SO_4^=$, despite the large concentrations of the latter. This suggests that HCl is produced in pollution but that it is apparently not neutralized by other ions before being removed by precipitation, in contrast to $SO_4^=$ which is also largely of industrial origin. The high chlorine content of coal is a factor which favors industrial production of HCl in this area. Macku *et al.* (1959) observed the highest Cl^- concentrations over Czechoslovakia in industrial regions. Georgii and Weber (1960) found that the Cl^- concentration in Frankfurt is 3 times higher than at the Taunus Observatory, 25 km farther north, almost identical with the $SO_4^=$ increase, indicating that industrial pollution is its source. Figures 17, 41, and Table 57 give further evidence of Cl^- pollution and suggest that anthropogenic Cl^- may be of regional importance in highly populated areas, such as England or Central Europe. The decrease of Cl^- concentration in Fig. 72, south of Central Europe, i.e., south of the main areas of industry, points in the same direction.

Another land source is the soil. In humid climates this source is unimportant due to the low chlorine content of rocks and sediments and to the rapid removal of any Cl^- by river runoff. However, in arid zones, salts dissolved in the ground water or deposited by rain can accumulate substantially at the surface. Hutton and Leslie (1958) suggest that in southern Australia a considerable fraction of rainwater Cl^- is recycled from the soil so that it is difficult to compute the accretion of sea salt in these areas.

It is apparent from this discussion that the major features of the chloride distribution in rainwater can be explained by sea salt and large-scale vertical mixing over land, but that differences in concentration for different land areas suggest additional nonmaritime sources. In the next section we will show that similar conclusions must be drawn for the other sea salt constituents and that their behavior differs from that of Cl^- only in that land sources are more important for most of them.

4.3.3 Ratio of Chloride to Sodium, and Sodium, Potassium, Calcium, Magnesium

The ratio of ions in sea water is rather constant all over the world and the comparison with ratios in precipitation can thus be useful for determining the origin of constituents. Table 58 gives a farily represen-

TABLE 58

OBSERVED Cl^-/Na^+ RATIO IN RAIN AND FRESH WATER ON ISLANDS AND IN COASTAL AREAS [a]

Observer	Location	Ratio
Leeflang (1938)	Netherlands—rainwater; average values for several years; variation with distance 0-86 km from the coast.	1.90–2.30
Gorham (1958 b)	Lake District, west coast of England—water from 18 tarns; variation with distance 0-50 km from the coast.	1.64–1.96
Oddie (1959)	Lerwick, Shetland Islands—rainwater; variation of monthly averages.	1.17–1.69
Eriksson (1960)	Average of 1958 rainwater:	
	Lista, southwest coast of Norway	1.71
	Rjupnahed, west coast of Iceland	1.78
	Lerwick, Shetland Islands	1.62
	Den Helder, coast of Netherlands	1.63
	Camborne, southwest England	1.79
Junge and Werby (1958)	Bermuda	1.72
	Tatoosh Island, Washington, U.S.	1.58
Gorham and Cragg (1960)	Falkland Islands—bog waters	1.98
Eriksson (1957)	Windward side of Island of Hawaii (near Hilo). Rainwater average for samples from 2 days 0-15 km from the coast.	1.90

[a] The ratio in sea water is 1.80.

tative compilation of Cl^-/Na^+ ratios observed on islands and in coastal areas. The low values found by Oddie (1959) in Lerwick were already mentioned in Section 2.3.2 when we discussed the possibility of HCl release from sea spray particles by the formation of H_2SO_4. Similar values are reported from other parts of the North Atlantic (Eriksson, 1960) and from the coast of the U.S. (Junge and Werby, 1958). However, other data show values equal to or higher than 1.80. The composition of the water in tarns in the Lake District of England's west coast is completely determined by precipitation, and we see that within the limits of accuracy the average ratio Cl^-/Na^+ is 1.8, i.e., equal to that of sea water. By far most of the NaCl deposited in this area by rain comes from the sea. Gorham (1958 b) showed that rains associated with winds from the industrial centers southeast of the Lake District had higher proportions of $SO_4^=$ and also excess Cl^-, both typical for pollution in England. Other rains, primarily light ones, showed some excess of Na^+. However, the total effect of these contributions to the tarn waters is apparently small as confirmed by the fact that highest Cl^- contents were always associated with storms from the west and with Cl^-/Na^+ ratios equal to that of sea water.

Table 58 also shows examples for Cl^-/Na^+ ratios *higher* than 1.8. In summarizing and completing the previous discussions to this point, we can list the following possible reasons for these deviations:

(1) Systematic errors in the analyses. In most instances the deviations from 1.8 in Table 58 do not exceed 10% and the ratio of two quantities is rather sensitive to errors. We would like to draw the attention to fact that the 1958 average for Den Helder is not in agreement with Leeflang's ratio.

(2) Possible modification of the composition of sea salt particles during the process of separation from the sea surface. Eriksson (1960) suggests that organic films which are often found on the sea surface may change the ionic composition by increasing the cation concentration of the surface water, which determines the composition of the sea spray particles, but so far no direct observations of this effect are known.

(3) Release of Cl^- from sea-salt particles subsequent to formation. In Section 2.3.2 we already discussed the fact that the escape of HCl by the formation of H_2SO_4 in or on sea-salt droplets is a probable mechanism. Progressive accumulation of $SO_4^=$ with time should thus lead to a decrease of the Cl^-/Na^+ ratio. If the rainout efficiency for these particles is higher than for HCl, a corresponding decrease of the ratio in rainwater should be observed. With increasing distance from the coast, it must be expected that the Cl^-/Na^+ ratio increases again, due to the accumulation of HCl.

(4) Pick up of mineral soil particles by wind. Since soil material, at least in humid climates, is generally low in chloride compared to the alkali metals, this results in a decrease of the Cl^-/Na^+ ratio. We will discuss this point in more detail in connection with the other constituents, K^+, Ca^{++}, and Mg^{++}.

(5) Residual amounts of mineral matter from other areas, e.g., the North American Continent. This is suggested by the composition of ice samples from the center of the Greenland ice sheet (Junge, 1960), given in Table 59. We see that the ratio of the constituents is quite diffe-

TABLE 59

IONIC COMPOSITION OF ICE IN THE CENTER OF GREENLAND; AVERAGE VALUES FOR THE TIME PERIOD 1915-1957 [a]

Ion	Concentration, mg/liter
$SO_4^=$	0.25
Cl^-	0.037
Na^+	0.029
Ca^{++}	0.035
K^+	0.011

[a] Junge (1960).

rent from that of sea water, although Greenland is surrounded by the ocean. Of particular importance here is the ratio of $Na^+ : Ca^{++} : K^+$. These data seem to indicate a background of mineral constituents in the air even after most other aerosols are removed, i.e., in very remote places or very clean atmospheres. It is likely that this background is higher on the west coast of Europe, but there is no way to distinguish it from other sources.

(6) Production of Cl^- by industry. This will *raise* the Cl^-/Na^+ ratio and may be indicated by Leeflang's data in Table 58, because most air that passes over the Netherlands has picked up pollution in England. Gorham (1958 b) showed that pollution in England has Cl^-/Na^+ ratios of 3 to 4.

In concluding this discussion we may say that the present data do not provide a sufficient basis for deciding if and to what extent the deviations of the Cl^-/Na^+ ratio in *coastal* areas are caused by a change in composition of the sea salt particles themselves [processes (2) and (3)] or by addition of Na^+ or Cl^- from other sources. Process (2) alone would, of course, result in a constant ratio Cl^-/Na^+ with increasing distance inland from the coast and the upper limit for this effect is set by the data in Table 58. Observations always show a decrease of the Cl^-/Na^+ ratio and much larger values. Processes (3), (4), and (6) allow for such variations.

Figure 75 gives average values of the Cl^-/Na^+ ratio for one year over the U.S., and shows a systematic decrease with increasing distance from the coast until values of 1/5 to 1/3 that of sea water are reached. Other observations, e.g., those made in Europe, Japan, and Australia consistently show the same phenomenon. In Figs. 76 and 77, the concentration of Na^+ and of *excess* Na^+ is plotted. The excess Na^+ is derived from the data in Fig. 76 by subtracting $Cl^-/1.8$ and represents the Na^+ of nonmaritime origin on the assumption that chloride is a conservative property for sea spray par-

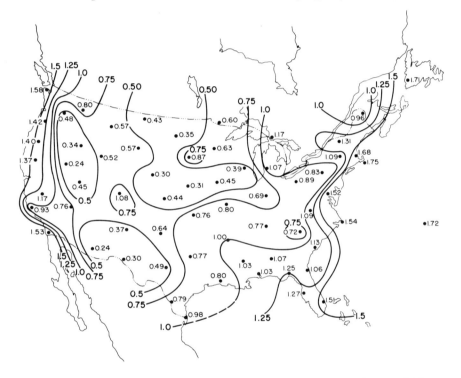

FIG. 75. Average ratio Cl^-/Na^+ in rain over the U.S., July 1955-June 1956 (Junge and Werby, 1958). (By courtesy of *Journal of Meteorology*.)

ticles, which may not be quite true. The values near the coast cannot be considered reliable since they are small differences of two large figures and thus sensitive to random and systematic errors in the analyses. The high values of excess Na^+ at the southern tip of Texas are due to "natural pollution" from large salt flats along the coast. There seems to be a tendency for higher excess values near the sea and there are areas of high and low concentration which seem to be related to the geographical features of the U.S. However, by and large, the source of the excess Na^+ is rather uniform.

Figure 78 shows the corresponding map of K^+ concentrations. The concentration of K^+ in sea water is so small that the map of *excess* K^+ after subtracting the values $Cl^-/50$ would not be much different from Fig. 78 except in coastal areas. The excess K^+ would be distributed fairly uniformly throughout the continent. If the excess concentrations of Na^+ and K^+ were the result of chemical modifications of sea salt particles according to process (3), it would have to be assumed

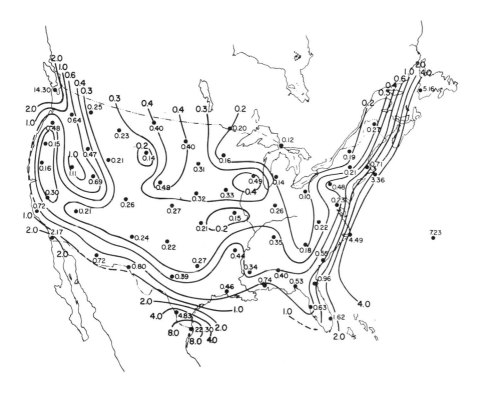

FIG. 76. Average Na^+ concentration (milligrams per liter) in rain over the U.S., July 1955-June 1956 (Junge and Werby, 1958). (By courtesy of *Journal of Meteorology*.)

that their modification and their removal by vertical mixing and rainout proceeds in such a way that almost constant excess concentrations result. This is rather unlikely. It is even more aggravating that the cation ratio K^+/Na^+, which is a conservative property for aerosols, increases from 1/20 in sea water to about 1 in the interior of the continent. There is no doubt that almost all the K^+ found over the U.S. must come from sources other than the sea and that the soil is the most likely one. Since the elements K and Na are chemically very similar and have similar abundances in soil material, we seem justified in concluding *that most of the excess* Na^+ *is also of land origin.*

The only process, other than the addition of soil material, that can alter the ratios K^+/Na^+, Mg^{++}/Na^+, and Ca^{++}/Na^+ in sea-salt particles would be (2), because a break up of salt particles and fractionation of the constituents *in the atmosphere* must be excluded, for reasons discussed in Section 2.3.2. Data for these ratios in *representative maritime* places

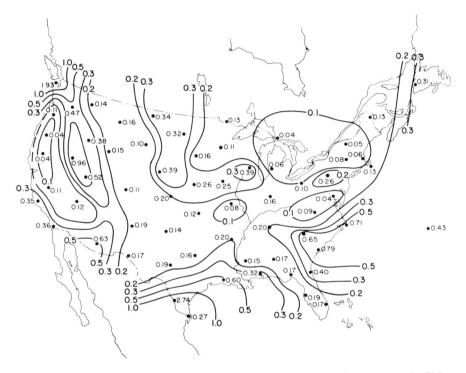

FIG. 77. Average excess Na^+ concentration (milligrams per liter) in rain over the U.S., July 1955-June 1956 (Junge and Werby, 1958). (By courtesy of *Journal of Meteorology*.)

should indicate the significance of process (2). Table 60 presents a collection of rather reliable analyses of such locations. It can be seen that the deviations from sea water are rather consistent, with the exception of Rosscahill which shows much higher deviations for K^+/Na^+ and Ca^{++}/Na^+ than the rest of the stations. There is good evidence that at least in this place, soil material is the major source for the observed variation. The other coastal places give an average increase of 36% for K^+/Na^+, 25% for Mg^{++}/Na^+, and 153% for Ca^{++}/Na^+, and these values can be regarded as upper limits for process 2. If we apply these figures for inland values (e.g., Figs. 78 and

TABLE 60

CONCENTRATION RATIOS K^+/Na^+, Mg^{++}/Na^+, AND Ca^{++}/Na^+ IN RAIN IN SOME MARITIME LOCATIONS IN WESTERN EUROPE

Location	K^+/Na^+	Mg^{++}/Na^+	Ca^{++}/Na^+
Rjupnahed,[a] southwest coast, Iceland	0.055	0.14	0.110
Lerwick,[a] Shetland Islands	0.040	0.13	0.050
Lista,[a] southwest coast, Norway	0.061	0.17	0.140
Den Helder,[a] west coast, Netherlands	0.040	0.17	0.085
Rosscahill, County Galway [b] west coast, Ireland	0.160	0.16	0.530
Average ratio, excluding Rosscahill	0.049	0.15	0.096
Sea water ratio	0.036	0.12	0.038
$\dfrac{\text{Average ratio}}{\text{Sea water ratio}}$	1.36	1.25	2.53

[a] Eriksson (1960).
[b] Gorham (1957).

79), it becomes clear that only a minor fraction of the change in the cation ratio $Na^+ : K^+ : Mg^{++} : Ca^{++}$ can be due to ion separation at the sea surface [process (2)] and that the major part must be due to soil material. Alkali and alkali earth metals are also produced in air pollution. This source can be important in industrial areas and big cities.

The map of Ca^{++} concentrations over the U.S. (Fig. 79) shows a pronounced maximum in the arid zones of the southwest, which should be expected if Ca^{++} is of continental origin. The Ca^{++}/Cl^- ratio in sea water is 0.021 (Table 32) and if excess Ca^{++} is computed from Figs. 73 and 79, considerable Ca^{++} concentrations remain along the coast, even in Bermuda. If this Ca^{++} enrichment is due to ion exchange processes at the sea surface, the effect should be easily detectable in laboratory experiments.

The possibility that the variation of rainwater composition with increasing distance from the coast may be caused by the superposition of maritime and continental aerosols was first discussed in detail by Kalle (1954). He used data from the Swedish network and showed that the calculated excess cation concentrations remain essentially constant, except for Na^+ which decreases somewhat inland. This decrease of excess Na^+ may be due to an enrichment of Na^+ in the soil solution by sea salt and ion exchange processes near the coast. The ratio of the excess cation concentration over Sweden is about

$$Na^+ : K^+ : Ca^{++} = 1 : 0.6 : 4$$

and is comparable to the composition of the earth's surface. Similar ratios are found in the U.S. and in South Australia (Hutton and Leslie, 1958). In the latter area the excess K^+ remains almost constant with increasing

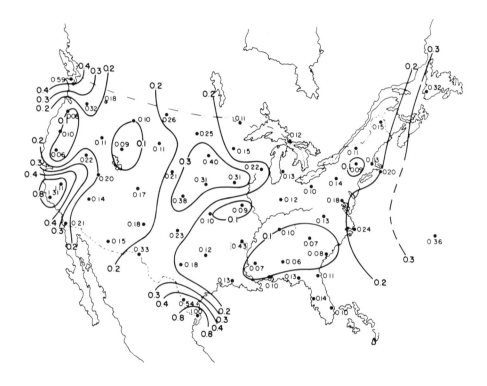

FIG. 78. Average K^+ concentration (milligrams per liter) in rain over the U.S., July 1955-June 1956 (Junge and Werby, 1958). (By courtesy of *Journal of Meteorology.*)

distance from the shore, whereas Mg^{++} increases slightly and Ca^{++} considerably. Hutton and Leslie suggest that these constituents are added from the soil and conclude that this must also be the case for part of the Na^+ and the Cl^-, since more than 50% of the soil solution in this area consists of NaCl. Thus Cl^- in rain cannot be considered a reliable indicator for the accretion of sea salt in some parts of Australia and other arid zones.

Almost constant excess concentrations of K^+, Mg^{++}, and Ca^{++} are found on the windward side of the Island of Hawaii within 15 km off the coastline (Eriksson, 1957).

Eriksson (1960) presents maps on the deposition rate of excess K^+, Mg^+, and Ca^{++} for Europe and finds generally higher values over maritime areas. When these maps are converted to concentration maps, the

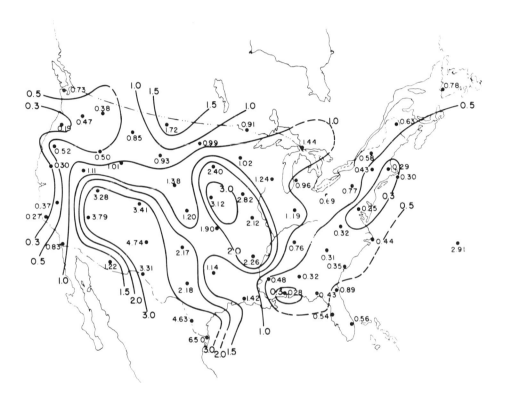

FIG. 79. Average Ca^{++} concentration (milligrams per liter) in rain over the U.S., July 1955-June 1956 (Junge and Werby, 1958). (By courtesy of *Journal of Meteorology*.)

highest values occur over continental Europe and low values over Scandinavia, with those of the British Isles in between. It is possible and likely that air pollution is of some importance as a source for these cations for industrialized areas of Europe.

So far we have considered only average conditions. In an interesting study, Rossby and Egnér (1955) showed that in Scandinavia the Cl^-/Na^+ ratio in precipitation depends on the general circulation. With advection of air masses from the Atlantic, the ratio is around 1.2 on the southwest coast of Sweden and drops to 0.25 toward the north. Advection of *arctic* air reduces the values to 0.0-0.3 throughout Sweden, but when the air comes from the *south*, the ratio is larger than 3 over most of southern Sweden. Rossby and Egnér explained these considerable differences by the release of chlorine from sea salt particles and by the assumption that the atmospheric residence time of HCl is longer than that of the aerosols. However, these findings can be explained equally well by assuming larger proportions of soil dust in arctic air and of industrial Cl pollution from Central Europe during advection of air from the south. This view is supported by the results from the U.S. network, which show that values larger than 1.8 are rarely observed and then only in the vicinity of industrial areas, and that there is no indication in Fig. 75 of a secondary increase of the Cl^-/Na^+ ratio farther inland due to removal of HCl.

The discussion of this section can be summarized as follows:

There is some indication that over sea or near the coast, the ratios Cl^-/Na^+, K^+/Na^+, Mg^{++}/Na^+, and Ca^{++}/Na^+ are higher than in sea water. It is possible that this is due to ionic separation at the sea surface or to release of HCl from sea-salt particles in the atmosphere. These effects are comparatively minor and are of no importance for the ionic composition farther inland.

The variation of excess cation concentration in precipitation with distance from the coast is small compared to the decrease of Cl^- and Na^+. *The ratio of excess cations* inland is quite different from that near the coast and is similar to that of soil material. This forces us to the conclusion that addition of soil material is the major factor which determines the cation ratio, with pollution being only of local importance.

4.3.4 Sulfate and pH Value

Sulfate is an important and interesting component of rainwater. The concentrations over land usually range from 1 to 10 mg/liter with an average over the U.S., for example, of 3 mg/liter. Over the oceans, values are usually between 1 an 2 mg/liter. Since the $SO_4^=/Cl^-$ weight ratio in sea water is 0.14 and the chloride concentrations are around 10 mg/liter the $SO_4^=$ concentrations over sea can be explained by sea water sulfate. However, a closer examination of the observations shows that even over very remote oceanic areas there is always some excess $SO_4^=$ which rapidly becomes dominant over land, where almost all $SO_4^=$ is of nonmaritime origin.

Figures 80 and 81, which show the total and excess $SO_4^=$ in precipitation over the U.S., demonstrate the general situation very well. The excess $SO_4^=$ increases inland and the isolines tend to follow the coastline of the U.S., particularly along the Atlantic. A broad maximum of excess sulfate appears over the northern and eastern part of the U.S., which is probably to a large extent of anthropogenic origin. For example, Knight (1934) reports that in Iowa during the recession when almost no coal was burnt in the winter of 1932/33, the $SO_4^=$ level in rain was at an all time low.

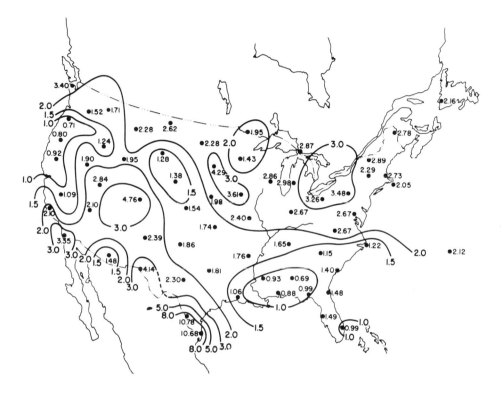

FIG. 80. Average $SO_4^=$ concentration (milligrams per liter) in rain over the U.S., July 1955-June 1956 (Junge and Werby, 1958). (By courtesy of *Journal of Meteorology*)

The maximum at the eastern borderline with Mexico is supposedly due to mineral dust from salt flats along the Gulf Coast and soil dust from the adjacent arid zones. We found similar "natural pollution" on the Cl^- and Ca^{++} maps.

In general the excess $SO_4^=$ has higher concentrations over land than over the ocean, where the level seems to be about 0.5 mg/liter. This points to the land as the major source area for the nonsea salt $SO_4^=$.

This picture is somewhat different in Europe. Here the concentration of sulfate is around 5 mg/liter over the British Isles and most of the northern part of Central Europe, and decreases toward the south and particularly toward the north. Values between 1 and 3 are common over most of Scandinavia. The high values over the British Isles and the adjacent area of the North Sea are of interest and raise the question to what degree they are due to natural or to artificial sources. Unfortunately, the network of stations is here not dense enough to determine details of the distribution,

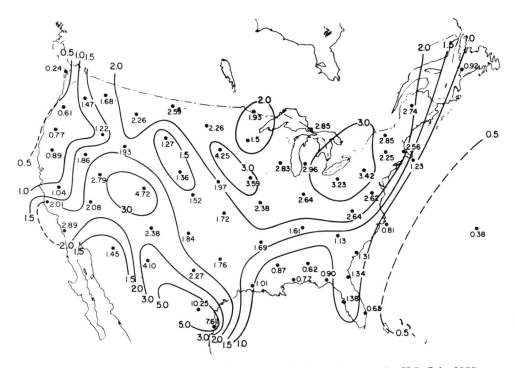

FIG. 81. Average excess SO₄= (milligrams per liter) in rain over the U.S. July 1955-June 1956 (Junge and Werby, 1958). (By courtesy of *Journal of Meteorology*.)

but apparently high concentrations start at or close to the western coast of Ireland. On the basis of deposition maps, Eriksson (1960) concludes that most of the excess $SO_4^=$ over Great Britain must come from the sea, perhaps as H_2S from the coastal areas. Gorham (1957) suggests that the high rainwater concentrations in Galway County in western Ireland originate from the release of H_2S from inshore marine muds and the numerous water-logged and oxygen-deficient peats of this area. A more careful study in Ireland, especially with respect to the potential sulfur sources in coastal and shelf areas, would be of interest.

It appears that Western Europe shows rather exceptional features with respect to the excess $SO_4^=$ level in coastal rains. In many places exposed to uncontaminated maritime air masses, viz., in remote oceanic areas, a rather uniform level of about 0.5 to 1.0 mg/liter excess $SO_4^=$ is observed, as demonstrated in Table 61. This table summarizes places with

TABLE 61

OBSERVED EXCESS $SO_4^=$ CONCENTRATIONS IN ISOLATED AND REMOTE PLACES [a]

Location	Observed Cl-	Observed $SO_4^=$	Calculated $SO_4^=$	Excess $SO_4^=$
North Sweden, 1955-1956				
Riksgransen	1.33	1.65	0.19	1.46
Kiruna	0.56	1.44	0.08	1.36
Arjepog	1.24	2.05	0.18	1.87
Ojebyn	0.85	2.85	0.15	2.70
(Current data on chemical composition of precipitation, *Tellus* **7** and **8**, 1955 and 1956.)				
West Ireland, 1955				
Rosscahill, County Galway				
(Gorham, 1957)	4.45	2.90	0.62	2.28
Russia				
Smolensk	3.10	1.20	0.43	0.77
Borowoje, Ssarnara	2.00	1.20	0.28	0.92
(From Eriksson, 1952 b)				
Greenland, 1915-1958				
Site II, Center of Ice Cap (Junge, 1960)	0.037	0.25	0.00	0.25
United States and West Atlantic, 1955/56				
Bermuda	12.41	2.12	1.81	0.38
Palm Beach, Florida	2.44	0.99	0.34	0.65
Tatoosh Island, Washington	22.58	3.40	3.16	0.24
Stevensville, Newfoundland	8.85	2.16	1.24	0.92
(Junge and Werby, 1958)				
Hawaii, 1955				
Hilo, average 0-20 km from windward coast (Eriksson, 1957)	3.54	0.98	0.49	0.48
New Zealand, 1884-1887				
Lincoln, Canterbury	8.80	2.65	1.23	1.42
(From Eriksson, 1952 b)				

[a] Values in milligrams per liter.

low excess $SO_4^=$ concentration is rainwater. Except for a few older measurements from the interior of Russia, all these data refer to maritime places. The lowest concentrations of excess $SO_4^=$ in Europe seem to be those of northern Sweden, where the values range between 1 and 2 mg/liter. Gorham's (1957) value from the west coast of Ireland reflects the generally high level over the West European islands. The other values from the U.S., the West Atlantic, and Hawaii are smaller than 1 mg/liter. However, some of these values are not too reliable because they represent a small difference of two large figures. The lowest reliable value of 0.25 mg/liter was observed in the center of Greenland (Table 59), where $SO_4^=$ is higher in concentration by about one order of magnitude than the other constituents.

This excess $SO_4^=$ concentration in unpolluted areas seems to be a world-wide phenomenon and apparently keeps within a rather narrow limit. It is likely that it represents that part of the SO_2 which is oxidized photochemically or in rainwater, as discussed in Section 1.5. If we accept the following average values for Eq. (1), $k = k_1 = 0.5$ mg $SO_4^=$/liter, $L = 2$ g/m³ and $c = 10$ μg SO_2/m³ or 15 μg $SO_4^=$/m³, the collection efficiency ε will be $2 \times 0.5/15 = 0.066$. This low value is in approximate agreement with our estimates in Section 4.2.4 for the removal of gases.

Figures 80 and 81 imply, of course, that the ratio $SO_4^=/Cl^-$ is always higher over the ocean than in sea water and increases rapidly inland over all continents. Table 61 and Fig. 81 seem to demonstrate that the sources of excess $SO_4^=$ are mostly over land. It is likely that the heavy SO_2 pollution over England (Fig. 18) may affect not only the island itself, but also the surrounding ocean to some extent so that it is difficult to estimate the contribution of natural sources with the data available.

Fog water in coastal areas can show remarkably high concentrations of $SO_4^=$ and ratios of $SO_4^=/Cl^-$. Houghton (1955) reports average concentrations of $SO_4^=$ between 6.5 and 52 mg/liter in sea fog at various places along the northeastern coast of the U.S. Air masses in this area are generally influenced by air pollution from the continent, but this alone can hardly account for the high values. It is possible that the long duration of these sea fogs, which can last for days, is an important factor in the accumulation of $SO_4^=$. The average $SO_4^=/Cl^-$ ratio in these fogs varied from 0.3 to 14. If we assume liquid water contents of these fogs between 0.1 and 0.5 g/m³, corresponding to visibilities of about 300 to 100 meters, the sulfate concentrations in air would range from 0.65 to 5.2 μg/m³ or 3.3 to 26 μg/m³, values which are quite high (see Figs. 41 and 42) for maritime places. In maritime aerosols, midway between the U.S. west coast and Hawaii, Lodge *etal.* (1960) found rather high $SO_4^=$ values in aerosols together with $SO_4^=/Cl$ ratios larger than 1. It is possible that these aerosols represent evaporated sea fogs.

Boss (1941) observed high concentrations of $SO_4^=$ in fog on the coast of southwest Africa. These fogs drift inland, and the sulfur fraction increases relative to the composition of sea water. He explains this increase by a preferential deposition on the soil and removal from the soil of constituents other than $SO_4^=$. Soil material enriched by SO_4 and picked up by the wind would then result in the observed increase of the SO_4/Cl ratio. However, it is likely that SO_2 oxidation is also involved just as along the U.S. coast.

The data on the composition of large particles (0.1-1.0 μ radius) in Section 2.3.3 (e.g., Fig. 39) indicate a pronounced correlation between the NH_4^+ and $SO_4^=$ content; these two represent major soluble constituents in a ratio less than but close to that of $(NH_4)_2SO_4$. The giant particles showed comparatively less NH_4^+. Since most of the large particles are washed out and thus contribute to the composition of rainwater, it may be of interest to look into the ratio $NH_4^+/SO_4^=$ in precipitation. Georgii and Weber (1960) found the values shown in the accompanying tabulation

	Winter	Summer
Frankfurt	0.25	0.27
Taunus Observatory (860 meters)	0.32	0.36
Zugspitze (3000 meters)	—	0.37
Theoretical for $(NH_4)_2SO_4$	—	0.37

for this ratio in rains. Except for some surplus $SO_4^=$, primarily in winter, the agreement with $(NH_4)_2SO_4$ is good. In Kentville, Nova Scotia, Herman and Gorham (1957) found a ratio of $NH_4^+ : SO_4^=$ of 0.1 in rain and 0.14 in snow. This is a predominantly agricultural area and the low NH_4^+ content is of interest. Larson and Hettick (1956) find a good correlation between the ionic concentration of $SO_4^=$ and the sum of $(NH_4^+ + NO_3^-)$ and suggest that this is due to the fact that all these compounds are produced by combustion. The data from the U.S. network generally show quite variable $NH_4^+ : SO_4^=$ ratios, between 0.1 and 0.3. Similar conditions are indicated by data from other countries.

We saw that considerable concentrations of Ca^{++} occur over most land areas. Calcium is picked up from the ground primarily as $CaCO_3$ and becomes partly soluble as bicarbonate. Another part is probably converted to $CaSO_4$ by the oxidation of SO_2. Larson and Hettick (1956) found a good relationship between the sum of $(HCO_3^- + SO_4^=)$ and the sum of $(Ca^{++} + Mg^{++})$ ions in Illinois rains, which suggests the indicated reactions for lime and dolomite particles. Gorham (1958 b) also found a good relationship between $SO_4^=$ and Ca^{++} concentrations in northern England; the Ca^{++} content here is partly due to air pollution.

The seasonal variation of $SO_4^=$ concentration in rain can serve as an indicator for the sulfur origin. In industrial areas there is a pronounced tendency toward higher values in winter than in summer, as e.g., indicated in Table 57. The northeastern U.S., i.e., east of the Missouri and north of Cape Hatteras, shows winter concentrations which are generally twice the summer concentration. This suggests the influence of larger fuel consumptions in winter, coupled with more frequent inversion layers which allow accumulation of pollution in populated and industrialized areas. In southeastern U.S. and in some areas in the West, the trend is partly reversed. In rural areas the higher production of H_2S in the soil may account for the summer maxima, although there are many factors which are superimposed. Similar yearly trends are observed in other parts of the world, for instance in Europe, where most sulfate data show a winter maximum corresponding to denser populations.

The discussion of rainwater $SO_4^=$ demonstrates that the major sources of atmospheric sulfur are sea salt, human activities, and land and sea areas with H_2S production. Table 15 shows the contributions of the various anthropogenic sources. The magnitude of the natural sources is roughly estimated in Fig. 20. The excess sulfate values seem to indicate that in most parts of the world, the continents are more important sources of natural sulfur than the oceans, which is not in agreement with the conclusion drawn from river runoff data that the shelf areas are a major source of H_2S (Section 1.5). More data are needed before the role of the various sources of sulfur and their variation from continent to continent can be properly assessed.

We will add a few remarks here about the pH value of rain. Numerous data from various parts of the world are available which show that the usual range is between 4 and 6 but that it can fluctuate from about 3 to 8. The pH data for one year from the Scandinavian rain analysis network were analyzed by Barrett and Brodin (1955). Through most of the year the pH is between 4 and 5 in southern Sweden and along the coasts of the Baltic and the Atlantic, as far as northern Norway. Farther inland, the values rise to about 6. The mean value for the whole network has a minimum below 5 from December through March, with a high spring peak of almost 6 in May. The factors which determine this general picture are complex. The low values in southern Sweden and partly along the coast are probably due to pollution from Central and Western Europe. This view is supported by the seasonal variations with the lowest values during winter, when the air flow is more southerly and the pollution is at a maximum. Since SO_2 is one of the major constituents of pollution, it is likely that sulfuric acid is the controlling factor of the pH in this area. However, the low pH values along most of the Norwegian coast and over the Baltic cannot be accounted for by artificial SO_2 and may be related to natural production of H_2S and may be related to natural production of H_2S in coastal areas or the sea as indicated for Western Europe. The higher pH values farther inland are caused by either progressive removal of SO_2 or the addition of cations, such as Ca^{++} or NH_4^+. In Section 4.2.4, we saw that traces of NH_3 can modify the pH drastically and the addition of Ca^{++} from the soil is well established.

Besides this general picture, which is more or less repeated each month, there are a few "alkaline islands" in southern Sweden and Denmark. There is evidence that these are caused by soil dust from limestone deposits in these areas and associated industries and/or by the production of NH_3 in agricultural activities.

The rains in the Lake District in England are strongly acid and the hydrogen ion concentrations show high correlation with the ($SO_4^= +$ NO_3^-) concentration (Gorham, 1958 b). The $SO_4^=$ can account for 30 to 70% of the H^+. The rains in the industrial areas were found less acid and had a higher Ca^{++} content. This suggests that H_2SO_4 is formed in the air outside the source area of pollution, in accordance with the concept that the aerosol sulfate is formed by slow oxidation of SO_2.

Gorham (1958 c, d) studied the composition of water in acid humus soils of such humid climates as England and found a high correlation between the hydrogen ion concentration and the $SO_4^=$ content. The water samples were collected from pools in rural districts in England and the U.S., which receive their mineral contents from precipitation. In certain urban areas in England, HCl can contribute to the pH of rainwater, perhaps because of the high Cl content of the coal used (Gorham, 1958 a), but in most polluted atmospheres $SO_4^=$ is the major constituent which reduces the pH.

All these observations point to H_2SO_4 as the important agent for low pH values in rainwater. The pH will be modified by cations from soil material and finally adjusted by reversible absorption of CO_2 and NH_3. This raises the question to what extent the pH of rainwater is determined by the condensation nuclei themselves. Let us assume that a cloud droplet has a pH of 5 in the absence of CO_2 and a concentration of total soluble material of 20 mg/liter. It this droplet evaporates in air of normal relative humidity, the concentration will rise to about 1000 g/liter, i.e., by a factor of about 10^5. This would result in a pH of 1, corresponding to 0.1 normal acids. The omnipresence of small traces of NH_3 in the atmosphere will soon neutralize such pH values. Therefore, it is reasonable to assume that the hydrogen ion concentration in rains is not a diluted aerosol component, but develops during the process of water condensation by fixation of SO_2, NO_2, or HCl. This is, among other things, evidence that the fixation of SO_2 in raindrops is a rather important process compared with photochemical oxidation of SO_2.

4.3.5 Ammonia, Nitrate, and Nitrite

Ammonia and nitrate were the first trace substances in air and rainwater to be studied thoroughly. In the second half of the 19th century the interest in these constituents was aroused by the suggestion that they supplied the soil with the fixed nitrogen necessary for plant life. This was before the discovery of bacterial fixation of nitrogen in the soil. Most studies in this field were made between 1870 and 1930 with the peak at the turn of the century. In recent times research was revived somewhat because of growing interest in problems of air chemistry.

The NH_4^+ concentration in rain varies considerably over a wide range from about 0.01 to 1 mg/liter, with the most frequent values around 0.1 to 0.2 mg/liter. Because of the small volume ratio of liquid water to air in clouds and rain, the NH_4^+ concentration in precipitation is considerably affected by the pH of the cloud water and the NH_3 content of the air, as discussed in Section 4.2.4. Thus, ammonia is not a conservative property of precipitation until the rain sample is collected, sealed, and protected against bacterial decomposition. Besides this soluble ammonia, the organic matter in precipitation contains NH_3, which can be released by oxidizing agents. Average values (milligrams per liter) of this "albuminoid nitrogen" over several years are available for a few places (Eriksson, 1952 a): Mt. Vernon, Iowa, U.S., 0.4; Ottawa, Canada, 1.1; Dehra Dun, India, 2.6; Rothamstedt, England, 2.0. These concentrations are considerable compared with the soluble fractions. It is likely that this organic nitrogen is associated with soil material picked up by the wind or is derived from gaseous components not yet identified. In the subsequent discussion we will deal only with the soluble form of ammonia.

In general the concentration of NH_4^+ in rain over or near the ocean is about half that over undisturbed land areas. A map from the Scandinavian network (Ångström and Högberg, 1952 b) shows the highest NH_4^+ values in southwestern Sweden (as is the case for all other constituents) and a decrease toward the north and towards the Atlantic and the Baltic coasts. Air masses of different origin have the following relative ratio:

Tropical : Polar : Arctic air = 1.00 : 0.74 : 0.49.

Both the latitudinal gradient and the higher content in air masses of southern origin over Sweden are apparently related to higher NH_3 concentrations in Central Europe, as suggested by a comparison of the Scandinavian data with the few sporadic values from Central Europe given in Section 1.7.3, Table 23, and Fig. 18. The same tendency toward higher values in Central Europe is indicated in rainwater concentration data. However, these features seem to be typical only for Europe and do not reflect a *general* decrease of ammonia with increasing latitude as suggested in older studies. This is clearly born out by Eriksson's (1952 a) compilation of data and by the results from the U.S. network for which Fig. 82 gives an example.

The data from the U.S. network show pronounced seasonal and geographical variations. The concentrations during late summer 1955 (Fig. 82) are higher over land than over the ocean. In contrast to $SO_4^=$, the distribution of NH_4^+ in Fig. 82, and for the other seasons, shows no

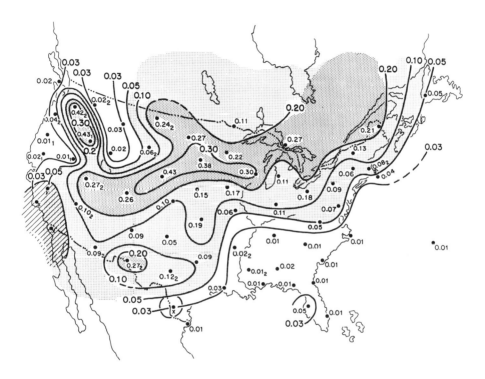

FIG. 82. Average NH_4^+ concentration (milligrams per liter) in rain over the U.S. July-September 1955 (Junge, 1958). (By courtesy of *Transactions of the American Geophysical Union.*)

obvious relationship to industrial areas, indicating that industrial production is not of great importance, at least over the U.S. Very low concentrations over the southeastern U.S. are consistent *throughout* the year and it is suggested that this reflects the low pH value of the yellow red laterite soils characteristic of this part of the country. The borderline of these soils runs closely parallel to the isoline 0.03 mg/liter from Texas to Cape Hatteras.

Low pH favors NH_3 absorption and/or prevents its release. The concentration in this area drops by about a factor of 10 compared to the rest of the country. This drop in NH_4^+ concentration and the steepness of the gradient across the borderline are similar in magnitude to those of Cl^- along the coastlines and suggest a similar explanation. This would mean that the area north and west of the borderline is a huge NH_3 source, that NH_3 is concentrated here primarily in the lowest layers above the ground, just as in the case of the sea spray over the ocean, and that it is diluted and depleted by vertical mixing and soil absorption whenever the air masses move southeast. The decrease of the NH_4^+ concentrations in the southeast may be supported by higher rainfall rates and liquid water contents of clouds in this region, but the influence of these and other meteorological factors can only be minor, as a comparison with concentration maps of other constituents indicates.

We have already mentioned the lower NH_4^+ concentrations along the coasts of Scandinavia. The values for Bermuda and the unpolluted parts of the U.S. coast are also low and vary during the year between about 0.01 and 0.04 mg/liter. Eriksson (1957) found somewhat higher concentrations, from 0.07 to 0.14 mg/liter on the windward side of Hawaii. In Section 1.7.3, we pointed out that the NH_3 air concentrations in Hawaii were higher below the trade wind inversion, but also higher than the equilibrium concentration calculated from the NH_4^+ content of sea water. It was suggested that the *sea*, but not the *sea water* itself, is a source and that organic films on the sea surface may be involved. The NH_3 concentrations in Hawaii (Table 24) are lower than those over undisturbed land by a factor of only 0.5 to 0.3, which indicates that they must be controlled by the sea and represent an equilibrium concentration. For land air, the sea thus acts as a partial sink of NH_3.

The seasonal variations of NH_3 are an important clue to its origin. The Swedish data (Ångström and Högberg, 1952, a, b) show a pronounced maximum in spring and minimum in the fall and winter. Long series of observations in Rothamstedt and in Ottawa (Eriksson, 1952 a) show a double maximum in spring and late summer, but generally a higher level during the warm season. The U.S. data exhibit a marked seasonal variation with the highest values from April to June, decreasing somewhat until September, and with a broad minimum during the winter.

The seasonal variation in *polluted* areas is sometimes reversed, indicating that NH_3 is produced by fuel consumption or similar processes, in agreement with the data in Fig. 18, but apparently this is not always the rule. In Berlin, e.g., (Table 57) there is no seasonal variation and no marked decrease of the NH_4^+ concentration from the center of the city.

Evidence is fairly strong that in most parts of the world the soil is the main source of NH_3, as was pointed out previously by Russell and Richards (1919) and later by Drischel (1940), whereas Eriksson (1952 a) considers fuel consumption to be of primary importance. The apparently high values in Europe may be attributed in part to this source, but intense or specialized agricultural activities in connection with alkaline soils are just as likely. California and Washington, e.g., have areas of high NH_4^+ concentrations in rain in springtime, which may be related to the use of liquid ammonia fertilizers in this part of the country. The usual spring and summer maxima are certainly somewhat modified by man's agricultural activities and in this sense some of the soil-produced NH_3 can be regarded as anthropogenic.

We see that the rainwater data contributed valuable information about the origin of atmospheric NH_3 and that the conclusions drawn from them are in good agreement with the direct observations of NH_3 in air discussed in Section 1.7.3. The large-scale horizontal distribution indicates that the land is the major source and that the ocean is only a partial sink, resulting in a lower equilibrium concentration of NH_3. The annual variation over land proves that the soil is the major source and that pollution is of local significance only. The studies of the release and uptake of NH_3 from soil lend support to this view. Allison (1955) points out that NH_3 is released from the ground if the pH is higher than 6 or 7 and is absorbed at smaller values. It is well known, e.g., that the loss of NH_3 to the atmosphere from fertilizers can be considerable in alkaline soils. Besides the pH value and the soil structure, the release of NH_3 is a function of the NH_3 production by decay of organic matter in the soil. We recall here the summer maximum of NH_3 concentrations in Scandinavia (Table 23) which approximately parallels the seasonal variation of the NH_4^+ concentration in rains and which reflects the bacterial activities in the soil. It is interesting to note that the highest NH_4^+ values over the U.S. in winter are found east of the Rocky Mountains in agricultural areas with *alkaline* soils.

The deposition of NH_3 by absorption on the soil surface can be substantial over soils with low pH. Experiments with acid dishes exposed to the atmosphere (see Eriksson, 1952 a) indicate that absorption can be 5 to 10 times higher than deposition by precipitation. A similar importance for direct soil uptake was reported for SO_2 and can also be expected for other trace gases.

Nitrate is another important form of fixed nitrogen in rainwater. The range of concentration in precipitation over land is about 1.0 to 2.5 mg/liter in Europe and somewhat lower, i.e., 0.3 to 2.0 mg/liter in other areas. Over sea or in coastal regions we find values between 0.15 and 0.5 mg/liter. The general distribution is thus similar to that of NH_4^+.

The data on NO_3^- are less numerous and less reliable than those for NH_4^+, due to analytical difficulties and bacterial or other decomposition during and after collection of the samples. Only a few of the data from the Scandinavian network have been evaluated. For Ultuna, north of Stockholm, Ångström and Högberg (1952 a, b) found a pronounced correlation between NH_4^+ and NO_3^- and an average weight ratio $NH_4^+ : NO_3^-$ of about 1 : 2. The concentration for different air masses varies as:

$$\text{Tropical : Polar : Arctic air} = 1.00 : 0.92 : 0.66,$$

i.e., similar but less pronounced than for NH_4^+.

These correlations between NH_4^+ and NO_3^- in Scandinavian rains reflect the fact that both constituents are transported into the area by air masses from the southwest. A tentative NO_3^- map of Sweden (Emanuelsson et al., 1954) shows the same general decrease from the southwest to the northeast and towards the Baltic and Atlantic coasts as do the maps of NH_4^+ and of other constituents, and suggests that Central and Western Europe are a common source area. The values for NO_3^- in Europe are again somewhat higher than for most other land areas of the world (Eriksson, 1952 a). The distribution over the U.S. (Junge, 1958) is strongly variable, both horizontally and with time, but certain patterns are consistent in all seasons and show a faint similarity to those of NH_4^+, suggesting some common sources, as e.g., the soil. Figure 83 for late summer shows large areas of high concentration over the north central part of the U.S., which is more pronounced during winter and is sometimes split into two sections by the Great Lakes region. Pollution may be partly responsible for this area, especially in its eastern section, but a comparison with the maps of $SO_4^=$ suggests that other sources are also involved. Another area of very high concentrations over California appeared only in late summer and may be related to smog formation in the Los Angeles Basin. The southeast has generally low NO_3^- concentrations, but less pronounced or regular than in the case of NH_4^+. It should be emphasized that these results for NO_3^- over the U.S. can be considered only tentative due to the quality of the analyses and to the large fluctuations in connection with the short period of observations.

The seasonal variations of the NO_3^- concentration are less pronounced than those of NH_4^+ and vary in character. In unpolluted areas like most parts of Sweden (Ångström and Högberg, 1952, a, b), in Australia (Anderson, 1915), and in the U.S. the maximum is in spring and/or summer, which points to a source in the soil. Over certain large areas of the U.S. which can be considered polluted, e.g., over the northeast, the maximum is in winter.

The data on the air concentration of NO_2, discussed in Section 1.7.2, lead to the tentative conclusion that soil and air pollution are the main sources. The present data on NO_3^- in rain support this view. The maritime values are lower and thus show that the ocean acts as a partial sink, at least for continental air masses which have mostly higher values. It is not possible to determine whether the soil or the industrial pollution is the dominant factor over land on a continental scale. Apparently, they are about equal, but the conditions will vary with the geographical location. We know that both the soil and human activities can produce NO_2.

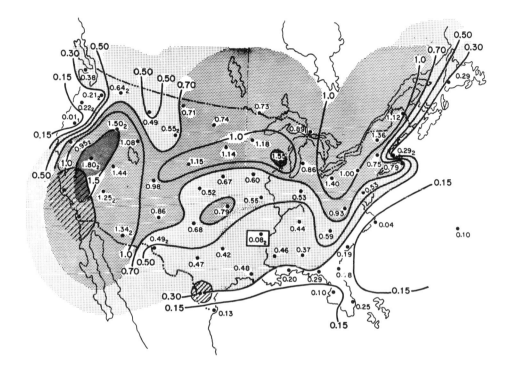

FIG. 83. Average concentration of NO_3^- (milligrams per liter) in rain over the U.S., July-September 1955 (Junge, 1958). (By courtesy of *Transactions of the American Geophysical Union.*)

Photochemical formation of NO_2 in higher atmospheric layers as a source of NO_3^- should result in a fairly uniform concentration in rainwater. Since observations show considerable fluctuations with time and space and also definite geographical patterns, most of the NO_3^- in rain over Scandinavia and the U.S. cannot come from this source. The seasonal variations, on the other hand, do not support the view that lightning is of great importance, in agreement with older estimates that it cannot account for more than 10% of all NO_3^- in rain. This is also confirmed by the N^{15}/N^{14} ratio of NO_3^- in rain, as discussed in Section 1.7.2. However, this does not exclude the possibility that electrical phenomena or processes can be of local influence. Reiter (1960) found that 40-80% of the NO_3^- in rains over the northern Alps is due to rainout in the clouds and that this amount increases with the frequency of changes of the electric field. His data seem to indicate that production of nitrogen oxides by corona discharge close to the ground is negligible.

The *nitrite* levels are usually very low compared with the nitrate concentrations. Older measurements quoted by Eriksson (1952 a) give a ratio NO_2^-/NO_3^- of about 0.1 or less. Anderson (1915) found ratios of 0.2 in fall and winter and of 0.025 to 0.1 in summer. A large number of data were collected by Reiter (1960) in the northern Alps. They show ratios of about 0.01 for various types of precipitation, except in hail and graupel where they were higher by a factor of 2 to 3. He suggested that in this case NO_2^- is "frozen in" and protected from oxidation.

We recall here that NO_2^- has never been found in aerosols. This indicates that oxidation of NO_2^- in cloud and rainwater proceeds fairly rapidly and that the NO_2^- concentrations can only be considered as minimum values. If nitrite represents approximately the fraction of NO_2 gas converted to NO_3^- in each condensation cycle, the NO_2^-/NO_3^- ratios can be interpreted as indicating that on the average each condensation nuclei goes through about ten cycles of condensation and evaporation before it is removed by wet removal.

List of Symbols

a = thickness of cloud layer
c = concentration of a constituent in air
d = diffusion coefficient of aerosol particle
D = deposition rate of a constituent on the earth's surface
f = factor for droplet evaporation
G = water vapor gradient
h = height of rainfall
H = height of cloud base
H' = height of tropopause
$\overline{H}$ = height of homogeneous aerosol layer
i = intensity of rainfall
k = concentration of a constituent in rainwater
k_1 = concentration of a constituent in rainwater due to rainout
k_2 = concentration of a constituent in rainwater due to washout
K = ion equilibrium constants in solution
L = total liquid water content of raining cloud
n = concentration of aerosol particles in air
r = radius of aerosol particle
t = time
v = fall velocity of particles; deposition velocity for constituents
z = altitude above ground
$a, \bar{a}, \bar{a}'$ = fraction of aerosols removed by rain
β = solubility constant of gases
γ = fraction of aerosols removed by washout
δ = absorption coefficient of gases in water
ε = rainout efficiency
φ = factor for washout
$\varkappa$ = exponent
η = collection efficienty for aerosol particles
ν = number of rainfalls
ϱ = density of water
τ = half-lifetime or residence time

Subscripts:

a = refers to absoprtion
b = refers to Brownian motion
c = cloud droplet
f = refers to attachment by Facy-effect
i = refers to impaction
n = condensation
p = refers to precipitation
s = refers to sedimentation
t = total

REFERENCES

ALLISON, F. E. (1955). The enigma of soil nitrogen balance sheets. *Advances in Agron.* **7**, 213-250.

ANDERSON, V. (1915). The influence of weather conditions upon the amounts of nitric acid and of nitrous acid in the rainfall at and near Melbourne, Australia. *Quart. J. Roy. Meteorol. Soc.* **41**, 99-122.

ÅNGSTRÖM, A., and HÖGBERG, L. (1952 a). On the content of nitrogen (NH_4-N and NO_3-N) in atmospheric precipitation. *Tellus* **4**, 31-42.

ÅNGSTRÖM, A., and HÖGBERG, L. (1952 b). On the content of nitrogen in atmospheric precipitation in Sweden. II. *Tellus* **4**, 271-279.

BARRETT, E., and BRODIN, G. (1955). The acidity of Scandinavian precipitation. *Tellus* **7**, 251-257.

BOSS, G. (1941). Niederschlagsmenge und Salzgehalt des Nebelwassers an der Küste Deutsch-Südwest-Afrikas. *Bioklim. Beibl.* **8**, 1-15.

BURTON, W. M., and STEWART, N. G. (1960). Use of long-lived natural radioactivity as an atmospheric tracer. *Nature* **186**, 584-589.

CHAMBERLAIN, A. C., and CHADWICK, R. C. (1953). Deposition of airborne radioiodine vapor. *Nucleonics* **11**, 22-25.

DHAR, N. R., and RAM, A. (1939). Formaldehyde in rain and dew. *J. Indian Chem. Soc.* **10**, 287-289.

DRISCHEL, H. (1940). Chlorid-, Sulfat- und Nitratgehalt der atmosphaerischen Niederschlaege in Bad Reinerz und Oberschreiberhau im Vergleich zu bisher bekannten Werten anderer Orte. *Balneologe* **7**, 321-334.

EGNÉR, H., and ERIKSSON, E. (1955). Current data on the chemical composition of air and precipitation. *Tellus* **7**, 134-139, and subsequent issues.

EMANUELSSON, A., ERIKSSON, E., and EGNÉR, H. (1954). Composition of atmospheric precipitation in Sweden. *Tellus* **6**, 261-267.

ERIKSSON, E. (1952 a). Composition of atmospheric precipitation I. Nitrogen compounds *Tellus* **4**, 215-232.

ERIKSSON, E. (1952 b). Composition of atmospheric precipitation II. Sulfur, chloride, iodine compounds. Bibliography. *Tellus* **4**, 280-303.

ERIKSSON, E. (1957). The chemical composition of Hawaiian rainfall. *Tellus* **9**, 509-520.

ERIKSSON, E. (1959). The yearly circulation of chloride and sulfur in nature; meteorological, geochemical and pedological implications. Part. I. *Tellus* **11**, 375-403.

ERIKSSON, E. (1960). The yearly circulation of chloride and sulfur in nature; meteorological, geochemical ane pedological implications, Part II. *Tellus* **12**, 63-109.

FACY, L. (1958). Les processus de congélation en atmosphère libre par capture des noyaux glacogènes. *Geofis. pura e appl.* **40**, 217-226.

GEORGII, H. W. (1960). Untersuchungen über atmosphärische Spurenstoffe und ihre Bedeutung für die Chemie der Niederschlage. *Geofis. pura e appl.* **47**, 155-171.

Georgii, H. W. (1952). Personal communication.

Georgii, H. W., and Weber, E. (1960). The chemical composition of individual rainfalls. Technical Note, Contract AF 61(052)-249, pp. 1-28. Air Force Cambridge Research Center, Bedford, Massachusetts.

Goldsmith, P., Delafield, H. J., and Cox, L. C. (1961). Measurement of the deposition of submicron particles in gradients of vapour pressure and of the efficiency of this mechanism in the capture of particulate matter by cloud droplets in nature. Paper presented at international Symposium on Condensation Nuclei, *Geofis. pura e appl.* **50**, 278-280.

Gorham, E. (1957). The chemical composition of rain from Rosscahill in County Galway. *Irish Naturalists' J.* **12**, 1-4.

Gorham, E. (1958 a). Atmospheric pollution by hydrochloric acid. *Quart. J. Roy. Meteorol. Soc.* **84**, 274-276.

Gorham, E. (1958 b). The influence and importance of daily weather conditions in the supply of chloride, sulfate and other ions to fresh waters from atmospheric precipitations. *Phil. Trans. Roy. Soc. London* B **241**, 147-178.

Gorham, E. (1958 c). Free acid in British soils. *Nature* **181**, 106.

Gorham, E. (1958 d). Free acid in Minnesota podsoils. *Ecology* **39**, 20.

Gorham, E. (1961). Factors influencing supply of major ions to inland waters, with special references to the atmosphere. *Bull. Geol. Soc. Am.* **72**, 795-840.

Gorham, E., and Cragg, J. B. (1960). The chemical composition of some bog waters from the Falkland Islands. *J. Ecol.* **48**, 175-181.

Greenfield, S. M. (1957). Rain scavenging of radioactive particulate matter from the atmosphere. *J. Meteorol.* **14**, 115-125.

Harvey, H. W., (1955). "The Chemistry and Fertility of Sea Water." Cambridge Univ. Press. London and New York.

Herman, F. A., and Gorham, E. (1957). Total mineral material, acidity, sulfur and nitrogen in rain and snow at Kentville, Nova Scotia. *Tellus* **9**, 180-183.

Heymann, J. A. (1927). Het jodiumgehalte van duin en regenwater. *Ned. Tijdschr. Geneesk.* **71**, 640.

Hinzpeter, M. (1959). Niederschlagselemente als Informationsträger über radioaktive Teilchen in der Atmosphare. Strahlungschutz No. 12. Schriftenreihe des Bundesministeriums für Atomenergie und Wasserwirtschaft. Gersbach und Sohn, Braunschweig, pp. 144-158.

Houghton, H. (1955). On the chemical composition of fog and cloud water. *J. Meteorol.* **12**, 355-357.

Hutton, J. T., and Leslie, T. I. (1958). Accession of nonnitrogenous ions dissolved in rainwater to soils in Victoria. *Australian J. Agr. Research* **9**, 492-507.

Johansson, O. (1959). On sulfur problems in Swedish agriculture. *Ann. Roy. Agr. Coll. Sweden* **25**, 57-169.

Junge, C. E. (1953). Die Rolle der Aerosole und der gasfoermigen Beimengungen der Luft im Spurenstoffhaushalt der Troposphaere. *Tellus* **5**, 1-26.

JUNGE, C. E. (1958). The distribution of ammonia and nitrate in rain water over the United States. *Trans. Am. Geophys. Union* **39**, 241-248.

JUNGE, C. E. (1960). Sulfur in the atmosphere. *J. Geophys. Research* **65**, 227-237.

JUNGE, C. E., and GUSTAFSON, P. E. (1956). Precipitation sampling for chemical analysis. *Bull. Am. Meteorol. Soc.* **37**, 244-245.

JUNGE, C. E., and GUSTAFSON, P. E. (1957). On the distribution of sea salt over the United States and its removal by precipitation. *Tellus* **9**, 164-173.

JUNGE, C. E., and RYAN, T. G. (1958.) Study of the SO_2 oxidation in solution and its role in atmospheric chemistry. *Quart. J. Roy. Meteorol. Soc.* **84**, 46-55.

JUNGE, C. E., and WERBY, R. T. (1958). The concentration of chloride, sodium, potassium, calcium and sulfate in rain water over the United States. *J. Meteorol.* **15**, 417-425.

KALLE, K. (1954). Zur Frage des "Zyklischen Salzes." *Ann. Meteorol.* **6**, 305-314.

KNIGHT, N. (1934). Analyses of the precipitation of rains and snows at Mount Vernon, Iowa. *Monthly Weather Rev.* **62**, 163-164 and previous papers on the same subject and in the same journal since 1931.

KUMAI, M. (1951). Electron-microscope study of snow-crystal nuclei. *J. Meteorol.* **8**, 151-156.

KUROIWA, D. (1953). Electron microscope study of atmospheric condensation nuclei. "Studies on Fogs" (T. Hori, ed.), pp. 351-382. Tanne Trading Co., Sapporo, Hokkaido, Japan.

LANDSBERG, H. E. (1954). Some observations of the pH of precipitation elements. *Arch. Meteorol. Geophys. u. Bioklimatol.* A7, 219-226.

LARSON, T. E., and HETTICK, I. (1956). Mineral composition of rainwater. *Tellus* **8**, 191-197.

LEEFLANG, K. W. H. (1938). De chemische Samenstelling van den Neerslag in Nederland. *Chem. Weekblad* **35**, 658-664.

LIESEGANG, W. (1934). Untersuchungen über die Mengen der in Niederschlaegen enthaltenen Verunreinigungen. *Kleine Mitt. Mitglied. Ver. Wasser- Boden- u. Lufthyg.* **10**, 350-355.

LODGE, J. E., MacDONALD, A. J., and VIHMAN, E. (1960). A study of the composition of marine atmospheres. *Tellus* **12**, 184-187.

MACHTA, L. (1960). A preliminary model of tropospheric aerosol removal. Paper presented at Symposium on Air Chemistry and Radioactivity, Helsinki, August 1960.

MACKU, M., PODZIMEK, J., and SRAMEK, L, (1959). Results of chemical analyses of precipitation collected on territory of Czechoslovak Republik in IGY. *Trav. Inst. Geophys. Acad. Tchec. Sc. No.* **124**, 441-519.

MADGWICK, H. A. I., and OVINGTON, J. D. (1959). The chemical composition of precipitation in adjacent forest and open plots. *Forestry* **32**, 14-22.

MASON, B. J. (1957). "The Physics of Clouds." Oxford Univ. Press; London and New York.

MATSUI, H. (1949). On the content of hydrogen peroxide of atmospheric precipitates. *J. Meteorol. Soc. Japan* [2] **27**, 380-381.

NEUMANN, G. H., FONSELIUS, S., and WAHLMAN, L. (1959). Measurements on the content of non-volatile organic material in atmospheric precipitation. *Intern. J. Air Pollution* **2**, 132-141.

ODDIE, B. C. V. (1959). The composition of precipitation at Lerwick, Shetland. *Quart. J. Roy. Meteorol. Soc.* **85**, 163-165.

REITER, R. (1960). Relationships between atmospheric electric phenomena and simultaneous meteorological conditions. Final Report Vol. 1, Contract No. AF 61 (052)-55, pp. 1-178. Air Force Cambridge Research Center.

ROSSBY, C. G., and EGNÉR, H. (1955). On the chemical climate and its variation with the atmospheric circulation pattern. *Tellus* **7**, 118-133.

RUSSELL, E. J., and RICHARDS, E. H. (1919). The amounts and composition of rain and snow falling at Rothamstedt. *J. Agr. Sci.* **9**, 309-337.

SMALL, S. H. (1960). Wet and dry deposition of fallout materials at Kjeller. *Tellus* **12**, 308-314.

SUGAWARA, K., OANA, S., and KOYAMA, T. (1949). Separation of the components of atmospheric salt and their distribution. *Bull. Chem. Soc. Japan* **22**, 47-52.

TURNER, J. S. (1955). The salinity of rainfall as a function of drop size. *Quart. J. Roy. Meteorol. Soc.* **81**, 418-429.

WEICKMANN, H. K., and AUFM KAMPE, H. J. (1953). Physical properties of cumulus clouds. *J. Meteorol.* **10**, 204-211.

WOODCOCK, A. H., (1960). The origin of trade-wind orographic shower rains. *Tellus* **12**, 315-326.

WOODCOCK, A. H., and BLANCHARD, D. C. (1955). Tests of the salt-nuclei hypothesis of rain formation. *Tellus* **7**, 435-442.

5.   *The role of air pollution in air chemistry*

5.1 Introduction

In the previous chapters, air pollution was frequently mentioned as a possible source for trace substances in the atmosphere. Therefore, it appears appropriate to summarize the features of polluted atmospheres in a separate chapter. We do not intend to go into details on the subject of air pollution itself, which is treated comprehensively, e.g., by Meetham (1952), Magill *et al.* (1956), Leighton (1961), and others, but rather to discuss those aspects which are of importance to our subject: The major constituents of polluted atmospheres, their relative abundance, and the zone of influence around polluted areas.

The definition of a polluted atmosphere is to a large degree arbitrary and is usually based on certain standards of concentrations set by air pollution control authorities. These concentrations are high compared with the natural background levels, and data on the chemical composition of the atmosphere in industrial and populated areas are generally not available unless these standards are approached or other nuisance occur. For practical reasons the interest is often concentrated on components, which may not be the most abundant ones, and only in a few cases as, e.g., in Los Angeles, do the studies comprise a large variety of constituents.

The selection of constituents investigated in polluted areas is determined by their potential hazard to health and plant life, or by other unpleasant properties. From a physical or chemical point of view these constituents are sometimes poorly defined as, e.g., "smoke," "dust," or "oxidants." For all these reasons a direct comparison with natural trace substances is therefore possible only for a very limited number of compounds, such as SO_2, NO_2, and a few others.

Most of the material injected into the atmosphere by human activities is not deposited within the source area but is removed by air motion. Once this material is removed from these areas, it is of little concern for air pollution research. However, the ultimate fate of this material in the atmosphere, i.e., its dispersion and its final removal, is a subject of special interest to air chemistry about which unfortunately very little is known.

The effects of air pollution depend to a considerable degree on secondary reaction products. The formation of such products is controlled by the relative composition of polluted atmospheres and by the climate. Broadly speaking one can distinguish two basic types of pollution: the sulfur dioxide-sulfuric acid-sulfate pollution and the oxidation-type air pollution. Famous for the first type is London where smoke and SO_2 accumulate in moist stagnant air masses during the cold season. Under these conditions sunshine is not able to destroy the ground inversion, and the conversion of SO_2 to H_2SO_4 or $SO_4^=$ on smoke particles is favored. The major effects of this smog are reduction in visibility and increase in mortality, e.g., by respiratory diseases.

The second type of smog is most serious in the Los Angeles Basin. The accumulation of material in the ground layer is favored here by the topography in connection with pronounced inversion layers. The relatively large amounts of nitrogen oxides and various hydrocarbons released by auto exhaust and other sources in connection with the sunny climate result in the formation of ozone and a number of other oxidants by photochemical reactions among the gaseous constituents. Eye irritation and plant damage are the main manifestations of this type of smog. It is of interest to note that the SO_2 level in both types of smog is not very different. The variety of pollutants released in cities and industrial communities and the variety of climatic and geographical conditions cause a corresponding variety of smog characteristics which modify these two basic types. However, for our considerations, which are concerned with the large-scale effects of air pollution, it will be sufficient to discuss the major features.

5.2 Composition of Polluted Atmospheres

5.2.1 Gaseous Pollutants

Normally, the concentrations of gaseous pollutants are considerably higher than those of particulate matter, in accord with the findings in unpolluted air. Table 62 gives a survey for a few locations with more complete data. If we disregard CO_2, the most abundant gaseous pollutant seems to be CO. *Carbon monoxide* is considered dangerous for exposures to more than 30 phm for more than 8 hours. Since the levels usually observed are much lower and since CO does not participate in any important reactoins subsequent to its release, it has not received much attention and the data are not very numerous.

TABLE 62

TYPICAL CONCENTRATIONS OF VARIOUS GASEOUS CONSTITUENTS IN POLLUTED ATMOSPHERES

		CO	SO$_2$	NO$_2$	Oxidant calculated as O$_3$	Hydrocarbons calculated as CH$_4$	Aldehdyes calculated as CH$_2$O	NH$_3$
Los Angeles, smog season, fall [a,b]	pphm	10–80	2–20	10–30	5–15 day 1–3 night	10–50	1–25	—
	μg/m^3	120–1000	60–600	200–600	100–300 day 20–60 night	70–400	10–300	—
Cincinnati, average conditions [c]	pphm	—	3–6	20	—	—	7	2
	μg/m^3	—	80–200	400	—	—	90	15
Baltimore, average conditions [c]	pphm	—	2–7	25	—	—	7	2
	μg/m^3	—	60–200	500	—	—	90	15
London [d,e]	pphm	480	20	1	1	—	—	—
	μg/m^3	6000	600	20	20	—	—	—
Leicester England [f]	pphm	—	15	—	—	—	—	—
	μg/m^3	—	400	—	—	—	—	—

[a] Renzetti (1955); [b] Faith et al. (1959); [c] Magill et al. (1956); [d] Meetham (1952); [e] Edgar and Paneth (1941); [f] Great Britain (1945).

Sulfur dioxide is one of the principal constituents of air pollution, both with respect to abundance and effects. It is produced in a large variety of industrial processes, such as melting and roasting of ores, oil refinery operations, and manufacturing of sulfuric acid, rubber, fertilizers, and other products. The main source of SO_2, however, is the burning of fossil fuels, i.e., coal, oil, and natural gas. They all contain sulfur in the range of a few tenths of a per cent up to 5%, with an average of about 1% (see, e.g., Magill *et al.*, 1956). Almost all this sulfur is converted to SO_2, which is thus a very common pollutant in all industrial and populated areas. In many cities in the U.S. and the U.K., the maximum concentrations range up to 50 pphm with averages between 2 and 10 pphm. Concentrations above 50 pphm cause damage of certain plants if the exposure lasts for hours.

In the U.S., the sulfur emission is higher than the consumpttion or production (Table 18), and the same is true for other countries. This and the fact that in some countries as e.g., in the U.S., the sulfur deposits are limited, show how important it is to recover sulfur from atmospheric wastes, both with respect to air pollution and economy. The trend to use fuels with lower sulfur content and to improve sulfur recovery has resulted in a decrease of SO_2 concentrations in some polluted areas in recent years. It is likely that this trend will continue in the future and will overcompensate the industrial expansion.

Contrary to SO_2, the release of H_2S by anthropogenic activities is rather limited. This was, e.g., demonstrated in Section 1.5 by the fact that the H_2S concentration in New York was almost the same as in the rural districts in New England. The reason is either that H_2S is easily converted to SO_2 during combustion and other industrial processes or that the release of H_2S is successfully prevented by recovery in gas purifiers. Hydrogen sulfide and other gaseous sulfur pollutants, such as mercaptans, are thus only of very local importance.

Nitrogen dioxide and, to a much lesser degree, other nitrogen oxides represent another major constituent of polluted air, especially in Los Angeles and other areas with oxidation-type smog. All combustion processes operating at high temperatures are important sources of NO_2, especially if the effluents are rapidly cooled. Effluents of industrial furnaces and automobile exhaust gases contain up to 0.05% by volume NO_2. In Los Angeles two-thirds of the NO_2 is produced by cars (Faith, 1961). The NO_2 levels in Los Angeles, Cincinnati, and Baltimore are not very different (Table 62); they are much higher than the level in London. However, the NO_2 data from London in 1940 may be too low due to less automobile traffic and thus may not be quite comparable.

Other nitrogen oxides, such as NO, NO_3, and N_2O_5, are also likely to occur in polluted atmospheres, but they have not been determined directly. Estimates based on the rates of reaction among themselves and with ozone indicate that their concentrations are less than a few per cent of that of NO_2 (Faith *et al.*, 1959).

Nitrogen dioxide is important for pollution and smog formation primarily because of its photodissociation into nitric oxide and atomic oxygen, which in turn forms ozone and oxidation products of hydrocarbons. The other nitrogen oxides may be important in the formation of intermediary products.

Only few data are available for *ammonia*. The concentrations in cities such as Cincinnati and Baltimore (Table 62) are rather low and only two to three times higher than those found in southern Sweden during the summer (Table 23). Ammonia is produced in small quantities in most combustion processes but may assume rather high concentrations in the vicinity of industries which use NH_3 as an important raw material (fertilizers, organic chemistry). In general, NH_3 is an unimportant pollutant by itself but may be instrumental in converting SO_2 into SO_4, as indicated by the composition of aerosols (Fig. 39) and by the discussion in Section 1.5.2.

The *oxidant* content is usually measured by the potassium iodide method. In clean air this method determines the ozone content, but in polluted atmospheres it also responds to other oxidizing compounds such as NO_2 which are present in considerable concentrations. The oxidant content is usually expressed in ozone equivalents.

Ozone in polluted atmospheres is primarily produced by the following reactions (Leighton and Perkins, 1958):

$$NO_2 + h\nu \longrightarrow NO + O$$
$$O + O_2 + M \longrightarrow O_3 + M$$
$$O_3 + h\nu \longrightarrow O_2 + O$$
$$NO + O_3 \longrightarrow NO_2 + O_2$$

The atomic oxygen formed by the dissociation of NO_2 will also react with other substances, e.g., organic, present in urban atmosphere, but Leighton and Perkins (1958) come to the conclusion that over 99.5% of the atomic oxygen reacts with molecular oxygen to form ozone and that less than 0.5% reacts by all other processes. The photodissociation of ozone is slow and does not substantially decrease the ozone concentration, but the nitric oxide-ozone reaction limits the concentration of ozone which can coexist with NO_2.

Ozone formation is apparently enhanced in the presence of olefins, whereas the production rate of ozone for most paraffins is small (Schuck and Doyle, 1959).

As a result of these processes the ozone-oxidant concentration in Los Angeles rises during the morning hours and reaches a maximum between 12 and 14 hours; it decreases toward night during which a level of 1 to 3 pphm (Table 62) is maintained, which is close to the natural background. The average maximum values in certain points of the city are as high as 17 pphm and individual maxima can be as high as 50 pphm.

Hydrocarbons are difficult to measure and values are available primarily from Los Angeles (Renzetti, 1955), where the concentrations range from 10 to 50 pphm. Most of these hydrocarbons seem to be paraffins (saturated hydrocarbons); the rest are composed of olefins (unsaturated hydrocarbons). They are emitted from automobiles, oil refineries, and gasoline service stations.

Hydrocarbons are not considered hazardous at the observed concentration levels, but certain olefins react with ozone or atomic oxygen to form a series of products, including formaldehyde, which contribute to eye irritation and plant damage. There is strong indication that the olefins are also dissociated photochemically into free radicals. The number of possible secondary reactions between these products is large and the entire subject is of extreme complexity (Leighton and Perkins, 1958).

Aldehydes are produced whenever organic compounds are burned, e.g., gasoline in cars or oil for heating. However, they are also produced in secondary reactions of olefinic hydrocarbons with ozone. A considerable fraction of the aldehydes consist of formaldehyde H_2CO. Their concentration in Los Angeles varies between 1 and 25 pphm, and similar concentrations are reported from Cincinnati and Baltimore (Table 62).

In atmospheres like that of the Los Angeles Basin and possibly in most cities with similar pollution characteristics, there is a host of other, primarily organic, compounds present such as organic acids, organic halides, cyclic hydrocarbons, and various oxidation products of organic compounds. Some of these compounds were identified and measured in Los Angeles (see, e.g. the individual Technical Reports 1 to 33 of the Air Pollution Foundation).

We will conclude this short review of gases in polluted atmospheres by pointing out differences between various polluted areas. Table 62 shows no pronounced differences in all five cities insofar as SO_2 is concerned. This demonstrates that the manifestations of the sulfuric acid-sulfate smog, e.g., in London, are due primarily to climatic conditions and that the oxidation of SO_2 in London is the result of processes other than photooxidation, most likely catalytic oxidation in fog droplets.

The concentrations of NO_2 and oxidant, on the other hand, are considerably lower in London, if conclusions may be drawn from the few data available for London. Such a difference is to be expected since most of the NO_2 is produced by automobile exhaust. Estimates indicate that in Los Angeles two-thirds of the oxides of nitrogen and three-fourths of the hydrocarbons come from motor vehicles.

5.2.2 Particulate Pollutants

The total concentration of particulate matter in polluted atmospheres is higher than the natural background by factors of 10 to 100, i.e., by about the same order of magnitude as some of the more important gaseous pollutants such as SO_2. The concentrations range from about 100 $\mu g/m^3$ in areas of low pollution up to 4000 $\mu g/m^3$ in London during severe smog conditions. Mean values for the center of large industrial areas and cities like Baltimore, Cincinnati, and Los Angeles range from 200 to 800 $\mu g/m^3$, and for smaller cities average concentrations of 100 to 200 $\mu g/m^3$ are very common. We recall here that the total burden of natural aerosols, including that of sea salt, is usually of the order of 5 to 50 $\mu g/m^3$.

Since studies of polluted atmospheres are dictated by special pollution problems of a certain area, the chemical compounds selected for studies of anthropogenic aerosols differ from those selected for natural aerosols, and a comparison is difficult. In numerous investigations in Great Britain and Canada, the particulate material was collected in deposition gages and analyzed in terms of such general categories as soluble matter, ash, or combustible material. Although the composition of deposited material cannot be expected to be identical with that of the total suspended material, it may still reflect the major features with good approximation. Table 63 gives some typical data from industrial and residential areas in

TABLE 63

AVERAGE COMPOSITION OF DEPOSITED PARTICULATE POLLUTANTS IN TERMS OF GENERAL CATEGORIES IN PER CENT WEIGHT

Category	London [a]	Greater Windsor Area [b]		
		Industrial	Industrial-residential	Residential-rural
Ash	40	50	57	58
Tar	2	2	2	5
Combustible matter other than tar	27	23	19	17
Total insoluble matter	69	75	78	80
$SO_4^=$	15	—	—	—
Cl^-	6	—	—	—
Ca^{++}	4	—	—	—
Others	6	—	—	—
Total soluble matter	31	25	22	20

[a] Meetham (1952)
[b] Magill et al. (1956).

polluted regions. We see that a considerable fraction, i.e., 70 to 80% of the material is insoluble and contains mineral and organic (combustible) compounds. A similar fraction of insoluble material was indicated in aerosols which were only slightly affected by pollution (see Section 2.2.3). The few data available show that the water soluble fraction is high in sulfate and that the solution is strongly acid. The figures in Table 63 refer to areas which are typical for burning coal or for heavy industry. Apparently, the composition in terms of these general categories does not differ much between London and the Greater Windsor area (Detroit), and it can be expected that this is also true for most other areas with similar smog characteristics.

The composition of the particulate material in terms of elements is more specific but leaves still open the important question of the actual chemical compounds present. Table 64 gives typical examples of some of the more abundant elements in particulate pollutants. Additional information is presented in Tables 33 and 34. All these data can only give an idea of the general composition, and, of course, local values can deviate considerably.

Elements such as silicon, calcium, aluminum, iron, and magnesium are also abundant in mineral dust and not specific for anthropogenic aerosols, whereas such elements as lead (from automobile exhaust) or manganin, zinc, and others are typical for certain sources of industrial pollution. Despite some variations in the concentrations, the data in Table 64 again indicate that by and large the average composition of particulate matter keeps within certain limits.

The aerometric survey of the Los Angeles Basin during the fall of 1954 (Renzetti, 1955) is the most comprehensive study of a polluted atmosphere made so far. Table 65 gives a few interesting data from this report comparing the concentration of a few chemical compounds which are also observed in natural aerosols. We see that $SO_4^=$ has about the same concentration in Los Angeles and New York-Chicago, but that it drops considerably in smaller cities. Since the average concentration of SO_2 in Los Angeles is about 10 pphm or 300 $\mu g/m^3$, the concentration ratio $SO_4^=/SO_2$ is about 0.1, similar to values in unpolluted areas (see Section 1.5.1 and Table 12).

For nitrate, the values in the Los Angeles Basin are notably higher than in equivalent cities such as New York or Chicago, although the data for the latter cities are not very reliable. This difference is noteworthy since the concentration of NO_2 in cities such as Cincinnati or Baltimore (Table 62) is of the same magnitude as in Los Angeles, so that it can be expected that NO_2 concentrations in New York and Chicago are not much lower. It is likely that the higher concentration of sea salt particles in the Los Angeles area is responsible for this difference, according to the discussion on nitrate formation in giant particles in Section 2.3.3. With an average

TABLE 64

AVERAGE CONCENTRATIONS OF IMPORTANT ELEMENTS IN PARTICULATE POLLUTANTS
IN $\mu g/m^3$ [a]

Element	Los Angeles	Cincinnati	Baltimore	Windsor Area	Average of 30 metropolitan areas in U.S. and Alaska [b]
Silicon	4	—	—	6	—
Calcium	2	16	—	3	—
Aluminum	4	4	4	3	—
Iron	14	12	15	3	5
Magnesium	2	7	—	1	2
Lead	3	3	1	0.5	2
Manganese	0.1	0.3	0.3	0.3	0.2
Copper	0.1	0.9	0.4	0.3	0.1
Zinc	—	2	—	0.2	—
Titanium	0.1	1	0.5	0.1	0.2

[a] Magill *et al.* (1956).
[b] Renzetti (1955).

TABLE 65

COMPARISON OF THE AVERAGE CONCENTRATION OF A FEW IMPORTANT COMPOUNDS
IN PARTICULATE POLLUTANTS [a]

Compound	Los Angeles Basin	New York and Chicago	Cities under 2 million
$SO_4^=$	22	25	4
NO_3^-	20	6	3
Organic material	60 [b]	40 [c]	25 [c]

[a] Renzetti (1955).
[b] Extracted by benzene.
[c] Extracted by acetone.

NO_2 concentration of about 20 pphm or 400 $\mu g/m^3$, we obtain a concentration ratio $NO_3^-/NO_2 = 0.05$, which is again of the same order as that for $SO_4^=/SO_2$, or as that for NO_3^-/NO_2 in unpolluted areas.

According to the data in Table 65 the concentration of *organic* material varies approximately with the size of the community. The

value for Los Angeles is likely to be a little too high because extraction by
benzene gives slightly higher values than where acetone is used. The organic
material is a complex mixture of a host of compounds and very little is
known about it. The best data are available from Los Angeles and some of
the more abundant compounds found in this area are listed in Table 66.

TABLE 66

Compound	Approximate fraction (%)
Organic acids and higly water soluble compounds (acids, dibasic acids, alcohols, etc.)	40
Saturated hydrocarbons	20
Two- to five-ring aromatics	5
Polynuclear aromatic hydrocarbons	5

5.3 Variation of Pollution in and around Polluted Areas

5.3.1 Variation with Time and Meteorological Factors

The concentration of constituents in polluted areas exhibits
daily, weekly, and seasonal variations. These variations are the result of
the interaction between the rate of production and the rate of dispersion,
the latter being a complex function of the meteorological conditions and
the topography.

The production rate of most pollutants has a minimum dur-
ing the night, a sharp increase in the early morning hours with the beginning
of traffic, heating, power generation, and other industrial activities, and a
decrease in the evening. In many instances, the production rate may have
a double peak during the day as for instance the production of SO_2 in residential areas by heating and cooking, or the production of automobile
exhaust due to heavy traffic in the morning and evening. Areas like Los Angeles, which are typical for the formation of smog by photochemical processes, show a pronounced peak of oxidant production during noontime.

Superimposed upon these production cycles is the variation
of the dispersion of the pollutants due to the natural ventilation of the atmosphere. This ventilation is a complex function both of the horizontal
wind velocity and of turbulent and convective mixing; the latter in turn
is controlled by wind velocity, topography, and thermal structure of the
ground layers. Under normal conditions, the diurnal variation of stability
and wind is such that the resulting ventilation has a minimum shortly
before sunrise and a maximum during the early afternoon. The combination

of production and ventilation yields a variety of daily concentration cycles, usually low values during night and high values in the morning and evening, with a secondary minimum around noon. In New York City, for instance, the average peaks of SO_2 concentration are around 8^h and 20^h (Greenburg and Jacobs, 1956), whereas in Los Angeles the SO_2 concentration has only one broad maximum during daytime (Renzetti, 1955).

As is to be expected, pollutants of industrial origin exhibit a weekly variation in concentration, with a minimum over the weekend. Any annual variations are again the result of production *and* ventilation. In heavily populated areas the production is higher in winter, and, in most parts of the temperate zones, the ventilation is at the same time at its lowest. Winter maxima of concentration in polluted areas are, therefore, very common. In New York City, for instance, the average SO_2 concentration in winter is more than twice the summer concentration and the severe smog conditions in London occur during the cold season. The Los Angeles Basin shows special features. Here the temperature inversions are most frequent during the fall and so is the frequency of smog.

The concentration level of pollutants is, under otherwise equal conditions, related to the size of the source area. Data from Great Britain (1945) indicate that the level is proportional to the square root of the population. A study in Nashville, Tennessee (Turner, 1961), gave correlation coefficients between concentration (e.g., of SO_2) and production rate, index of thermal stability, and wind velocity of about $+ 0.6$, $+ 0.5$, and $- 0.5$, respectively. However, these relations will certainly vary from case to case and can only serve as an example of the general trend.

5.3.2 The Area of Influence around Centers of Pollution

The decrease of the concentration of pollutants with increasing distance from source areas is of special interest to air chemistry. One of the best sources of information on this subject is still the 3-year study at Leicester in 1945 (Great Britain, 1945). The densely populated area of this town in Central Great Britain of about 3 km diameter is surrounded by a residential belt about 4 km wide. A network of 13 stations was established to monitor the concentration of SO_2 and smoke.

The isolines of the average SO_2 and smoke concentration closely match the shape of the populated area. The mean concentration of SO_2 and smoke in the center of the city of about 400 $\mu g/m^3$ drops by a factor of 2 to 3 within the residential belt. At a distance of about 5 km the level of the background concentration is approached. However, the background concentration in this part of Great Britain is still considerably higher than the natural level, due to the influence of more distant pollution sources (see, e.g., Fig. 17).

The effect of wind on the configuration of the isolines is surprisingly small. For velocities up to 15 km/hour, the maximum of the concentration is still close to the center of Leicester. The asymmetry of the isolines due to the prevailing westerlies is only of the order of 2 km with respect to the outlines of the town, and the concentration level in the center varies only slightly with wind velocity.

Similar results have been obtained in other studies, e.g., by Flach (1952) who studied the distribution of Aitken particles in various cities in Central Europe as an index for pollution. The isolines of concentration follow closely the outlines of population density and the effect of wind is not pronounced. Gorham and Gordon (1960) measured the SO_4 content in pond waters downwind from a smelter area and found a rapid decrease within the first 5 km from the smelter, a slow decrease by about 25% between 5 and 15 km, and almost no further decrease beyond 15 km. This result is of particular interest with respect to data of rainwater analysis, as it apparently indicates that smaller polluted areas have no measurable effect beyond about 15 km. The influence of pollution on rainwater corresponds, of course, more to the integrated effect within a vertical column of air than to the surface concentration. In the Leicester Report the total amount of smoke within a vertical column was roughly measured by the attenuation of sunlight, particularly of the ultraviolet radiation, and the data show that the variation with wind is more pronounced and the decrease with distance somewhat slower than for surface concentrations.

These studies give a fairly good idea of the average distribution of pollutants in the immediate vicinity of the source area. Information on the distribution at greater distances is rather scanty. Figure 17 shows that large portions of Great Britain can be considered influenced by the various industrial areas. The Leicester Report gives some rough estimations which seem to indicate that between distances of 50 and 150 km downwind from a source, the concentration in $\mu g/cm^3$ can be approximated by

$$C_1 = 7 \times 10^4 \, m/x^2 \text{ for smoke}$$

and

$$C_2 = 2 \times 10^4 \, m/x^2 \text{ for } SO_2,$$

where m is the size of the population in millions and x the distance in kilometers. A city of 2 million with British heating habits will thus raise the concentration at a distance of 100 km by 14 and 4 $\mu g/m^3$ for smoke and SO_2 respectively. These concentrations are comparable to aerosol and SO_2 concentration in unpolluted air.

There are *theoretical considerations* about the average decrease with distance from the source, but the results are not very reliable and are difficult to apply to actual conditions. It is clear that unpolluted areas, in the sense that the contamination level due to human activities is small compared to natural levels, no longer exist in areas such as Western and Central Europe or the northeastern part of the United States. This was already pointed out on several occasions throughout the book and shows that the interpretation of data from so-called unpolluted areas has to be made with care.

REFERENCES

EDGAR, J. L., and PANETH, F. A. (1941). The determination of ozone and nitrogen dioxide in the atmosphere. *J. Chem. Soc.* **144**, 511-519.

FAITH, W. L. (1961). *Air Pollution Foundation (Los Angeles) Final Rep.* pp. 1-62.

FAITH, W. L,, RENZETTI, N. A., and ROGERS, L. W. (1959). *Air Pollution Foundation (Los Angeles) 5th Tech. Progr. Rep. No.* **27**, 1-77.

FLACH, E. (1952). Über ortsfeste und bewegliche Messungen mit dem Scholzschen Kernzähler und dem ZEISSschen Freiluftkonimeter. *Z. Meteorol.* **6**, 97-112.

GORHAM, E., and GORDON, A. G. (1960). Some effects of sulfur pollution northeast of Falconbridge, Ontario. *Can. J. Botany* **38**, 307-312.

GREAT BRITAIN, Department of Scientific and Industrial Research (1945). Atmospheric pollution in Leicester: a scientific survey. *Tech. Papers Atmos. Pollution Research* **1**, 1-161.

GREENBURG, L., and JACOBS, M. B. (1956). Sulfur dioxide in New York City atmosphere *Ind. Eng. Chem.* **48**, 1517-1521.

LEIGHTON, P. A. (1961). "Photochemistry of Air Pollution." Academic Press, New York.

LEIGHTON, P. A., and PERKINS, W. A. (1958). Photochemical secondary reactions in urban air. *Air Pollution Foundation (Los Angeles) Rep. No.* **24**, 1-212.

MAGILL, P. L., HOLDEN, F. R., and ACKLEY, C., ed. (1956). "Air Pollution Handbook," pp. 2-45. McGraw-Hill, New York.

MEETHAM, A. R. (1952). "Atmospheric Pollution: Its Origins and Prevention," pp. 1-268. Pergamon, New York.

RENZETTI, N. A., ed. (1955). An aerometric survey of the Los Angeles Basin, August-November, 1954. *Air Pollution Foundation (Los Angeles) Rep. No.* **9**, 1-333.

SCHUCK, E. A., and DOYLE, G. J. (1956). Photooxidation of hydro-carbons in mixtures containing oxides of nitrogen and sulfur dioxide. *Air Pollution Foundation (Los Angeles) Rep. No.* **29**, 1-104.

TURNER, D. D. (1961). Relationships between 24 hour mean air quality measurements and meteorological factors in Nashville, Tennessee. *J. Air Pollution Control Assoc.* **11**, 483-489.

Author Index

A

Ackley, C., 59, 66, 71, *107*, 353, 355, 356, 359, 361, *365*

Adams, C. E., 241, *283*

Adel, A., 82, 83, *100*

Aitken, J., 112, 154, *202*

Alexander, L. T., 263, *283*

Allington, K., 276, 280, *283*

Allison, F. E., 86, 91, *100*, 343, *348*

Almeida, J. G., 230, 236, *286*

Altshuller, A. P., 86, 95, 96, *100*

Anderson, E. C., 30, 31, 35, *100*, 233, *283*

Anderson, V., 313, 344, 346, *348*

Angström, A., 313, 340, 342, 344, *348*

Arnold, J. R., 30, 31, 35, *100*, 230, 234, 236, 237, *283*, *285*

Arnold, P. W., 83, *100*

Arons, A. B., 157, 158, *205*

Aufm Kampe, H. J., 292, *351*

Ault, W. V., 74, *100*

Aurand, K., 217, 218, 220, 221, 222, 226, *285*

B

Baer, F., 160, *206*

Bannon, J. K., 10, *100*

Barclay, F. R., 6, 7, 27, *100*

Barrett, E. W., 8, *100*, 304, 338, *348*

Barth, C. A., 77, 84, *100*

Bates, D. R., 80, 83, 96, *100*

Baus, R. A., 215, 217, 229, 254, 255, *283*, *285*, *286*

Becker, F., 216, *285*

Begemann, F., 19, 20, 75, 76, 78, *100*, 269, 270, 271, 272, *283*

Benesch, W., 96, 97, *100*

Bigg, E. G., 197, *202*

Birkeland, J. W., 82, *100*

Bischof, W., 27, *101*

Bishop, K. F., 19, *101*, 272, 273, 274, *283*

Black, R. W., 254, 255, 258, 260, *286*

Blanchard, D. C., 156, 157, 158, *202*, 205, 294, *351*

Bleichrodt, J. F., 260, *283*

Blifford, I. H., Jr., 215, 217, 227, 228, 229, 254, 255, 268, *283*, *285*, *286*, *287*

Blok, J., 260, *283*

Boato, G., 14, *102*

Bodenstein, M., 82, 84, *101*

Bolin, B., 29, 31, 35, 93, *101*

Boss, G., 337, *348*

Boville, B. W., 276, 280, *283*

Bowen, I. G., 49, *101*

Brasefield, C. J., 8, *101*

Braverman, M. M., 61, *106*

Bray, J. B., 28, *101*

Brewer, A. W., 4, 43, 44, 47, 49, 50, 54, *101*, 192, 193, *202*, 250, 269, 278, *283*

Bricard, J., 148, *202*

Bridge, H. S., 9, *101*

Brocker, W. S., 267, *283*

Brodin, G., 304, 338, *348*

Broecker, W. S., 75, *105*

Brown, F., 7, *101*

Brown, H., 29, *101*, 266, *283*

Buddhue, T. D., 199, *202*

Bullrich, K., 146, *202*, *203*

Burch, D. E., 82, *100*

Burckhardt, H., 157, *202*

Burris, R. H., 77, *105*

Burton, W. M., 228, 229, *283*, 301, *348*

Buswell, A. M., 77, 94, *101*

Byers, H. R., 164, *202*

367

C

Cadle, R. D., 59, 69, 95, *102*, 167, 168, 207

Callendar, G. S., 27, 28, *102*

Carter, H. J., 8, *100*

Cauer, H., 59, 68, 91, 93, 98, *102*, 154, *202*

Cernoch, 160, *206*

Chadwick, R. C., 310, *348*

Chagnon, C. W., 65, *106*, 188, 189, 192, 198, *202*, *205*, 252, *285*

Chamberlain, A. C., 93, 94, *102*, 214, 220, 223, *283*, 310, *348*

Chambers, L. A., 177, 178, 179, *202*

Chapman, R. M., 87, *107*

Chapman, S., 38, *102*

Chen, M. C., 77, *109*

Chepil, W. S., 181, *202*

Cholak, C. E., 177, 178, 179, *202*

Cloud, P. E., 77, *102*

Collins, W. R., 261, *283*

Conway, E. J., 65, 71, *102*

Costa, N. L., 230, 236, *286*

Cowper, G., 235, 236, *284*

Cox, L. C., 292, *349*

Cragg, J. B., 323, *349*

Craig, 44

Craig, H., 20, 29, 30, 31, *102*, 230, 233, 269, 270, 271, *284*

Craig, R. A., 14, 38, 42, *102*

Crooks, R. N., 228, 253, 259, 261, *287*

Crozier, W. D., 163, 199, *202*

Cruikshank, A. J., 235, 236, *283*

Cunningham, R. M., 11, *102*

D

Damon, P. E., 79, *102*

Dansgaard, W., 12, 13, 15, 16, *102*

Davis, C. N., 125, *202*

Day, G. J., 188, *203*

de Bary, E., 11, *102*, 146, *203*

Dekker, R. H., 260, *283*

Delafield, H. J., 19, *101*, 273, *283*, 292, *349*

Deming, L. S., 38, *110*

Dessens, H., 114, 160, *203*

de Turville, C. M., 9, 10, *102*, *104*

de Vries, H., 36, *103*

Dhar, N. R., 98, *103*, 316, *348*

Dillemuth, F. J., 58, 94, *103*

Dilworth, C., 9, *101*

Dinger, J. H., 8, *107*

Dobson, G. M. B., 279, 281, *284*

Doherty, D. J., 113, 116, *206*

Dole, M., 18, *103*, *106*

Dombrowski, N., 156, *205*

Dondes, S., 84, *105*

Doyle, G. J., 357, *365*

Drevinsky, P. T., 242, 252, 254, 257, 259, 260, 261, *285*, *286*

Drischel, H., 315, 343, *348*

Dütsch, H. V., 38, 41, 42, 44, 45, 49, 51, *101*, *103*

Dunham, S. B., 155, *203*

Dyson, E. D., 214, 220, 223, *283*

Dzens-Litovskiy, A. I., 94, *103*

E

Eaton, J. H., 66, *103*

Eaton, S. V., 66, *103*

Eckhardt, D. L., 167, 168, *207*

Edgar, J. L., 85, *103*, 355, *365*

Edvarson, K., 240, *284*

Effenberger, E., 122, *203*

Eggleton, A. E. J., 19, *101*, 273, *283*

Egnér, H., 61, 62, 88, 89, 91, *103*, *109*, 317, 320, 331, 344, *348*, *351*

Ehmert, A., 44, 49, 50, 51, 54, *103*

Ehmert, H., 51, *103*

Eldridge, R. G., 138, *203*

Elliott, M. J. W., 6, 7, 27, *100*

Emanuelsson, A., 320, 344, *348*

Epstein, S., 12, 14, 15, 16, 17, *103*

Eriksson, E., 24, 29, 31, 35, 61, 62, 65, 66, 67, 71, 72, 86, 88, 89, 92, *101*, *103*, 159, 165, 166, *203*, 271, *284*, 308, 309, 310, 315, 317, 320, 323, 324, 329, 331, 334, 335, 340, 341, 342, 343, 344, 346, *348*

Evans, H. D., 69, *110*, 155, *208*

F

Facy, L., 292, *348*

Faith, W. L., 355, 356, 357, *365*

Faltings, V., 19, 75, *104*

Farkas, A., 77, *104*
Farkas, L., 77, *104*
Farlow, N. H., 241, *283*
Faucher, G. A., 183, 185, 190, *207*
Feely, H. W., 246, 281, *284*
Fellenberg, T. V., 93, *104*
Fenn, R. W., 122, *203*
Fergusson, G. J., 230, 233, 267, *284*
Fisher, E. M., 228, 253, 259, 261, *287*
Flach, E., 364, *365*
Flohn, H., 157, *202*
Foitzig, L., 145, *203*
Fonselius, S., 317, *351*
Forster, H., 154, *203*
Fournier d'Albe, E. M., 159, *203*
Friedlander, S. K., 119, *203*
Friedman, H., 215, 217, 229, *283*, *285*
Friedman, I., 12, 14, 75, 76, 77, 78, *100*, *102*, *104*, 272, *283*
Friend, J. P., 196, *203*
Frith, R., 10, *104*

G

Galt, R. I., 152, *206*
Garvin, D., 78, *107*
Gates, D. M., 8, *104*
Georgii, H. W., 59, 60, 61, 63, 85, 86, 87, 92, *104*, 119, 141, *202*, *203*, 295, 304, 305, 306, 307, 309, 311, 313, 314, 315, 322, 337, *348*, *349*
Gerhard, E. R., 68, *104*, 154, 166, *203*
Glawion, H., 182, *203*
Glu`e`kauf, E., 2, 75, 76, 78, 79, 94, 95, *104*
Gmelin, L., 65, 87, 91, *104*
Godson, W. L., 47, *104*
Goel, P. S., 228, 236, *284*
Goetz, A., 114, 180, *203*, *204*
Götz, F. W. P., 44, 53, 54, 55, 57, *104*
Goldberg, E. D., 181, *207*, 230, *285*
Goldberg, L., 82, 87, 94, 95, *104*, *107*
Goldsmith, P., 6, 7, 27, *100*, *101*, 292, *349*
Gonsior, B., 77, *104*, 272, *284*
Goody, R. M., 82, 83, *104*
Gordon, A. G., 364, *365*
Gorham, E., 310, 312, 313, 314, 315, 316, 320, 322, 323, 324, 325, 329, 334, 335, 336, 337, 339, *349*, 364, *365*

Gray, J., Jr., 27, *105*, 267, 268, 269, 270, 271, *284*
Green, H. F., 7, *101*
Green, H. L., 114, *204*
Greenburg, L., 61, *104*, 363, *365*
Greenfield, S. M., 293, *349*
Grosse, A. V., 19, 75, *104*, *105*
Groth, W., 78, *105*
Grumitt, W. E., 235, 236, *284*
Gruner, P., 197, *204*
Gustafson, P. E., 298, 317, 319, 320, *350*

H

Hagemann, F., 27, *105*, 267, 268, 269, 270, 271, *284*
Hallden, N. A., 261, *283*
Hare, F. K., 9, *105*, 276, 280, *283*, *284*
Harrison, E. R., 10, *104*
Harteck, P., 19, 74, 75, 76, 77, 78, 79, 84, *104*, *105*
Harvey, H. W., 24, *105*, 303, *349*
Hawkins, T. D. F., 6, 8, *105*
Haxel, O., 227, 228, *284*
Helliwell, N. C., 7, *105*
Hendrix, W. P., 135, *206*
Hering, W., 49, 50, *105*
Herman, F. A., 316, 337, *349*
Herndon, L. R., 8, *100*
Herzberg, G., 97, *107*
Hesstvedt, E., 7, *105*, 193, 199, *204*
Hettick, I., 315, 337, *350*
Heymann, J. A., 315, *349*
Hinzpeter, M., 294, 312, 313, *349*
Hoch, G. E., 77, *105*
Hochheiser, S., 61, *106*
Hodge, P. W., 198, *204*
Högberg, L., 313, 340, 342, 344, *348*
Hoering, T., 86, *105*
Holden, F. R., 59, 66, 71, *107*, 353, 355, 356, 359, 361, *365*
Holland, J. Z., 243, *284*
Holt, A., 7, *101*
Honda, M., 230, 234, 236, 237, *285*
Houghton, H., 336, *349*
Houghton, J. T., 6, 7, 8, *105*
Huber, B., 23, *105*

Hurd, F. K., 135, *206*
Hutchinson, G. E., 33, 94, 95, *105*
Hutton, J. T., 320, 322, 330, *349*

I

Isono, K., 169, *204*
Israël, H., 112, 113, 115, 116, 151, *204*, 211, 213, 215, 219, 220, 227, *284*, *285*
Israël-Köhler, H., 216, *285*

J

Jacobi, W., 135, 170, *204*, 217, 218, 220, 221, 222, 226, *285*
Jacobs, M. B., 61, *104*, *106*, 363, *365*
Jelly, J. V., 6, 7, 27, *100*
Jensen, J. H. D., 74, *105*
Jensen, M. L., 73, 74, *106*
Johansson, O., 66, 67, *106*, 310, *349*
Johnson, F. S., 44, 45, *106*
Johnston, R. L., 19, *104*
Johnstone, H. F., 68, *104*, 154, 166, *203*
Jones, S., 250, *285*
Junge, C. E., 56, 60, 65, 68, 70, 71, 72, 73, 90, 92, *106*, 112, 114, 117, 118, 119, 123, 127, 130, 133, 134, 135, 137, 138, 144, 147, 148, 149, 150, 151, 152, 153, 154, 162, 163, 166, 167, 170, 174, 186, 187, 188, 189, 190, 192, 194, 195, 197, 198, *202*, *204*, *205*, *206*, 252, 253, *285*, 298, 305, 308, 317, 319, 320, 323, 324, 325, 326, 327, 328, 330, 331, 333, 334, 335, 341, 344, 345, *349*, *350*

K

Kalkstein, M. I., 252, 275, 277, *285*
Kalle, K., 329, *350*
Kanazawa, T., 260, *287*
Kanzwisher, J., 24, 25, 36, *106*
Kaplan, L. D., 21, *106*
Katcoff, S., 239, *285*
Katsuragi, K., 260, *287*
Katz, M., 64, *106*
Kay, R. H., 49, 50, 54, *106*
Kayana, T., 166, *207*
Keefe, D., 149, 150, *205*
Keeling, C. D., 25, 26, *106*

Keily, D. P., 138, *205*
Kellogg, W. W., 241, 285
Kennan, E. L., 150, *206*
Kientzler, C. F., 157, 158, *205*
King, P., 229, 254, 255, *285*, *286*
Kirschenbaum, A. D., 75, *105*
Kirschenbaum, I., 13, *106*
Kitt, G. P., 75, 76, 78, *104*
Knelman, F., 156, *205*
Knight, N., 333, *350*
Koehler, H., 132, *205*
Koffler, H., 77, *106*
Koide, M., 230, *285*
Kosmath, W., 215, 217, *285*
Koyama, T., 313, *351*
Krogh, M. E., 82, *109*
Krumbein, W. C., 129, 181, *205*
Kulkarni, R. N., 45, 47, *108*
Kulp, J. L., 75, 79, *102*, *105*
Kumai, M., 293, *350*
Kup, J., 114, 122, *205*
Kuroiwa, D., 138, 139, 169, *205*, 294, *350*

L

Laevastu, T., 199, *205*
Lal, D., 20, *102*, 228, 230, 231, 232, 233, 234, 235, 236, 237, 238, 269, 270, 271, 284, 285
Landsberg, H. E., 113, 120, 122, 157, *205*. 297, *350*
Lane, G. A., 18, *103*, *106*
Lane, W. R., 114, 204
Larson, T. E., 315, 337, *350*
Lassen, L., 149, 150, *205*, 222, 223, 224, *285*
Lazarus, A. J., 9, *101*
Leeflang, K. W. H., 320, 323, *350*
Lehmann, L., 227, 228, *285*
Leighton, P. A., 95, *108*, 353, 357, 358, *365*
Leslie, F. E., 6, 8, *107*
Leslie, T. I., 320, 322, 330, *349*
Lettau, H., 10, 51, 80, *106*, *107*, 125, *205*, 275, *286*
Libby, W. F., 19, *104*, *107*, 233, 241, 243, 266, 269, 270, 271, 272, 280, 281, *283*, *286*

Liesegang, W., 316, *350*
Lindblom, G., 236, *286*
Lippert, W., 135, 170, *204*
List, R. J., 243, *286*
Little, H. N., 77, *105*
Locke, J. L., 97, *107*
Lockhart, L. B., Jr., 215, 217, 227, 228, 229, 254, 255, 258, 259, 260, *283, 285, 286*
Lodge, J. E., 159, 160, *206*, 336, *350*
Löw, K., 240, *284*
Ludlam, F. H., 199, *206*
Lundegardh, H., 21, 22, *107*
Lyon, E. F., 9, *101*

M

Mac Donald, A. J., 336, *350*
Mc Dowell, M. R. C., 80, *100*
Machta, L., 27, *105*, 219, 229, 241, 243, 259, 267, 268, 269, 270, 271, 281, *284, 286*, 300, 301, *350*
Mac Kay, C., 234, 266, *287*
Mackenzie, J. K., 7, *105*
Mc Kinley, J. D., Jr., 78, *107*
Macku, M., 313, 314, 317, 322, *350*
Mc Master, K. N., 160, *207*
Mc Math, R. R., 87, *107*
Madgwick, H. A. I., 304, *350*
Magill, P. L., 59, 66, 71, *107*, 353, 355, 356, 359, 361, *365*
Malhorta, P. K., 230, 231, 232, 234, 235, 236, *285*
Manson, J. E., 65, *106*, 192, 194, 195, 197, 198, *205*, 252, *285*
Marquez, L., 230, 236, *286*
Martell, E. A., 242, 252, 254, 257, 259, 260, 261, *285, 286*
Mason, B. J., 118, 122, 156, 158, 159, *206*, 293, 296, *350*
Mastenbrook, H. J., 8, *107*
Matsui, H., 316, *351*
May, K. R., 114, *206*
Mayeda, T. K., 14, 16, 17, *103*
Meetham, A. R., 61, 63, 68, 69, 72, *107*, 353, 355, 359, *365*
Mellis, O., 199, *205*

Metnieks, A. L., 120, 121, 122, 152, 158, 159, 187, *206, 207*
Middleton, W. E. K., 144, *206*
Migeotte, M. V., 44, 84, 87, 94, 96, 97, *100, 101, 107*
Milford, J. R., 44, *101*
Millen, S. G., 138, *205*
Miller, L. E., 82, *107*
Milton, J. F., 177, 178, 179, *202*
Miyake, Y., 260, *287*
Möller, F., 11, *102*
Mohler, O. C., 87, *107*
Monteith, J. L., 24, *107*
Moordy, W. A., 136, *206*
Moore, D. J., 118, 122, 159, 160, 162, *206*
Moreland, W., 54, *110, 259, 288*
Moss, T. S., 6, 8, *105*
Mueller, E. A., 82, 94, 95, *104*
Müller, H., 129, *206*
Mueller, H. F., *101*
Münnich, K. O., 267, 269, *287*
Murcray, D. G., 6, 8, *104, 107*
Murcray, F. H., 6, 8, *107*
Murgatroyd, R. J., 50, *107*
Muth, H., 217, 218, 220, 221, 222, 226, *285*

N

Nakai, N., 73, 74, *106*
Narasappaya, N., 228, 236, *284*
Neumann, G. H., 317, *351*
Neumann, H. R., 158, *206*
Neuwirth, R., 63, *108*
Neven, L., 84, 96, 97, *107*
Newitt, D. M., 156, *205*
Nolan, P. J., 113, 116, 149, 150, 152, *205, 206*
Noyes, W. A., Jr., 95, *108*

O

Oana, S., 166, *207*, 313, *351*
Oddie, B. C. V., 166, *206*, 323, *351*
Öpik, E. J., 195, 198, *206*
Östlund, G., 73, 74, *108*
Ohta, S., 262, *287*
Ohtake, T., 138, 139, 169, *208*

Orr, C., 135, *206*
Orvig, S., 9, *105*
Osmond, R. G. D., 259, 261, *287*
Ovington, J. D., 309, *350*
Owers, M. J., 261, *287*

P

Pack, D. H., 219, *288*
Paetzold, H. K., 37, 38, 40, 41, 44, 45, 46, 47, 48, 51, *101*, *108*
Pales, J. C., 53, 54, 57, *108*
Palmer, C. E., 280, 281, *286*
Pandow, M., 234, 266, *287*
Paneth, F. A., 75, 76, 85, *103*, *108*, 355, *365*
Parham, A. G., 7, *101*
Parker, R. P., 236, *287*
Patterson, H. S., 129, *208*
Patterson, R. L., Jr., 229, 254, 255, 258, 260, 268, *285*, *286*, *287*
Pauling, L., 266, *287*
Peabody, C. O., 19, *101*, 273, *283*
Peirson, D. H., 261, *287*
Penndorf, R., 184, 188, *206*
Perkins, W. A., 357, 358, *365*
Perl, E., 57, *108*
Peters, B., 230, 231, 232, 234, 235, 236, *285*, *287*
Piscalor, F., 44, *101*
Podzimek, J., 122, 160, *206*, 313, 314, 317, 322, *350*
Pollak, L. W., 152, 187, *206*, *207*
Prabhakara, C., 228, 246, *284*
Preining, O., 114, 180, *204*
Price, S., 53, 54, 57, *108*
Przibram, K., 111, 151, *207*
Purcell, J. D., 44, 45, *106*

R

Ram, A., 98, *103*, 316, *348*
Rama, T., 228, 236, 237, *284*, *285*
Ramanathan, K. R., 45, 47, *108*
Rau, G., 149, 150, *205*, 222, 223, 224, *285*
Rau, W., 120, 122, 160, *207*
Reed, R. J., 43, *108*
Regener, E., 44, 49, *108*

Regener, V. H., 44, 49, 51, 53, 54, 58, 59, *101*, *108*
Reiter, M., 86, *109*
Reiter, R., 86, *109*, 436, *351*
Renzetti, N. A., 59, *109*, 355, 357, 358, 360, 361, 363, *365*
Revelle, R., 28, 29, 30, 31, 32, 34, 35, 36, *109*
Rex, R. W., 181, *207*
Reynolds, W. C., 85, *109*
Rich, T. A., 149, 150, 152, *205*, *207*
Richards, E. H., 343, *351*
Rinehart, T. S., 198, *204*
Robbins, R. C., 167, 168, *207*
Rogers, L. W., 355, 357, *365*
Rosenstock, H. B., 227, 228, *283*
Rosinski, J., 252, *287*
Rossby, C. G., 91, *109*, 331, *351*
Rossi, B., 9, *101*
Rudd, D. P., 18, *103*
Russell, E. J., 343, *351*
Ryan, T. G., 68, *106*, 167, *205*, 305, *350*

S

Sagalyn, R. C., 183, 185, 190, *207*
Saruhashi, K., 260, *287*
Saunders, A. W., Jr., 254, 255, 258, 260, *286*
Schadt, S., 95, *102*
Schell, W. R., 241, *283*
Scherb, F., 9, *101*
Schlarb, G., 187, *207*
Schmolinsky, F., 144, *207*
Schraub, A., 217, 218, 220, 221, 222, 226, *285*
Schröer, E., 38, *109*
Schubert, C. C., 58, 94, *103*
Schuck, E. A., 357, *365*
Schulz, L., 112, 113, 115, 116, *204*
Schuman, L. M., 86, *109*
Schumann, G., 215, 227, 228, *284*, *287*
Seely, B. K., 163, *202*
Seeley, J. S., 6, 7, 8, *105*
Sharp, R. P., 16, 17, *103*
Shaw, C. C., 8, *104*
Shaw, J. H., 82, 94, 96, 97, *100*, *109*
Sherwood, R. D., 196, *203*

Sievers, J. R., 164, *202*
Simpson, G. C., 145, *207*
Sisefsky, J., 240, 241, *284*, *287*
Sisler, F. D., 77, *102*
Sittkus, A., 227, 228, *285*
Skidmore, D. R., 58, 94, *103*
Slobod, R. L., 82, *109*
Slocum, G., 27, *109*
Sloss, L. L., 129, 181, *205*
Small, S. H., 253, 261, 263, *287*, 294, *351*
Spar, J., 246, 281, *284*
Squires, P., 73, *109*, 192, *207*
Sramek, L., 313, 314, 317, 322, *350*
Steele, L. P., 10, *100*
Stern, S., 250, *287*
Stewart, K. H., 138, *207*
Stewart, N. G., 228, 220, 253, 259, 261, *283*, *287*, 301, *348*
Stockham, J., 252, *287*
Störmer, C., 7, *109*
Storebö, P. B., 240, 253, *288*
Suess, H. E., 28, 29, 30, 31, 32, 34, 35, 36, 75, 76, 77, *100*, *105*, *109*, 233, *288*
Sugawara, K., 166, *207*, 313, *351*
Szeicz, G., 24, *107*

T

Taylor, B. T., 19, *101*, 272, 273, 274, *283*
Taylor, H. A., 77, *109*
Teichert, F., 51, 52, 54, *109*
Tousey, R., 44, 45, *106*
Tucker, G. B., 4, 6, *109*
Tufts, B. J., 164, *202*
Turkevich, A., 27, *105*, 267, 268, 269, 270, 271, *284*
Turner, D. D., 363, *365*
Turner, J. S., 295, 296, *351*
Twomey, S., 73, *109*, 135, 137, 138, 156, 159, 160, 163, 182, 192, *207*

U

Urey, H. C., 78, 80, *110*

V

Verzár, F., 69, *110*, 112, 155, *207*, *208*
Viemeister, P. E., 86, *110*

Vigroux, E., 44, *101*
Vihman, E., 336, *350*
Vogel, J. C., 267, 269, *287*
Volman, D. H., 77, *110*
Volz, F., 53, 54, 55, 57, 58, *104*, *108*, *110*, 141, 143, 144, 146, 197, *208*

W

Wahlman, L., 317, *351*
Walshaw, C. D., 82, 83, *104*
Walton, A., 263, 264, 266, *288*
Watanabe, K., 44, 45, *106*
Weber, E., 295, 307, 311, 313, 314, 315, 322, 337, *349*
Weickmann, H., 187, *208*, 292, *351*
Weichsel, H., 149, 150, *205*, 222, 223, *285*
Went, F. W., 95, *110*, 180, *208*
Werby, R. T., 319, 323, 324, 326, 327, 328, 330, 331, 333, 334, 335, *350*
Wexler, H., 54, *110*, 219, 259, *288*
Weyant, W. S., 54, *110*, 259, *288*
Wheeler, L. B., 163, *202*
Whipple, F. J. W., 149, *208*
White, F. D., 219, *288*
Whytlaw-Gray, R., 129, *208*
Wiffen, R. C., 93, *102*
Wigand, A., 187, *208*
Wilkening, M. H., 215, 217, 226, *288*
Willet, H. C., 41, *110*
Williams, W. J., 6, 8, *107*
Wilson, P. W., 77, *106*
Witherspoon, A. E., 83, 96, *100*
Wolfgang, R. L., 19, *104*, 234, 266, *287*
Woodcock, A. H., 114, 118, 119, 121, 123, 156, 157, 158, 159, 162, 163, 164, *202*, *205*, *208*, 294, *351*
Wright, H. L., 144, 146, 148, 162, *208*
Wulf, O. R., 38, *110*

Y

Yamamoto, G., 138, 139, 169, *208*
Yudkin, J., 77, *104*

Z

Zankelies, F. A., 18, *103*
Zebel, G., 130, *208*
Zutski, P. K., 228, 236, 237, *284*, *285*

Subject Index

A

Abundance of gases, see Gases

Actinon, 211

Aerosols, 111-199
  between 0,1 and 1 μ, see Large particles
  chemical composition, 153-182
  chemically important size range, 112, 118
  distribution in troposphere, see Aitken and Large particles
  electrical properties, 146-153
  electrically important size range, 112, 146
  extraterrestrial, see Extraterrestrial dust
  in polluted atmospheres, see Particulate pollutants
  in stratosphere, see Stratospheric aerosols
  larger than 1 μ, see Giant particles
  mass distribution, see Volume distribution
  nomenclature, 112
  optical properties, 141-146
  optically important size range, 112, 141, 143
  over continents, see Continental aerosols
  over oceans, see Sea salt particles
  physical constitution, 131-135
  residence time in troposphere, 190-191, 227-228, 236-238, 253-254, 298-301
  role as condensation nuclei, see Condensation nuclei
  role in atmosphere, 113
  scattering, see Scattering
  size distribution, see Size distribution

  smaller than 0,1 μ, see Aitken particles spectrum,
  see also Size distribution, 112, 114
  washout efficiency, see Washout efficiency

Air pollution, 353-365
  aerosols in, see Particulate pollutants
  area of influence, 363-365
  definition, 353
  gases in, see individual constituents
  global extent
  see Sulfur, Carbondioxide, Iodine
  types of, 354
  variation of concentration, 362-363

Aitken particles 112-113, 118, 120, 122, 152-157, 183-191
  background concentration, 189, 191
  chemical composition, 157
  coagulation, see Size distribution
  counter, 113
  decrease of concentration with pressure, 185, 187
  definition, 112
  electrically charged, see Ions
  global budget, 190-191
  growth with humidity, 157
  mass concentration, 118
  mean radius and concentration, 152
  nature and origin of, 153-157
  number concentration, 120, 122
  removal rate by rain, 190
  role as condensation nuclei, see Condensation nuclei
  size distribution, see Size distribution of aerosols
  sources, 154-156
  in stratosphere,
  see Stratospheric aerosols
  vertical distribution, 183-191

Aldehydes in polluted atmospheres, 358

Ammonia, 87-91, 174, 304, 343-346, 357,
   170-177
   in aerosols, 170-177
   atmospheric abundance, 87-91
   in polluted atmospheres, 357
   in precipitation, 343-346
   ratio to ammonium in aerosols, 87, 174
   seasonal variation, 89
   solution in water, 304
   sources and sinks, 88-91

Angström's formula, 142-143, see also
   Scattering of radiation, wave length
   dependence

Artificial radioactivity, 209, 238-266, see
   also Fission products
   deposition on earth's surface, 261-266
   distribution, in stratosphere, 243-252
     in troposphere, 252-261
   production, 238-242

Atomic tests, 241-242

B

Beryllium-7,
   see Cosmic ray produced isotopes

Biosphere, role in air chemistry, see
   Carbon dioxide, Hydrogen, Hydro-
   gen sulfide, Nitrous oxide, Ammonia,
   Methane

Bishop ring, 145

Blue sun, 145

Brewer-Dobson circulation,
   see Ozone in stratosphere,
   Water vapor,
   Fission products
   Stratospheric circulation

C

Calcium in precipitation, 328-332

Carbon, reservoirs of, 30

Carbon-14, 29, 31-34, 36, 210, 233-234,
   266-269
   artificial, 266-269
   increase in atmosphere, 267-269
   in stratosphere, 268-269
   natural, 29, 31-34, 36, 210, 233-234

Carbon dioxide, 21-36, 303
   assimilation by plants, 22-23
   budget, see Cycle
   exchange at the ocean surface, 24-36
   exchange rate with ocean,
   see Residence time
   fast cycle, 29-36
   hemispherical exchange, 26
   industrial production, 34
   partial pressure over ocean, 24
   pH-value in rain,
   see pH-value
   production and removal over land 21-24
   production in soil, 21
   residence time, 30-33
   seasonal variation, 25-27
   secular increase, 27-29, 34-36
   slow cycle, 29
   solution in water, 303
   stratospheric concentration, 27
   system atmosphere-ocean, 35
   variation in surface air, 22-23

Carbon monoxide, 96-98, 354
   in polluted atmospheres, 354
   atmospheric abundance, 96-97
   sources and sinks, 96-98

Chloride in aerosols, see also Sea salt
   particles, 170-177

Chloride in precipitation, 317-326
   over continents, 321-322
   ratio to sodium, 323-326
   sources, 317, 322, 324-325
   variation with distance from coast, 318-
   321

Chlorine, see Chloride in precipitation,
   91-92

Cloud droplets, 137-140, 291, 294-295
   concentration of chemical constituents,
   291, 294-295
   evaporation residues, 138-140
   formation, 137
   sizes, 138-140

Coagulation of aerosols, see Size distribution of aerosols

Condensation nuclei, see also Aerosols,
   112-113, 136-140
   activation, 113, 136-140

definition, 112-113
supersaturation, critical, 135-136
  spectrum, 137-138
Continental aerosols, size distribution,
  see Size distribution of aerosols
Continental aerosols, 113-124, 168-182
  and rain water composition,
  in precipitation, 168-169,
  see also individual ions
  atomic composition of urban and nonurban aerosols, 177-180
  chemical composition, in precipitation,
  168-182, see also individual ions
  electron micrographs, see Electron micrographs
  organic compounds in, 179-180
  soil as source of, 181-182
  total mass concentration, 180
  variation of composition with geographic location, 173-177
Cosmic ray produced isotopes, 209, 230-
  238
  beryllium-7, 235-236
  concentration in air, 234, 236
  isotopic ratio, 237-238
  phosphorus-32 and -33, 236-237
  primary particles, 231, 234
  production rate, 231-237
  removal by rain, 236-237
  secondary activity, 234-235
  sulfur-35, 236-237
  vertical distribution, 234, 236

D

Decay products of radon and thoron,
  212, 220-230, 300-302
  attachment of aerosols, 220-226
  diffusion coefficient, 220, 223
  in stratosphere, 229-230, 301-302
  life time, 223-224
  long lived, 226-230
  primary particles, 220, 222-224
  removal by precipitation, 227-229,
  300-302
  secondary activity, 220, 223-226
  vertical distribution, 300-302
Deposition velocity, 309-310

Deuterium, 12-19, 76-78
  in hydrogen, see Hydrogen
  in precipitation, 14
  in water, see Water
Diffusion coefficient of molecules, 125
Diffusion coefficient of particles, 113,
  125-126
Dry layer in stratosphere, see Water
  vapor

E

Eddy diffusion coefficient, 127, 190
Electron micrographs of aerosols, 134,
  169-170
Emanations, see Radon and Thoron
Escape of gases, see Hydrogen, Helium
Exchange layer, 183
Exhalation of emanations, see also Ra-
  don and Thoron, 211, 213-215, 217
Extinction of radiation, see Scattering
  of radiation
Extraterrestrial dust, 198-199
  concentration in stratosphere, 198
  spherules, 199
  zodiacal dust cloud, 198

F

Fall velocity of particles, 125-126, 308
Fission products, see also artificial radioactivity, 239-281
  attachment to inert material, 240-241
  budget, 266
  composition, 239
  deposition on earth's surface, 263-266
  formation, 239-240
  fractionation, 240
  hot particles, 241-242
  injection into stratosphere, 241
  local fallout, 241
  long lived, 240
  in rain water, 254, 256-258
  ratio Barium-140/Strontium-90, 254,
  256-257
  ratio Strontium-89/Strontium-90, 245-
  248, 254
  rhodium-102, 249, 275-278, 280-281

seasonal variation of fallout, 259-261

size distribution, in stratosphere, 250
  in troposphere, 252-253

stratospheric circulation,
see stratospheric circulation

stratospheric distribution, 243-248

stratospheric fallout, 261

stratospheric residence time, 247-249, 269

strontium-90, 244-248, 261-266, 280

in surface air, 254-259

tropospheric fallout, 241

tropospheric residence time, 253

tungsten-185, 249-251, 258-259, 280

washout and rainout, 261-266

Fog droplets, *see* Cloud droplets

Formaldehyde, 98

Fractionation factor for isotopic constituents in water, 12

Frequency of clouds with altitude, 11

G

Gases, 1-4
  abundance, 3
  reservoirs, 2
  residence time, 2-4
  units, 5
  variability, 1-2

Giant particles in troposphere, 112, 123, 127-128, 168-182
  chemical composition, 168-182
  definition, 112
  number concentration, 123
  vertical distribution, 127-128

Growth of particles with relative humidity, 124, 131-135
  measurements, 134
  theory, 131-134

H

Haze, *see* Scattering by aerosol particles

Helium, 79-81
  escape into space, 80-81
  isotopic composition, 79
  residence times, 79-81
  sources of Helium-3, 80
    of Helium-4, 79-80

Hemispherical exchange, *see*
  Carbon dioxide,
  Methane,
  Tritium content,
  Fission products

Hydrocarbons, 179-180, 358
  in polluted atmospheres, 358
  natural, 179-180

Hydrogen, 74-79
  atmospheric abundance, 74-76
  biological production, 77
  deuterium content, *see* Deuterium
  escape into space, 78
  photooxidation, 77
  production by photolysis, 77,
  sources and sinks, 77-79
  tritium content, 76, 78-79

Hydrogen sulfide, 59-70
  distribution in atmosphere, 59-65
  oxidation, 69
  production in coastal areas, 65
  role of pollution, 61
  sources, 61, 65-70

Hydrogen, tritium content, 76, 78-79, 272-273

I

Ice nuclei, 141

Industrial production, *see* individual constituents

Insoluble matter, in aerosols, 178-182
  in precipitation, 316-317

Iodine, 93, 315
  adsorption on aerosols, 93
  in rain water, 315
  sources and sinks, 93

Ionisation equilibrium, 141, 152

Ions, 111-113, 115-116, 147-152
  line structure, 115
  medium and large, 112
  mobility, 149
  multiple charges, 149-150
  ratio to uncharged particles, 148, 150-151
  recombination coefficients, 147-149
  small, 111
  spectrum, 113, 115-116

variation of electrical properties with particle size, 149-152

K

Koschmieder's formula for visibility, 143

L

Large particles in troposphere, 112, 122, 127, 168-182, 188-192
  ammonium sulfate in, 171-173
  background concentration, 189
  chemical composition, 168-182
  definition, 112
  number concentration, 122
  in stratosphere,
  see Stratospheric aerosols
  vertical distribution, 127, 188-192
Liquid water in clouds, 291, 293
  residence time, 11
Loess particles, 129

M

Magnesium in precipitation, 328-332
Mass distribution of aerosols,
  see Volume distribution
Meteoritic material, see Extraterrestrial dust
Methane, 94-95, 274-275
  atmospheric abundance, 94
  destruction, 95
  sources, 94
  tritium content, 95, 274-275
Mie's theory of scatterng, 141
Mixed ocean layer, Carbon-14 age, 32
Mixed particles, 131-134, 169
Mobility of particles, 125
Mother of pearl clouds, 199
Multiple charges, see Ions

N

Nitrate, in aerosols, 167-168, 171-177, 179
  in precipitation, 343-346
Nitric oxide, 84
Nitrite in precipitation, 346

Nitrogen compounds, isotopic composition, 86
Nitrogen dioxide, 85-86, 174, 356, see also Nitrate in precipitation
  atmospheirc abundance, 85-86
  in polluted atmospheres, 356
  ratio to nitrate in aerosols, 85, 174
  sources, 86
Nitrogen oxides in the atmosphere, 81-82
Nitrous oxide, 82-84
  atmospheric abundance, 82
  photochemical destruction, 83
  production in soil, 83
  residence time, 83
  sources, 83-84
  vertical distribution, 82
Noctilucent clouds, 199

O

Organic matter in aerosols, 179-180
Oxidant content, 357
Oxygen, 18
  isotopic composition, see Oxygen-18
Oxygen-18, 12-19
  and salinity of ocean water, 17
  in ocean water, 18
  in oxygen, 18
  in precipitation, 16
  in water, see Water
  seasonal variation in ice, 16
Ozone
  in stratosphere, 37-49, 58
    adjustment time to photochemical equilibrum, 41
    and Brewer-Dobson circulation, 47
    as conservative property, 41
    chemical reactions, 38-39, 41
    comparison of measurements with theory, 45-46
    measurement of vertical distribution, 44
    photochemical equilibrium, 39-40
    residence time, 58
    theory of formation, 38-41
    variation with altitude, 39-40, 44-49
    variation with season, 45-48

stratospheric circulation, *see* Stratospheric circulation
total, 42-44
  seasonal and latitudinal variation, 42-43
  variation with weather, 43
in troposphere, 49-59, 357
  budget, 56-59
  decrease in surface air, 51-53
  destruction rate, 56-58
  origin, 49
  production in polluted atmospheres, 59, 357
  reaction with trace gases, 58-59
  representative average values, 53-56
  seasonal variation, 53-57
  vertical flux, 51, 58
  vertical profiles, 50
Ozone units, 37

P

Particulate pollutants, 359-362, *see* also Continental aerosols, Aitken, large and giant particles
  composition in various places, 360-362
  general composition, 359
pH-value of precipitation, 340-343
Phase enrichment for isotopic constituents in water, 13-14
Phosphorus-32 and -33,
  see Cosmic ray produced isotopes
Pollen, 128
Potassium in precipitation, 327-332
Precipitation chemistry, *see* Rainout and Washout
Primary particles, *see* Decay products of radon and thoron or cosmic ray produced isotopes
Proton influx into atmosphere, 10, 78
Purple light, 197

R

Radioactive fallout, *see* Artificial radioactivity or Fission products
Radioactivity, units, 210-211

Radon, 209, 211-230
  concentration in air, 215-216, 217-218
  decay products, see Decay products
  in soil, 214-215
  over continent and ocean, 218-219
Rain chemistry, *see* Rainout and Washout
Rainout, 289-295, 302-306
  definition, 289-290
  efficiency, 291-294, 306
  of aerosols, 291-295, 306
  of ammonia, 304
  of fission products, *see* Fission products
  of gases, 302-306
  of sulfur dioxide, 305
Rainwater composition, 295, 311-321, 364
  individual constituents, *see* Chloride etc.
  ionic ratios, *see* Chloride etc.
  rarely observed constituents, 315-317
  variation with amount of rain, 311-315
  variation with distance from source, 316, 318-321, 364
  variation with droplet size, 295, 296
  variation with type of precipitation, 314-315.
Raoult's Law, 132, 134
Ratio of cations in precipitation, 326-332
Rayleigh distillation, 13-15
Recombination coefficients, *see* Ions
Removal of trace substances, 289-311
  by absorption, 310
  by impaction, 309-310
  by precipitation, 291-306, *see* also Rainout and Washout
  by sedimentation, 307-308
  survey, 289-290
Residence time, *see* Gases or Aerosols
Rhodium 102, *see* Fission products

S

Scattering of radiation, 141-146
  by aerosol particles, 141-144
  cross section, 142
  molecular or Rayleigh, 143

scattering function and size distribution of aerosols, 145-146
total, 143
variation with humidity, 144-145
wave length dependence, 142-144
Schlarb effect, see also Aitken particles, decrease with pressure, 185, 187
Sea salt particles, 119-122, 124, 126-128, 135, 145, 157-168, 173-176, 323-332
budget, 162-163, 165
chemical composition, 159, 165-168, 173-176, 323-332, see also individual ions in precipitation
modification of composition, 166-168
nitrate formation on, 167-168
over land, 120, 160, 163-165
phase transition, 135, 145
process of formation, 157-158
production rate, 159, 163
removal over land, 165
role as condensation nuclei, 160-162
size distribution, 119 122, 124, 126 128, 158-160, see also Size distribution
sulfate formation on, 166-167
vertical distribution, 163-165
Sea water composition, 165
Secondary activity, see decay products of radon and thoron
Sedimentation equilibrium of aerosols,127
Sedimentation of aerosols, see also Size distribution of aerosols upper limit, 126, 308
Size distribution, modification by water vapor condensation, 136-138, 226
Size distribution of aerosols, 113-131, 136-138
definition, 115
exponential decrease, 116, 118-119
line structure, 115, 119
lower limit, 116, 129-131
maximum, 116
methods of determination, 113-114
model distributions, 123-124
modification by coagulation, 129-131
by relative humidity, 124, 136
by water vapor condensation, 136-138

observations, 116-122
over land, 116-119, see also Continental aerosols
over sea, 119, see also Sea salt particles
upper limit, 116, 126-128
Sodium in aerosols, 170-172, see also Sea salt particles
Sodium in precipitation, 324-326
excess, 326
sources, 324-325
Solution of gases in water, 302-304
Spherules, see Extraterrestrial dust
Stokes-Cunningham correction factor, 124-125
Stratospheric aerosols, 123, 153, 192-199
chemical composition, 194-196, 197
extraterrestrial components, see Extraterrestrial dust
influence on air conductivity, 153
latitudinal distribution of large particles, 193-194, 196
optical effects, 197
origin of sulfate particles, 196
size distribution, 123, 194-196
vertical distribution of Aitken particles, 192-193
of large particles, 193
Stratospheric circulation, 4-12, 44-49, 243-248, 278-281
fission products, 243-248, 280-281
ozone, 44-49, 279
water vapor, 4-12, 278-279
Stratospheric exchange over winter pole 8-9
Stratospheric mixing coefficients, 250
Strontium-89, see Fission products
Strontium-90, see Fission products
Sulfate in aerosols, 166-167, 170-177, 179
Sulfate in precipitation, 332-339
and pH-value, see pH-value
excess, 333-336
in fog water, 336-337
ratio to other ions, 336-339
sources, 334-338
Sulfur, see also Sulfate in precipitation, 59-60, 70-74, 174
budget, 70-73

cycle, 72-74
  forms of atmospheric, 59-60
  isotopic composition, 73-74
  ratio of gaseous compounds to sulfate
    in aerosols, 59-60, 174
  residence time, 72
  seasonal variation, 66
  total deposition in rain, 70-72
Sulfur-35,
  see Cosmic ray produced isotopes
Sulfur dioxide, 59-70, 305, 356, 362-364
  distribution in atmosphere, 59-65
    in Europe, 63-64
  in polluted atmospheres, 356, 362-364
  industrial production, 66
  oxidation, 64, 68-69
  role of pollution, 61
  seasonal variation, 62
  sinks, 66-69
  sources, 65-70, 305
  vertical distribution, 63
Suess effect, *see* Carbon 14

T

Thomson's formula, 132
Thorium decay, 211-212
Thoron, 209-230
  concentration in air, 215-216
  decay products, *see* Decay products
  in soil, 214-215
Tritium, 19-20, 76, 78-79, 95, 233, 269-275
  artificial, 269-275
  deposition, 270-271
  in hydrogen, *see* Hydrogen
  in methane, *see* Methane
  in water, *see* Water
  inventories, 270-271
  natural, 20, 233
  reservoirs, 19

unit, 19
  variation with sun spot cycle, 20
Tungsten-185, see Fission products

U

Uranium decay, 211-212

V

Visibility, 143, *see* also Scattering
Volume distribution of aerosols, 118, 126-131
  definition, 115
  effect of coagulation, 129-131
    of sedimentation, 126-128
  observations, 118

W

Washout, 140, 289-290, 295-298, 306, 314
  of aerosols, 295-298, 314
  definition, 289-290
  efficiency, 140, 295-297
  of fission products, *see* Fission products
  of gases, 306
Water, 12-20
  isotopic composition, 12-20, 269-272
    deuterium content, 12-19
    oxygen-18 content, 12-19
    tritium content, 19-20, 269-272
Water vapor, 4-20
  dry layer in stratosphere, 4, 7-8
  extraterrestrial origin, 10
  increase in upper stratosphere, 7-10
  residence time, 10
  source of stratospheric, 8-10
  stratospheric circulation, *see* Stratospheric circulation
  vertical distribution, 4-12